UP THE CREEK

Once past the island, Doc said, 'There's a lovely little creek behind the weir, and I know the old lady who lives along there. She'll let us fish from the bottom of her garden.'

So saying, he swung the boat hard-a-starboard (who says I know nowt about it?) round the back of the island, and headed for the creek. The current was flowing strongly and we found ourselves moving swiftly towards the weir.

'Soon be there,' said Doc.

'Oh, what's it say on that board sticking out of the water?' he said.

'D-A-N-G-E-R ... danger,' I said (as in 'banger'). My mind must have been on something else. 'No! Oh-my-gawd! It's DANGER! As in "ranger"!'

'As in what?' shouted Doc over the noise of the engine.

'Ranger! As in Lone Ranger! Tonto! Hi-yo Silver ... away!'

DOCTOR ROBERT CLIFFORD

It's A Long Story, Doctor!

Illustrated by Larry

THERE YOU ARE, DOCTOR!
ON HOLIDAY AGAIN, DOCTOR?
YOU'RE STILL A DOCTOR, DOCTOR!

WARNER BOOKS

Prologue

Life is a tragedy, for we are all born eventually to die. We survive our tragedies by laughing at them.

> *A friend once told me that when he was under the influence of ether he dreamed he was turning over the pages of a great book, in which he knew he would find, on the last page, the meaning of life.*
>
> *The pages of the book were alternately tragic and comic, and he turned page after page, his excitement growing, not only because he was approaching the answer, but because he couldn't know, until he arrived, on which side of the book the final page would be. At last it came: the universe opened up to him in a hundred words: and they were uproariously funny.*
>
> *He came back to consciousness crying with laughter, remembering everything. He opened his lips to speak. It was then that the great and comic answer plunged back out of his reach.*

Christopher Fry

THERE YOU ARE, DOCTOR!

For Cliff, Joyce, Clive, Petra, Janet and Sarah

Contents

CHAPTER 1

Naked Truth

An urgent message was waiting for me when I arrived at the surgery; it was another of those ambiguous calls from Mrs Sanderson. No details, but would the doctor come straight-away, please?

Dare I leave it until after my surgery? I had been on so many wild-goose chases to Mrs Sanderson's that it seemed a reasonable risk. The first time she called me out urgently she had a ruptured appendix; another time she had broken a hip; but quite often – at least thirty or forty times – I had been summoned in haste to find that she hadn't even been in, having miraculously recovered and gone out to the launderette or somewhere. I decided to wait until after the surgery.

I saw my first patient, who had arrived ten minutes before time. Then Grace, one of our receptionists, rang through to say there was nobody waiting for me. The town must have been smitten by a sudden outbreak of health. 'Oh hell,' I thought, 'let's get this over with.'

I shot over to Mrs Sanderson's. It meant leaving the surgery and crossing the bridge to go up to the uphill part of Tad-chester, then down through a long winding estate to an old Victorian house. The house was completely unkempt, barely

1

furnished and filled with all sorts of lodgers and hangers-on, plus Mrs Sanderson's four daughters. It had been suggested that a red light outside the place would not be amiss.

I banged at the front door. There was no reply. This wasn't unusual. I went round to the back door and shouted – again, no reply, though the back door was unlocked. There were altogether about seven or eight bedrooms in this tumbledown house. I would have to find out which one she was hiding in. I climbed the stairs shouting, 'Hallo—oo! Hallo—oo!' Still no reply.

I looked around the first landing, trying to decide which room to attempt first. The choice was made for me when, from the second room on the left, there came a tremendous groaning. Thank God I had come urgently; there was obviously something really amiss. I tried the door handle. It would not budge. There didn't appear to be anybody else in the house and the door was almost falling off its hinges, so I put my shoulder to it, bursting into the bedroom.

There, instead of the ailing Mrs Sanderson, was one of her not unattractive daughters. She lay naked in the middle of a large double bed, covered by an equally naked middle-aged man in the middle of something his wife certainly would not have approved of. His activities could not have been helped by the door's crashing down beside the bed; a sort of added climax, as it were.

The naked man, stilled by my entrance, lay with his head tucked into the pillow, obviously not wanting to be recognised, but there seemed to be something familiar about the boil on the back of his neck.

Meanwhile Miss Sanderson, smiling sweetly over her companion's rotund shoulder, said, 'Oh, there you are, Doctor. Thank you for calling. Mother felt better so she's gone out to do the shopping.'

With a friendly wave of her hand I was dismissed and so I hurried back to the surgery for my next appointment.

* * *

Unnecessary calls, happily, were not too frequent. One of the most irritating came one evening from Tommy Charles, a sort of male Mrs Sanderson, who actually lived only three or four doors away from her. His call came at the end of a long and tiring day. He, like Mrs Sanderson, had presented me now and again with something serious so I couldn't ignore his call. I wearily strode up the path to his old people's bungalow.

'Well, Tommy,' I said, 'what is it this time?'

Tommy was sitting in front of a roaring fire enjoying a mug of tea and a piece of toast.

'I don't feel all that bright, Doctor,' he said. 'But the main thing that's worrying me is all these empty medicine bottles.' He waved towards a box containing about thirty empty bottles, representing several months of his medication, all washed and tidied up in the box.

'Would you mind taking them back to the surgery?' he said. 'I don't like the empties hanging about.'

The fact that we didn't re-use bottles was of no consequence.

3

I didn't feel like upsetting Tommy with a dressing-down, but he never knew how near he came to having the whole box dropped on his head.

During the time I had been in general practice, the amount of home visiting had dwindled from being a major part of the work to a relatively minor one. This wasn't because the nation's health was getting better, but simply because more people had transport of their own or knew somebody who could give them a lift into town. The only time that home visits did pick up was in the summer months when Tadchester Bridge was so crowded with holidaymakers that it often took half an hour to cross it. Some patients felt that they would rather waste the doctor's time than their own, but thankfully they were a very small minority.

As new drug treatments improved, night calls became fewer but were never ignored. It was very rare, if ever, that one was unnecessarily called out after twelve o'clock. Often the only treatment required was the appearance of a doctor who could take responsibility for the situation. I still deemed such calls necessary. Patients who felt they just couldn't cope needed help or reassurance and could have worried themselves to death if they waited until morning for their fears to be allayed.

Also I was not brave enough to refuse to go on these calls. On the odd occasion that I hadn't gone, when it seemed as if some reassurance over the phone might be enough, I had spent a sleepless night wishing I had gone and wondering if I had given them the right advice.

I was the fourth partner in a group of five and a half partners in a little Somerset town called Tadchester. It was a market town with a rising populaton of about eight thousand. It stood on the estuary of the River Tad in one of the most beautiful parts of the Somerset coast, with the resorts of Sanford-on-Sea and Stowin about equidistant east and west of it.

Although primarily a market town, it had in the past centred on its coal mine; there was some fishing, an increasing amount of light industry and a great deal of farming. The town was split in two by the River Tad and further split by the large hill which dominated one side of the river.

You are not just a Tadchester resident, you are strictly Up-the-Hill or Down-the-Hill. In years past this had important social distinctions in that the populations of Up-the-Hill tended to be the have-nots, whereas Down-the-Hill tended to be the haves. They had levelled off over the years with the coming of light industry which was mainly Up-the-Hill. It had encouraged the building of big housing estates, which had created the effect almost of two towns.

There were even two football teams. Tadchester United was the traditional Tadchester football side. It was Down-the-Hill and had a history going back more than 150 years. The team Up-the-Hill called itself Tadchester Royal. This was because at some point way back in the past, a King Charles or Richard or possibly even Henry VIII stayed at an inn on that side of the river. It made the Royals feel they were much superior to poor old Tadchester United, which in some ways they were as they had a better ground and were a better team.

* * *

We were the only general practice in the town and we also took care of the local hospital. Of the five full partners, each had his own area of responsibility in the hospital. Steve Maxwell, the senior partner, had a special interest in medicine. Henry Johnson, the second senior, was the surgeon. Jack Hart, the third partner, was the anaesthetist.

I, as the fourth partner, was reckoned to be the expert of midwifery, although in recent years this meant just pointing the expectant mothers in the direction of the hospital. Midwifery had changed so much that instead of doing three home confinements a fortnight I now was lucky if I did one or two a year, the rest being handled by the big new maternity hospital at Winchcombe.

Our fifth partner was Ron Dickinson, an accomplished athlete who spent a great deal of his time running, jumping, swimming, sailing, water-skiing and removing all the local tonsils.

When I had a coronary bypass operation a couple of years before, we had a locum, Catherine Carlton to cover my work. Catherine, the wife of a local dentist, was kept on as a half-time partner when I returned to duty.

Catherine was a delightful girl who balanced the load by sharing weekend and night duties, and who increased the practice lists by two when she produced twins just a year after she had been made a half-time partner.

In my advancing years, all young doctors look as if they should still be sitting their 'A' levels rather than practising medicine, and Catherine was one of these. Like her husband Tony, who not only practised dentistry but played a vigorous part in the affairs of the town council, both of them had pilots' licences. Whereas my family would think we were adventurous motoring through France, Catherine and Tony would fly to Malta or some other such place, piloting their own machine.

We were a happy and well-balanced team and having a new part-time lady member to add to the five was what we needed to round us off. There are some subjects that ladies only want to talk about to ladies.

We were all very lucky to be practising medicine in such delightful surroundings. Doctors in Tadchester were very important people. They ranked with vicars and solicitors as the leading lights of the town. If someone was to be successful in any other field apart from farming, then he had to go away up to London or to one of the big cities. It gave us an inflated idea of our own importance. Talking to a colleague who was in practice in a large town in Berkshire, I found that doctors there came much further down the batting order. They had to compete with airline pilots, merchant bankers, members of Parliament and property dealers. As my friend said, he often felt that he was just a clerk who had to supply notes before a patient could see a specialist.

We were indeed lucky. We had the championship golf course at Sanford-on-Sea; a flourishing sailing club at Stowin; the River Tad and its companion the River Tod, at Winch-

6

combe, not far away. There was much unspoilt country and, as yet undiscovered by too many of the general public, coves and tiny beaches tucked away in quiet corners. It was a good place both to live and work in.

CHAPTER 2

Horses for Courses

Following the death of the octogenarian vicar of St Peter's Church, Up-the-Hill, the new young vicar had made a disastrous start. At his welcoming party, his heavily built hostess's right breast broke loose from its moorings, and was exposed for all to see. Instead of what I understand is the classical way of repairing the situation — gently returning the object with a warm tablespoon — the bright young man shouted, 'Look out of the window everybody!' Everybody looked out of the window. And there on the lawn were two dogs mating.

It was the beginning of a series of disasters in Tom Leatherbridge's new ministry. Part of this was that any new vicar represented such change: the previous incumbent had held the post for more than sixty years. At his first christening, young Tom dropped the baby in the font and cut its head, leaving it in need of two stitches. This was a first as far as I was concerned.

Tom was a northerner, with a hearty sense of humour and bonhomie not in tune with the rather fixed southern ways of Tadchester. He was a leg-puller, but many of his parishioners didn't understand his humour. Slowly, an area of viciousness and gossip sprang up round him. Three middle-aged ladies in

8

the Mothers' Union implied that he had made improper suggestions to them. The only thing the three had in common was they would have been a great success at a Hallowe'en ball, even without masks. They were leaders in the behind-the-scenes whispering campaign against this poor young man.

Two choirboys who were obviously avid readers of one of the Sunday newspapers, where there were countless stories of misbehaviour between vicars and choirboys, reported to their parents that he had looked at them in a funny way. Before long this amounted almost to homosexual rape, and the parents withdrew them from the choir.

An atmosphere of hate and viciousness that only a small community can generate grew up round this unfortunate, but most likeable, young man, all stemming from the one un-happy incident at his introduction to the parish. It was almost now as if he bore a coat-of-arms that included a pair of mating dogs. He was progressively shunned by his parishioners as more and more people imagined he had insulted them or done something. He wasn't invited out. His congregation began to fall away and there was even talk of the three harridans having complained to the police of his improper advances. It was beginning to destroy him.

What I knew, but nobody else knew, was that soon after he had arrived he had been steadily and properly courting a sister from the fever hospital. It was she who persuaded him to talk to me about his troubles.

He came to me one evening in utter misery, pouring out all the unjustified troubles that had been heaped upon him.

I listened sympathetically and tried to reassure him. When he asked me what to do I said, and I believed it, that I'd always felt there were horses for courses. The answer was simple: he probably wasn't the right horse for this course.

I said, 'I think your employer,' pointing upwards towards the Almighty, 'really means you to do work elsewhere.'

'Do you really mean that, Doctor?' he said.

'Yes, of course,' I said, breaking one of my rules that I wouldn't behave like a deity myself. 'I think a change of scene is the only answer.'

Tom Leatherbridge was a northern lad used to northern people, brought up in an industrial town.

'You don't think I'm running away?' he said.

'No,' I said, pointing upwards again. 'I think it's Him. He's just trying to show you you ought to be somewhere else.'

Perhaps there was something in Tom that had lain hidden. He had escaped from the hard industrial north to the balmy south; something on his conscience told him he ought to go back to the muck and brass of the north, a move which was now often being suggested by his parishioners.

I appeared to have lifted a tremendous load from him.

'Thank you, Doctor,' he said. 'God bless you.'

He handed in his resignation to his local church council which was readily accepted, served about a month's notice, and easily found a parish near to where he was brought up in the north. A couple of months later his fiancée from the fever hospital went up and married him. Pam and I went up to the wedding and found he was already happily settled in an adoring parish with a packed church, and he had become a most popular young man.

His abrupt departure from Tadchester brought all sorts of more vicious rumours about him: that he had made three girls pregnant, that he had been unfrocked, that he had gone to South Africa, that the BBC had taken him on. I was utterly amazed at the bad feeling people had got for this very innocent, inoffensive, sincere, hard-working young man.

I am not usually vindictive, but when I came back from his wedding I went round to everybody I knew who had been unpleasant or had made half hints about him. The three harridans who were supposed to have been improperly propositioned I interviewed independently with a little notebook at my side, frightening them that police action was going to be taken for slander. The simple answer in their case was that there was nothing more they would have liked than to have been propositioned, but the chances of it were almost nil. Their only hope lay in stumbling across a blindfolded sexmaniac. I roasted the parents and the choirboys who had cast aspersions, and for a few days anybody who had said anything detrimental about Tom Leatherbridge got the sharp end of my tongue. There was, of course, nothing against him. He had been just a round peg in a square hole.

Eventually the community Up-the-Hill became sufficiently ashamed to send him an overgenerous wedding present, with many thanks for all his care of them.

A full time minister was found to replace Tom; an older man, Ross Stone, and his wife Bettine. Ross Stone's first job after ordination many years before, had been as a curate at St Peter's so he and his wife knew the people and the area very well. Ross was the epitome of everything that was good in an Anglican minister or any minister, or in fact any person. He was just a good man. His wife, Bettine, was a handsome and gracious woman, perfect as a vicar's wife, joining in every single activity connected with the female side of the church, all the women's organisations and the children's organisations, many of which must have thoroughly bored her, but whether they did or not she always appeared to enjoy them.

Ross was a true man of God. Whenever I was called out to a death, whether the patient was a churchgoer, Roman Catholic, Jewish or nonconformist, I would usually find Ross there when I arrived or he would arrive as I left. The aged and lonely whom I visited routinely, so did he, and we seemed to follow each other around. He was a kind, caring, comforting man who went about amongst his flock just doing good.

I am afraid that Pam and I were not churchgoers. The only time that we did go to church was usually for funerals or weddings. This did not stop us from becoming good friends with the Stones. We often used to dine at the vicarage and they often came and had a meal with us.

Unfortunately, Ross was approaching retiring age when he arrived back in Tadchester, so was with us in all far too short a time. But we have kept in touch and seen each other from time to time, and they have happily always remained good friends.

St Peter's was at its best under Ross. He cut out the cant and hypocrisy and his influence of good spread amongst the parishioners. It's amazing how a community can make about-turns so quickly. I think my day of spitefulness had helped Ross, for the three harridans, the choirboys and their families, and one or two others, never appeared at the church again. It was some dead wood well cut out. Some had become Methodists and some Baptists, so they obviously couldn't do without a church of some sort. I hoped they hadn't taken their ability to poison the atmosphere with them.

CHAPTER 3

Round and About

Whenever the rare occasion of a sunny day and time off coincided, my wife Pam and I would slip away and drive to Green Cliff. We knew of a secret path that led to a little ledge that gave a panoramic view of the whole area of coast.

Most days, particularly if the sun was going to be followed by rain, Puffin Island, twenty miles off the coast of Sanford-on-Sea, stood out etched on the horizon. In years gone by it was a pirate stronghold, but it was now owned by the National Trust with a dozen residents, rare species of plants and assorted animals, including peacocks, and a herd of wild goats that destroyed everything in front of them. Two-and-a-half miles long and half-a-mile wide, the island was a natural paradise. There was one hotel and a dozen cottages that were let out in the summer.

If we were lucky we would see, like dots, the crowds on the beach at Sandimere, the great pebble ridge sweeping in an arc over several miles right to the mouth of the Tad, the drab-looking huts of the holiday camps, a couple of fishing boats trawling and a paddle steamer taking day-trippers from Coomten, a port twenty miles west of Winchcombe to Puffin Island. The trippers would struggle up from the island's rocky

landing stage just in time to buy some souvenirs before they came back.

To the south we could see Hovery, the most picturesque village in the area, like a cleft in the rocks, with steep cobbled streets that went down and down and down. Goods were transported by donkey and sledge, and every year three or four holiday-makers had coronaries after climbing down just a bit farther than they meant to.

We could see from our vantage point small sailing dinghies from the Stowin Yacht Club, a few pleasure boats bobbing up and down with fishing parties on board, a coastal vessel making for Tadchester and the regular supply ship, a small forty-five-foot trawler, the *Puffin*, carrying the essentials out to Puffin Island and often a dozen holiday-makers as well.

Peargate with its shipyard stood out clearly, and even from several miles away the clanging noises of shipbuilding could be heard. The Peargate lifeboat lay patiently moored out in the sea on the sea side of the sand bar, ready whatever the state of the tide to dash off to a rescue.

I don't think there was anywhere that provided a more picturesque scene than this, providing the sun shone. Alas, we had one of the heaviest rainfalls in the country. If we were caught in our vantage spot by an unpredicted rain shower, not only did it spoil the view, we would get soaking wet in the two-mile scramble downhill to reach our car.

It is amazing what changes had taken place since the Industrial Revolution. Only a hundred years ago it took a day to travel from Hovery to Tadchester, so people didn't often do it. They lived in self-contained little communities in every access to the beach all the way round the bay. What in those days used to be a whole day's journey, with probably a few highwaymen to be negotiated, was now covered by twenty-five minutes in the car.

Tadchester had not been too spoilt by modern developments. Many of the buildings dated back to the 16th century, and the place engendered a feeling of safety and stability. Most of the buildings were white, and there was even a town song about the little white town by the sea.

* * *

One of the most attractive features of Tadchester was that it was one of the cleanest ports that I have ever seen, one of the few that had no accompanying railway. All that came into Tadchester was two or three regular fishing boats and a few timber boats from Scandinavia, an occasional collier, gravel dredgers from the Channel, then boats with loads such as concrete and occasionally flour. There was usually one boat moored on Tadchester quay, very rarely two, and I think that the maximum in tonnage that they could take that far up the river was 2,000 tons.

We were about three-and-a-half miles upstream from where the Tad and the River Tod, coming from Winchcombe, joined. Stowin was at the middle of the confluence of these two

rivers and on the Tadchester side was the shipbuilding area of Peargate.

Most of Tadchester's spotless quay was an auxiliary car park. About once every two years a visitor would put his foot on the accelerator rather than the brake and we would have a tragedy, whether the tide was in or out.

There were few more picturesque sights on a sunny day with the tide going out, than to see the licensed seine-net fishermen with their nets fishing from the bridge pools. I could watch them for hours, fascinated, but it was when the tide was in that Tadchester looked at its best.

I remember one day at a wedding on the Up-the-Hill side of the water at a hotel near Stowin, seeing a couple of fishing boats coming up the river, bathed in glorious sunshine. A little coaster having unloaded its cargo on to Tadchester's neat quay, was moving downriver. A couple of rowing fours from the Tadchester rowing clubs, the Reds and the Blues, were making even time with a couple of sailing boats. It was all peace and tranquillity.

The clean, peaceful, unindustrialised quay changed suddenly, literally almost overnight, into a filthy place with queues of lorries, snarled-up traffic and boats queuing up to come into the berths. The reason for this was the coal strike of 1984. Tadchester was an unlicensed port and was a loophole by which coal could get into the country. There never seemed to be any pickets down there trying to stop it.

From a leisurely timber boat once a fortnight, we had four or five coal boats from all over the place unloading on to the quay, with coal dust and grit sweeping all over the main quay road. A stream of lorries stretched back as far as the huge new Western Counties offices at the end of the quay. There was Polish coal, Australian coal, American coal, Chinese coal, Russian coal, Rumanian coal. I used to have a good look at it, as just before going up to medical school I had had two years in the mines as a Bevin Boy and reckoned I was an authority on coal. My coal was the rich, gleaming Barnsley bed from South Yorkshire. The stuff I saw coming in was a mixture of slate and coal dust and this was how it seemed to burn.

It went on for months and months. I forget the precise figures of the coal import into Tadchester but it went from something like six thousand tons in one year to 760,000 tons. A good 700 tons of that seemed to get into my eye every time I walked along the quay. It completely changed the town for a while. Every man who could drive a lorry had a job. The unloading went on day and night and seemed to go on for ever. We wondered when eventually the strike finished whether things would ever return to normal.

A lot of money was spent by foreign ships' crews and lorry drivers, so one man's loss was another man's fortune. For a time Tadchester thrived, but it was losing its character. The miners' strike eventually came to an end, but we wondered if

17

the coal would still keep coming. Perhaps somebody had found that this was cheaper than buying coal produced in England. The boats kept coming in numbers for two weeks after the strike then they started to dwindle; finally they disappeared altogether. It was a further three months before the stains and coal dust were washed away by a combination of winter snow and rain and the municipal street sweepers. But, come the spring, the quay was restored to its old beauty again.

It did show how nothing is settled, how quickly in this moving world things that seemed permanent can change. It seemed mean in a way to grumble; we hadn't been inconvenienced a lot, we hadn't gone short of fuel. A lot of people had found employment, though at somebody else's expense. But the big grumble was that our sleepy, beautiful little town had for a few long months been turned into a grimy industrial suburb.

A year later, a new bridge was begun over the Tad, of a structure which meant that none of the coastal vessels would be able to pass above it to the quay. Until the bridge was finished, we wouldn't know whether it would enhance the town or be an eyesore, though one thing was sure: it would protect us from ever becoming a hectic industrial port again.

Selfish? Perhaps. But the world holds plenty of dirt and squalor. It doesn't hold too many places like Tadchester.

CHAPTER 4

A Collection of Characters

I'm sure that every general practice feels that it has more than its share of eccentrics. I know that we in Tadchester did. We perhaps had some grounds for this as the town had plenty of out-of-the-way places where people could almost disappear from public view. But if perhaps we over-estimated the quantity of our eccentric patients, certainly they didn't lack in quality.

One of our prizewinners was Hamish Richardson. His eccentricity was such that we didn't learn much about him until after he died. He came to Tadchester before I arrived – a well-educated man with a little money of his own – and proceeded to build himself a stockade in a copse near Elfin Cross. He had the absolute minimum of contact with the outside world and was almost completely self-sufficient. He had an arrangement with a local farmer that if he was ever in distress or needed help, he would fly a white flag from the tall flagpole sticking out from the middle of his stockade.

One day I was summoned by the farmer. Would I go and see Hamish Richardson?

'It'll be quite safe,' he said.

I didn't quite know what he meant but I got there, having

driven up to Elfin Cross, then driven two miles along a muddy lane, then walked a further mile to a wooden stockade straight out of *Treasure Island*.

The stockade consisted of an area of about a hundred yards long by thirty-five yards wide surrounded by tree trunks, sharpened at the top and standing twelve feet high. In the middle of this area was a log cabin and nearby was a wire cage with two bull mastiffs trying to tear their way out. Normally, apparently, they were left to roam at will. The one incongruous thing about the whole back-to-nature atmosphere, was two large Calor gas cylinders behind the cabin.

As I walked to the cabin, I took a quick look round. There were hens scuttling around inside the stockade, there were pigs grunting in one corner, and a goat very much in milk tethered to one side. There was a well with a shiny bucket attached to a rope and outside the gate at the back of the stockade was about half an acre of immaculately-kept garden, jammed full of every possible vegetable.

I had been asked by the farmer to bring some cough medicine and antibiotics; Mr Richardson had a chest infection.

I entered the log cabin. It was plain but comfortable and everything was neat and tidy. There were wooden tables, a rocking chair, a wood-burning stove, Calor gas stove, a couple of Calor gas lights and some oil lamps. There was no radio, no television, and just one row of books, all about gardening and growing things.

Mr Richardson was in the next room, a quiet, neatly-kept bedroom, in a sleeping bag on a bunk. He had an obviously bad chest, and asked me politely if I had brought him some antibiotics and cough medicine.

'Yes,' I said.

'Thank you very much, Doctor,' he said. 'I'll let you know if I require you again. Don't ever try and come here without being sent for. The dogs could tear you to bits.'

I could quite believe that.

Back in Tadchester, I enquired about Mr Richardson's background. Nobody was very forthcoming. He was about as self-sufficient as any man could be. Joe and Lynne Church had a nodding acquaintance with him. He was a keen fisherman, lobster catcher and prawner, and they would bump into him as he combed the beaches each day, travelling there by an old bike with a huge basket on the back. He had a map of all the lobster holes in the coves in the area, and usually made a good haul of lobsters, which he sold to hotels in the town. He appeared in the town once a week on Fridays at the local pannier market, just off the High Street.

Every Friday he sat behind a table piled with the very best vegetables, free range eggs, the odd chicken, goat's cheese, and occasionally such delicacies as smoked trout. His was always the first stall to make for, as the quality of all his goods was so much better than anybody else's. He was quiet and personable, did not communicate with his fellow stallholders but again was not rude. He never got into personal conversation, just brought his goods, set them up, and sold them.

I doubt if he sold enough to cover his expenses, or to make a proper living out of it but, as he just about fed himself completely, perhaps he did.

When the pannier market closed, he would go round the town making a few essential purchases like flour and salt, go into the hardwear shop for nails, screws and odd implements, then back to his stockade. The only other time that you were likely to see him was if he was nipping off on one of his fishing expeditions. There was no report ever of his shooting rabbits or birds, but that is not to say that he didn't; there was always somebody, usually poachers, banging off at something in Elfin Cross.

I was only called to see him once more and that was about ten years after the first visit. He had an infection of one leg which I had to open and dress. I gave him an antibiotic and was able to question him a little about his life and about how he fed himself. There was no doubt he had an adequate and balanced diet. There was a brine barrel in the corner with joints of pork and goat in salt. He had his own smoking room and there were rows of smoked brown trout and sea trout hanging from the

wall. When I started to ask about his past or where he had
come from, he clammed up and dismissed me saying, 'Thank
you very much. That'll be all for today, Doctor. I'll let you
know if I want you again.'

He never ever did send for me again. And he never put up
his white flag again.

One severe winter, his farmer contact became suspicious
that he hadn't seen anybody around for some time and con-
tacted the police. The bull mastiffs were loose, so nobody
dared to go in, but both dogs looked emaciated – and there
wasn't a sign of another living thing, pig, goat or chicken. It
would appear that the mastiffs had eaten the lot.

A vet was called, who threw some drugged meat to the dogs,
who wolfed it up straightaway. Within an hour they were
sound asleep and I was with the police when they broke
through. First the vet dragged the dogs into the wire cage and
then we went into the house to find Hamish Richardson very,
very cold and very, very dead in bed. He was frozen stiff and
had probably been dead for weeks. The post mortem revealed

22

that he had died from natural causes and only after his death did we learn the details of his life.

He had been a university professor with an MSc and a PhD. He had a brother and a sister in Scotland and apparently his university work had been in some midland university. He had suddenly walked out one day with no explanation, and now it was so long ago there weren't too many people about who remembered him at all.

As far as I could gather, he had lived in his stockade for probably forty years, and was round about his eighties when he died. He had lived completely alone, apart from his animals, and it would appear was quite happy. He never interfered with anybody and he made sure that nobody interfered with him.

I often wondered what started it all. Was it a scandal? Some broken love affair? We would never know. All we knew was that a distinguished man of learning had suddenly thrown it all up to go and live the life, the very lonely life, of a primitive backwoodsman.

He had done this successfully and I could not help but admire him. He really could not be classified as a true eccentric: he was just different. He must have been a man of tremendous inner strength and self-sufficiency to cope single-handed and create his own domain. I knew that I would never have wanted to live like that, even if I could have coped.

His life and lonely death moved me in a way I couldn't explain. There was something rather fine about it all. I went to his funeral, to which none of his family came. Any survivors were too old, too far away and too out of touch to make it. When the vicar said, 'God rest his soul,' I felt myself echoing those words.

* * *

Zackovitch Hebden lived in two caravans in a small copse of trees about fifty yards from the walls of a small brickmaking plant on the outskirts of Tadchester. He was not a Romany. We had our own Romanies – they were much too respectable

23

to be called Gypsies – who lived in five settled caravans on the other side of Tadchester. These caravans were immaculate, very expensive, had every mod con, were filled with precious china and the owners were as nice a group of people as one could wish to meet anywhere.

I looked after only one member of this group, a Miss Rowley. She explained that although they were settled, two or three times a year they felt the urge to be on the move, and would go off and join some travelling Romanies.

'It's in the blood, Doctor,' she said. 'The year is never the same unless I do some travelling.'

Zackovitch Hebden never travelled anywhere. He never left Tadchester and its precincts. His two caravans were broken down, derelict, with no electricity, water or sanitation. His wife – who was almost crippled with arthritis – had to walk across a field with a milk churn to get the water from a stand pipe. What they did about sanitation, I never enquired. I just noticed that the grass in the area of the caravans looked rather richer than the grass beyond them.

Zackovitch – who was always Zackovitch, nobody would ever think of calling him Zack – lived in a daytime caravan which was equipped with Calor gas and where his meals were cooked by his long-suffering wife. At night he slept in the other caravan which was warmed by a smelly paraffin stove. He made up for any lack of heating by wearing layers and layers of grubby clothes. I was continually urging him to go into housing and the social services offered him council flats and council houses. Though his wife was keen, he always refused. He wasn't short of money and always ran a good car, new enough to have cost him a fair amount.

I never knew the derivation of Zackovitch's name. He was in actual fact a Yorkshireman, from where in Yorkshire I don't know, unless it was Hebden Bridge. He was of indeterminate age: he could have been old enough to have served in the First World War or he could have been a First World War baby. There was a rumour during the First World War that the Russians were passing through England because somebody had seen them at a railway station up north with snow on their boots. Perhaps Zackovitch's mother had happened to be in the station waiting room at the time.

Why he chose to live in such discomfort, nobody knew. In winter it used to be appalling. I treated him for pneumonia and had to go through eight or nine layers of clothes to reach his chest. But he recovered, refusing all along to go to hospital.

One Monday I came back from a weekend off to find an urgent call from him – he would never see any doctor but me. He had been having a little waterworks trouble for some time and hadn't passed any water since the Friday night. Finding that I wasn't on duty he was determined to wait until I came back.

I went early and found him in considerable pain with a stomach so swollen that he looked pregnant. There was a tremendous argument about whether he should go into hospi-

tal or not. I refused to try and catheterise him on the spot and told him he would probably need an operation. In the end he reluctantly agreed to go to hospital. A catheter was inserted and he was back in his caravan that night.

'No more hospitals for me,' he said. 'Once is enough.'

At the time Zackovitch had his trouble, catheters were not as sophisticated as they are today. They were made of a substance that meant they would eventually block off, and had to be changed at least once a month, sometimes more. I spent a lot of time in the most unhygienic surroundings, particularly in mid-winter, inserting new catheters into Zackovitch in the most difficult circumstances, with only the relevant piece of anatomy on display, surrounded by a mass of grubby clothing.

I had a patient when I first went into practice who became an expert at catheterising himself, keeping a catheter wrapped in newspaper in his hat. He never washed it, just fished it out and inserted it whenever he felt his tank was full. Zackovitch couldn't take his own catheter out; by this time they had progressed to the extent that they were kept in the bladder by a little balloon. The balloon was filled with water through a tube that ran alongside the catheter and would blow up to the size of a small tangerine.

One weekend the catheter became clogged. Zackovitch rang up to enquire whether I was on duty and being told 'No' he said, 'Never mind'. Henry who was on duty for the weekend, rang to tell me of the call, so I thought I had better look in at the caravans.

I found Zackovitch quite happily wandering round the copse.

'How are things?' I said. 'I've come to change your catheter.'

'No need doctor,' he said. 'I pulled it out myself.'

The very thought of him pulling it out with this tangerine–sized bag attached to the end, made me wince.

'I'm not having one of those things in again,' he said. 'No need. I've passed water fine ever since.'

Zackovitch had done the equivalent of a man efficiently cleaning a rifle barrel. How on earth he had done it I don't know but his good pull-through seemed to work. From then on he had no further trouble with his waterworks.

I never knew much about him, nor could I find out even how he had landed up in these two caravans. His wife, a simple soul, was so concerned with her own troubles (she was getting progressively crippled with arthritis), that she was not much help either.

I had got quite fond of Zackovitch in a way and certainly admired his courage, and a doctor is always flattered when a patient will only see him and nobody else. But after his pull-through, he bothered me less and less. I would occasionally see him and his wife in the town, shopping. I was called once more to the caravans, this time to see Mrs Hebden who had sprained an ankle carrying the water across the field. Again I pleaded with Zackovitch to find better accommodation, but he wouldn't hear of it.

After my coronary bypass operation I was off work for six months. When I came back I started to pick up the threads and contact my old patients. One day I popped in to see Zackovitch and his wife. They were gone. The dilapidated caravans were empty and had been vandalised; windows were smashed, doors torn off and scanty bits of furniture thrown all over the place. There was no record of Zackovitch going into any housing accommodation locally and as far as I knew he had no family. That was the last I thought that I would hear or see of them.

A year later Steve Maxwell was driving up north to see some relative near Birmingham. Turning off the motorway just south of Birmingham he spotted two dilapidated caravans in the cutting underneath the motorway. There was a crippled old lady struggling with a milk churn towards the caravans and a man wrapped in grubby clothing sitting at the caravan door, impatiently waiting. 'I could have sworn they were the Hebdens,' said Steve, 'but there was no way I could pull off the road.'

I'm afraid I wasn't prepared to get my car out and shoot up to Birmingham just to see if it was Zackovitch, so I never knew what became of him.

*   *   *

Miss Peabody worked at the income tax office on Tadchester Quay. She was the sort of person who could not be called anything other than Miss Peabody, nor work anywhere other than in an income tax office.

She was short, plump, grey haired, wore glasses and was completely ageless. At a guess I would have said she was seventy-five but, knowing that she was a civil servant with a retiring age of sixty, I realised she must be less than that unless she had special dispensation.

She was such a permanent fixture at the local income tax office that I had visions of the cleaning ladies dusting her as part of their duties.

She was much like one of our venerable bishops whom I saw when watching a royal wedding at Eric's Radio and TV shop one day. Seeing this snowy-haired, round-shouldered old man tottering up the aisle with only his shepherd's crook keeping him from falling on his face, I said, 'There's a grand old man.'

28

'Do you know how old he is?' said Eric.

'No,' I said, 'but I should think he's creeping up towards the Queen's telegram.'

'In fact,' said Eric, 'he's only forty-five. He's been practising being eighty ever since he's been forty.'

Miss Peabody was of this ilk. She lived in a neat council flat in the centre of the town. But she had an ambition.

If you asked her what she was going to do in the future she said, quite assuredly, 'I'm going to win the football pools. When I've won them I shall buy a villa in Spain, and when I retire I shall go and live in Spain in the sunshine.'

Although everybody else that I'd ever met was sure that one day they were going to win the pools, I never met anybody quite like Miss Peabody who was absolutely, positively certain she was going to win. It was as if she had had some divine message.

On her annual holiday to Hastings each year, Miss Peabody made several day trips to Calais and Boulogne, so she had already acquired a taste for Continental life.

The win didn't come in a hurry as she filled her pools in, week after week, year after year, on a very modest stake. But Miss Peabody pressed confidently on.

She was very rarely ill, but one Monday morning, she came to the surgery, grey-faced and tight-lipped, and asked for two tranquillisers.

It was taking every bit of her self-control to hold herself together, but she would give no reason.

'Could I just have two tranquillisers doctor? Just the two tablets. I don't mind how much it costs.'

It was the sort of request I got from people who were taking their driving tests for the tenth time and wanted something to steady their nerves the night before. I acceded to her request, wondering what emotional traumas had induced this state in this most staid little lady. Perhaps it was a love affair. No. On second thoughts ...

I learnt two days later that Miss Peabody, as she had always said she would, had won the football pools. She hadn't won a

29

giant amount, just £20,000. True to her word, she spent £15,000 of it on buying an apartment in southern Spain. To my amazement I found that she was only fifty-five and she was going to use the apartment for holidays until she reached her retiring age of sixty, when she would go to live there. It was nice having the extra £5,000 for furnishing and incidental expenses.

Miss Peabody went off and had three weeks in Spain, thoroughly enjoying it and getting to know the people. It should have been the end of a happy story.

But, alas, when she went back next spring for an early holiday, she found her apartment had been vandalised. The electricity had been cut off and there were all sorts of complex Spanish regulations to deal with. It was all more than she could cope with. She put the flat up for sale. She lost a bit of money on it, not too much, but her dream of living in the sunshine in Spain disappeared.

With the money she salvaged, she bought a nice little house near the park in Tadchester, quiet and away from the noisy council block she lived in. So her winning had been a great bonus, even if her main objective hadn't been achieved. She duly worked on until her retirement, then spent the time in her own house with its nice little garden. She had her library books, belonged to several women's organisations and was a strict churchgoer, so time didn't hang heavily on her hands.

She had bronchitis a couple of winters after she had retired. I popped in to see her. She was lying, covered in blankets, on a chaise longue in her dining room. Covering the dining room table was a mass of football pool forms from about every pools firm in the land. Having checked her over, I asked about her pools. Was she having another go?

'Yes, Doctor,' she replied. 'I'm quite certain that I'm going to win the pools again but this time I think I might look for an apartment in France. I think they're rather more civilised than the Spanish.'

I prescribed for her condition, wished her luck and left her. I thought the chances of her having a second win on the pools were absolutely minute. But for her it was an objective; it might happen any week. If it never happened at all, which was the most likely, she was doing that most important thing, travelling hopefully – which by definition, is supposed to be better than arriving.

* * *

Problems that arose in the practice were not just confined to the patients. Not infrequently they involved the partners and their families as well. I remember once coming to the surgery, being handed the phone and told, 'Just listen to this.' There was a child screaming at the top of its voice. When I spoke to the mother I found it was Pam, and it was Paul, one of my own children, who had scalded his hand.

Jack Hart had decided to bring his parents to Tadchester so he could keep a better eye on them. Jack was a gentle, reserved man who was easy to underestimate. It was very difficult to get him to talk about his wartime experiences but he was a doctor working in Hull when the war broke out. He volunteered for the airborne forces, landed in a glider in France soon after D-Day and landed again in a glider during the Rhine crossing. In his second landing the glider came down smack in front of a German machine gun, leaving the troops no alternative but to surrender. Jack spent the rest of the war behind barbed wire in a German prisoner-of-war camp.

During the war Jack's father had served in the Forces as a surgeon, mainly in Africa and sub-tropical areas. Not only did he have to battle for the health of his patients but also spend a tremendous amount of his time and energy on the hygiene of the medical station and the instruments, reducing the chances of cross-infection by making sure that they were sterile and didn't go rusty in the humid surroundings.

Jack's father was a bit eccentric and his mother an absolute dear: one of those little old ladies who was always smiling and who looked as though she were made of porcelain. She was handicapped with arthritis and her husband had to do most of the household shopping and, indeed, most of the housework.

In his later years, his eccentricities became more noticeable, probably a reversion to his army surgical days in the jungle. Obsessed about things not being clean and going rusty, he was one of the few people who could empty the whole of a house hot-water system simply by doing the washing-up for two people. Every single item had to be washed thoroughly under a running tap. It had to be dried and then had to be blow-dried with a specially powerful drier. He gave the silver teapot an extra boost on his heater and eventually managed to melt it.

His eccentricities were all quite harmless but they did mean that a great deal of his day was occupied in the simple act of washing a few pots, pans, knives and forks (but alas no more his silver teapot) for two people.

Dr Hart senior had one other idiosyncrasy: his bed. He always refused to buy a new one. The middle of the bed had sunk so much that although his feet and head were at the same level, the rest of his body was down in a deep pit. It was the sort of bed that a camel would have been very happy in, providing it could stick its four feet up in the air. There was a theory that

32

his dipping bed felt like a hammock and reinforced his feeling of being back in the jungle.

He had to go to hospital for a few days and, as Jack's mother couldn't manage on her own, his mother-in-law volunteered to come and hold the fort. There was a difficulty in that there were only two bedrooms in the flat; one occupied by Mrs Hart senior and the other by the bed with the bump in it in old Dr Hart's room. A new bed was ordered to coincide with the day that he was to be admitted to hospital so that it would be a *fait accompli* by the time he came back.

When the time came for him to go to hospital, he decided that he wanted Jack to cut his hair – not that Jack had ever done it before. There was no arguing with his father, so they went into the kitchen and Jack started chopping off a few of his grey locks. In the midst of this the new bed arrived. There was then a sort of French farce, Jack trying to keep his father pinned in the kitchen while the bed was hidden in his wife's bedroom until they eventually got him out of the house.

His stay in hospital wasn't long, but long enough to get him used to a flat bed. He came home and made no comment about the new bed; he seemed to assume that it had always been there. But as soon as he got home, even before he got his coat off, he washed all the cups, plates, knives, saucers, spoons, and anything else he could lay his hands on, carefully drying them, before extensively blow-drying them, including the inside of the new china teapot.

Then he said, 'Thank God. For the first time for days I'll be able to have a clean cup of tea.'

* * *

William Jessop lived in a row of Edwardian houses in a road near the hospital which, in Edwardian times, must have housed the *crème de la crème* of Tadchester society. Many of the houses had been subdivided, some turned into flats, but William Jessop's house was in no way touched; on entering the house you felt you were back in the Edwardian age. It was still filled with the Edwardian furniture of his parents and William himself was an Edwardian figure with a wing collar and a silk cravat with a large diamond pin stuck in the middle of it.

He was an incredible man who knew more about everything than anybody else I've known. He shared his house with a housekeeper-companion, a Miss Winmaker, who was a sort of mental playmate. She could have been a physical playmate too, but somehow I don't think she was, and they were both staunch supporters of the Methodist chapel.

To my knowledge William never went out to work. He played around with stocks and shares and was obviously not short of money. He had a tremendous appetite for knowledge of every kind. He read, and he loved Miss Winmaker to read to him. He played the piano and the organ and was a great authority on music. He was a ham radio operator and conversed with people all over the world. He could speak several languages fluently. And he seemed to know everything about everything.

One day when I had called to see Miss Winmaker, he came down and stopped me.

'Do you know how the distance a furlong developed?' he said.

'No,' I said, thinking about my next case and not wanting to get into a long intellectual discussion with William.

'Well,' he said, 'it was one of the first distances of measurement. What happened was that they got some oxen and they hitched them to a plough and they made a note of how much they could plough in a certain period of time. From then on, that length was called a furlong.'

'Thank you very much, William,' I said, shoving the information into my own memory bank. Perhaps I could get the garage to change the speedometer in my car from miles to furlongs.

William loved to travel.

'So many people think it's the sights of places that are exciting but, to me it's the smells,' he said. 'I love the smell of a place.'

He wrote three philosophical books: when I say wrote, he

always used a typewriter, nothing handwritten, and he could type away as fast as the best shorthand typist.

I first met him when he was in his middle sixties and all the time I knew him, he was as busy as a bee. No moment of the day was wasted. If he sent for me it was usually to query me about some new medical advance. He always knew far more about it than I did. He was a very nice man, if a little brusque in manner, and tremendously perceptive. I only had to walk into the room on a visit and he would say, 'What's bothering you today, Dr Clifford?' or 'You seem pleased with yourself today, Dr Clifford,' before I had even opened my mouth, and he was always right. He seemed to have an extra sense about people.

He had some wealthy gentlemen-farmer friends with whom he toured the Continent, Miss Winmaker always making up the party. One of the farmers told me that one day they were driving through Paris and were suddenly lost. They were aiming for Le Touquet.

'I don't know which way to turn,' said the farmer.

'Can you see Notre Dame?' asked William.

'Just,' said the farmer.

'Can you see its shadow?'

'Just,' said the farmer. 'It's pointing to the right.'

'Well, it's twelve o'clock now,' said William, 'take the next turning left and we should be on the road to Le Touquet.'

The farmer did and William was right.

Unfortunately I could never make a friend of William. Not that he was unfriendly, he just lacked the warmth of the old philosophical bookseller at Sanford-on-Sea, Bob Barker, with whom I had many chats. William was really far too intellectual to be chummy.

I would wager an even bet if you asked him any question, be it political, historical, geographical, he would know the answer. He was right up-to-date with current affairs. He always knew who would win an election and by how much. The only thing he wasn't so good on was the weather.

William was quite a remarkable man. In fact, when I look back, probably one of the most remarkable, knowledgeable men I have ever met. The most remarkable thing about him was that you honestly couldn't call him blind, in spite of the fact that at the age of eleven he had completely lost the sight of both eyes.

CHAPTER 5

Family Matters

Pam first started complaining about pains in her hip ten or eleven years back: a bit of stiffness, a bit of pain getting out of bed in the morning. I took notice because Pam was probably the least complaining person I ever knew. (Putting up with me for all these years should confirm that.)

Initially a couple of aspirin put everything all right. There would be no problem for two or three months, then her pain would return, calling for a few more aspirins. During the winter months she had more persistent pain and I or one of my partners would put her on one of the anti-inflammatory drugs that ease joint pain. Oiling the joints, I call it. The drugs relieve pain by taking the inflammation away. By removing inflammation they remove the local pain, as opposed to a pure pain-reliever which relieves any sort of pain. One of the anti-inflammatory drugs would help a little bit with toothache, but not as much as a straightforward pain-killer.

Pam was always better in the summer, and better still if we had been on the Thames with Joe and Lynne. I deduced, thinking man that I am, that having her leaping up lock sides with a rope between her teeth and pulling the boat in was doing her hip good. Anyway, I resolved that from her health point of view, it was much better if I did the steering and she did all the leaping about. She didn't mind this and was actually sure that it kept her pain-free and stopped her being stiff. I encouraged her in this activity and became one of the best steerers on the river.

Pam, Paul, Jane and I once took a canal boat on the Brecon-Abergavenny Canal, a unique canal running parallel to the River Usk, surrounded by villages that seemed to be thirty years back in price as well as time and customs. Paul even caught a trout in the canal and was so confused to find such a beautiful game fish that he unhooked it and put it back in, as he would any coarse fish.

It was a complicated canal full of locks, and Pam had to run across the planks (I haven't a very good head for heights), perch right over the tall locks, and tug on ropes while I hung on grimly to the steering wheel. It was one of the best years her hip ever had. I did think at one time of prescribing boating, or at least land-crewing for patients with painful hips.

However, her hip steadily worsened. She had spells when she was in a good deal of pain. We both accepted the fact that one day we would have to do something about it, but Pam hoped that day was many, many years off.

Her mother, who had been a most courageous lady, had both hips operated on years before artificial hips were thought of. In those days it meant going into hospital for a minimum of twelve weeks in traction, having one hip operated on and then going back six months later for a further twelve weeks while the other hip was done. The operation didn't leave the patient walking about as if nothing had happened, as modern hip operations do. It meant the patient could get about and was relatively pain-free, but that was all.

We gradually went on to stronger and stronger anti-inflammatory preparations. At last Pam agreed to have an X-ray of her hip, and it did show gross arthritic changes. Although by now the anti-inflammatory drugs had begun to upset Pam's stomach a bit, she still wasn't keen on an operation. She had the brilliant idea of joining the over-fifties badminton club; the activity was almost like leaping from a boat. She went to the club twice and thoroughly enjoyed herself, but each time she came back with progressive pain and from then on her hip was sheer agony.

'My love,' I said, 'we've no alternative. We must seek advice.'

There was an orthopaedic surgeon in Winchcombe, Pat Chesterfield, whom I'd known since our student days. 'Let's see him,' I said.

There seemed to be a lot of obstacles.

'I can't have it done before Christmas,' said Pam, 'and then there's Trevor's birthday.'

'Never mind darling,' I said. 'Let's just go and see Pat.'

Pam had a further X-ray which showed that over a period of three months the condition of her hip, almost certainly aggravated by the badminton, had deteriorated markedly. The head of main bone in the leg, the femur, had almost disintegrated.

'You must get this hip done as soon as possible,' said Pat Chesterfield when he saw the X-rays. 'I don't know how you've managed to walk on it.'

Pam went over to Winchcombe to be operated on, coincidentally a year to the day that I had had my coronary bypass operation. She was to have a total hip replacement which would mean removing the whole of the diseased joint and putting in a new artificial one. She felt pretty rough the first day after the operation and was in some pain. The second day she was sitting up taking notice, eating and reading a paper. The third day she was swinging her legs out of bed, thoroughly enjoying being waited on. By the fifth day she was beginning to walk. By the sixth day she was doing some stairs. By the twelfth day she was home, determined not to use sticks, and climbing the stairs unaided.

Within a few weeks she was driving the car and walking into town. Nobody would believe that she had ever had anything wrong with her hip.

We both had our operations on November 23rd. For both of us our first major social event was a New Year's Eve dinner with friends, a sort of first-footing.

Pam was a different woman with her new hip. She was pain-free. She could turn over in bed without any trouble. She was off all drugs. It really was a miracle. We were so fortunate to be born in an age when these great advances in surgery had been made. I certainly, without my operation, would have had to give up work. If there hadn't been these marvellous new artificial hips Pam would have had to undergo the same traumatic experience as her mother and would have finished up, not fully mobile but just pain-free and able to get about only moderately well.

At the time Pam was in hospital there was somebody else having an artificial shoulder put in and somebody else having an artificial knee put in.

Jack Kitchen, an old friend, used to call in and see us with his French wife, Pierette. Now a consultant orthopaedic surgeon at Bath, Jack was the British, if not the world, authority on ankle replacements. He was a huge, broad shouldered, gentle giant who played in the front row with me in my medical student days.

The rugby team called him Garth, after a cartoon character in the *Daily Mirror*, who was a cross between Tarzan and the

Incredible Hulk. Jack was rarely ever roused, but on the rare occasions that the opposing pack did rile him enough to lose his cool, he would seem to swell up about twice his size and sling the opposing set of forwards all over the field.

He had met his wife on a French rugby tour when we were playing in Bordeaux. They always said I had introduced them. I never quite worked out how this had happened but anyway, thirty years later, they were still very happily married. Whenever we met, Jack and I used to have a semi-scrum down to remind us of old times.

As well as being an orthopaedic surgeon, he had written several books on the history of British surgery and had a great passion for literature.

Jack would sit there, brow furrowed, and say, 'It's quite incredible. Who would ever think of two front-row forwards writing books?' The true front-row forward was supposed to be bone from the neck up and with his ears coming out on his shoulders. If you weren't born like that, by the time you had played rugby, that's the shape you became.

It was so good to see Pam free of pain and mobile again. She started to ride her bike, went swimming, and said tentatively, 'What about squash?'

'I should leave it just a little while,' I said. 'Certainly until the scar has healed.'

The children had all visited their mother in hospital and were at the house when she was discharged. They were standing at the door to meet her as I brought her home in the car.

There stood Trevor, Jane, Paul and Gill with a big bunch of flowers.

'We won't say "Welcome Home Mother",' said Trevor. 'We'll just say "Hip, Hip, Hooray!"'

*   *   *

We were fortunate in the spacing of our children's ages that none of them was close enough to have to compete with each other. There was three-and-a-half years between Trevor, the eldest, and Paul, and ten years between Trevor and Jane, our

41

youngest who although having two much older brothers, was neither a tomboy not spoilt. Jane developed into a good-looking, fair-haired young woman who never said a nasty word about anybody, was always a delight to have around, and was the true definition of a 'good sort'.

When I look back over my life, the best times I had were holidays with the children. The practice was good in that it allowed us to have a month in the summer so that, even when the children were quite young, we would roam all over the Continent on camping trips or get out on a boat. Even when the children had all left home, we would always try and have a few days together somewhere.

Trevor, after taking a masters' degree in law and spending a couple of years lecturing in law, went to drama school and joined the acting/writing profession which he loved. Although to date he has not become a front-line star, he has done very well and never seems to be unemployed. Part of this is because he mixes writing with acting, and mainly because he works very hard at it. If there's not much acting about, there's usually a bit of writing and vice versa. We are all of us Trevor groupies and follow him around to watch him in his various perform-ances. To York to see him in an Alan Bleasdale play, to Southampton for a Melvyn Bragg musical. One memorable evening in London, memorable because of the heat which I thought was going to make me pass out, we sweated it out watching him play Rosencrantz and the first gravedigger in *Hamlet*, with Robert Lindsay a brilliant Hamlet.

Trevor did a bit of everything. He wrote a few episodes for *Tucker's Luck* for the BBC, as well as appearing in one. He wrote several episodes of *Albion Market* for ITV, became the Schweppes' man for the New Zealand market where he had to play a barmaid, a yokel and a butler, as well as doing commer-cials for Shell, some Scottish ales and various other companies.

Paul, married to the delightful Gill who painted and made jewellery, was in a job in a micro-electronics factory in Tad-chester. When he had gone there initially they had given him a specifically named post and then kept on moving him sideways. He eventually finished up as a progress-chaser which is a job where everybody hates you, both the people you chase and the people who chase you.

'Never mind,' said his employers. 'If you work hard enough you will eventually become . . . ' and they gave the name of the job he had been originally appointed to.

Paul desperately searched round for new jobs. It would mean his leaving Tadchester, as prospects in his kind of work were limited locally. Eventually he found just the job for him in the Thames Valley. He worked for a component firm who were part of a much larger group. They really knew how to look after their employees. From the beginning Paul was encouraged: people would ring him up and say how well he was doing. He had to cover vast areas by car and spend Sundays writing reports. But most important, the firm continually encouraged and supported him, as they did all their employees. They did seem to have the art of getting the best out of people and in the nicest possible way. He enjoyed his work and was successful at it and he and Gill settled down very quickly in Berkshire.

One of the perks of the job was that Paul got a large brand-new car, a good expense account and a free telephone. It was a complete contrast to the way that he had been treated at the micro-electronics firm.

Jane was at Brighton at the polytechnic, doing a degree in the history of design. One of the criticisms of the course was that the course itself had never ever been properly designed. During the first year of her course she had only to appear two mornings a week; sometimes the lecturer didn't appear and nobody was quite sure what they were supposed to do. It would appear to an outsider that there were two careers open to you after you had completed this course. One was to write a book on how it should be done and the other was to get yourself appointed as a lecturer to tell other people what it should be about. Or shouldn't, as the case may be.

Her second year did improve. I found it all a bit confusing. Their work included photography. They went up north, visited factories, went down a coal mine and had a magnificent trip to Vienna. Jane was an industrious, interested little girl. On completing her second year it did look as if she was going to come away with a reasonable degree, whatever that was.

She loved Brighton with all its shops, the sea and the theatre. She was much more of a Trevor groupie even than we were. Trevor would always have his sister up for a few days whenever he was in a play that was running for a long time. Jane thought that when she finished her course she would like to work somewhere behind the scenes in television, theatre or radio, but that was a year or two off. First she had to get a degree.

It was a great adjustment suddenly to find it was just Pam and I in the house. We not only missed the children but we missed all the friends of the children. When Paul had been with us and his musical group was functioning, there had always been lots of young people coming and going and lots of noise and bustle. At the time it used to be a bit hard going, but how we missed it now. We felt just like Darby and Joan.

The children always came home as often as they possibly could. We always tried to make it that coming home was something they could look forward to and not an obligation. We also made trips to see Jane, to Aldermaston to call in at Paul and Gills' cottage. The only disadvantage of staying with them was that the traffic in this beautiful old Georgian village had steadily increased over the years and I could swear that from five o'clock in the morning all the heavy traffic used to come in through the bedroom window, and go out through the bathroom. I do hope that some day they will put a bypass round it. Many of the houses are three or four hundred years' old and the constant rumble of heavy goods vehicles cannot help.

General practice was time-consuming for me, and Pam, with time on her hands, now did quite a lot of work for Oxfam, had part time jobs at various times in bookshops, went to French classes and swimming with the Evergreens. I was never sure whether this was a group of people who were coloured green, some people called Evergreen, or a darling little swimming bath with a lot of foliage.

We gradually built up a life of our own together. We were fortunate that we had many good friends locally but it was difficult. There was no doubt that we'd been dependent a lot on the children. Pam felt that she was too old for camping now so our visits to the Continent would be bed-and-breakfast in inexpensive French hotels, and we found that we increasingly tried for short trips, often only two or three days and occasionally five days. We had a long weekend in Paris with our old friends Eric and his wife Zara, which included a trip on the Seine, an evening in Monmartre and inadvertently a very saucy night show which beggared description. We had river trips with Lynne and Joe Church. A trip with two new friends, Des and Joan when we took our car from Newhaven to Dieppe. A night in Beauvais with its huge cathedral and the site where the Zeppelin R101 had crashed. A wonderful day's

driving through the Compiègne forests and a night in the lovely old French family hotel in a place called Noyon which was famous in the First World War. This again had a church about as big as St Paul's Cathedral. The hotel was a lovely rambling old place; huge rooms with showers, a vast dining room with marvellous service; a meal and a bottle of wine. Our total bill each was £7 for dinner, bed and breakfast; it was unbelievable.

Then we had a trip with Primrose and Frank Squires. I had always talked about inexpensive trips to France so it was left to me to arrange a five-day trip, hopefully to explore the Loire Valley.

We spent our first night in Vitré, a town that seemed to have more churches than houses, and had a fairly indifferent meal at the hotel. The indifference of the meal was highlighted on our second night at Chinon, Rabelais' birthplace, when Pam and Frank were stricken with a tummy bug and were very ill. The only accommodation we had been able to find at Chinon was of a pretty poor standard. If you're feeling poorly and having to rush to the bathroom frequently, it's no help to your condition to see hundreds of cockroaches scuttling away every time you turn the light on. Frank was in a bad way.

'We must find a hotel with a bathroom, toilet, and telephone,' he said. 'I don't think I'm going to survive this trip.'

We went on to Tours and after a lot of wandering round, found a magnificent hotel. It was not too expensive, and had beautiful marble staircases, plush rooms with every facility under the sun. It was a lovely summer's day and the streets were filled with market stalls, including many outside cafes. We ventured out in the evening — those that were eating, that is — to one of these kerbside cafes for kebabs.

This trip was some sort of record in that during the five days that we were away there was no single meal that all of us were fit enough to eat together. On the first night it had been Primrose with a migraine. On the second night George and Pam. Then intermittently until we got home, there was always one at each meal who dined solely on Perrier water. From

Tours we moved on to St Malo where Frank recovered but Pam still seemed a bit shaky. It was Primrose's birthday on our second night there and Frank had found a magnificent restaurant where, apart from Pam, we all did justice to our meal.

I always go armed with a pharmacopoeia of medicines when we go abroad. I don't know how people manage without them. Certainly this trip would have been a disaster if I hadn't been able to supply the appropriate drugs. In the end we all put it down as a great experience. We put the hotel in Virtré into the Bad Food Guide that we were compiling and arrived home safely, all of us a bit thinner but none of us too much the worse for wear.

* * *

Pam half promised that when I retired, which wasn't in the too far distant future, she and I might do a bit of camping again together. When we had camped with the children, often with our friends Margaret and Sally as well, the car was usually so jam-packed with things that we could hardly move. Now we felt that with just the two of us, a tent and a few cooking things and sleeping bags thrown in, would be enough.

Neither of us were big eaters. Lunches in France were always a set routine. First a village where we could buy pâté, a bottle of wine, some cheese; next a river bank in the sunshine, preferably with a nice shady tree nearby. There are very few pleasures better than being stretched out on the river bank in the sunshine after your bread, pâté, sausage and cheese, washed down with half a bottle of wine and a cup of coffee boiled on the little gas stove. An extra treat was a French cigar called a Voltagar which although about ten times the size, was the same price as a cigarette. There was a picture of a camel on the front of the packet: Eric said it was unique in being the only packet which carried a picture of the animal that produced the material for the tobacco.

Yes, we loved France. Not that in any way we didn't love England, but France had one particular more or less guaranteed

47

ingredient that if you went far enough south you could always find what we lacked. Sunshine.

* * *

Pam and I decided to spoil ourselves with an expensive holiday. We chose Madeira, which I had visited once before and had always hoped to take Pam to, and which many of our friends talked of as some sort of paradise.

We flew out on a cold February morning and landed at this delightful island noted for its short runway which limited the size of planes that could land there. Traditionally, all the passengers cheered as the pilot landed the plane safely.

We were driven to the best hotel I have stayed at in my life. The towels in the room were changed twice a day. This worried me so much that I used to go and dampen unused towels just to show the room attendant how clean I was. There was a large swimming pool, surrounded by lawn, with special couches to lounge on. And a man assigned to carry your mattress and towel and make you comfortable on your couch. I would hate to be called a sybarite, but this was heaven.

It was a pleasant walk down to Funchal, which had not been spoilt by tourists. The indigenous population had held its own. There was a marvellous fish market, an abundance of flowers, some lovely old buildings and pleasant places to sit out in the sun having coffee and just watching people go by.

The hotel had been designed by the same architect who designed Brasilia and he had designed it on the same scale. You entered the restaurant, with room for a thousand diners, down a huge sweeping ramp to a vast room surrounded by windows about forty feet high.

There's an old cliché about its being a small world. There's a more recent one about not being able to take your mistress anywhere these days. Wherever you go, however far from home, you're bound to bump into somebody you know.

As Pam and I sat down to our first meal, a lady from the next table got up and said, 'Isn't it Dr Clifford?'

It was Jean Davis who used to be the health visitor in

48

Tadchester, staying there with another health visitor friend. On the plane coming over we met the local baronet from Tadchester, who came over every winter and spent a month at Reid's Hotel, in the same room. He said he had come specifically this year to practise tying his flies. Being a bit slow on the uptake, and especially as I knew he hadn't been well, I thought for heaven's sake, why doesn't he buy himself a zip? But of course he meant tying his flies for his fly fishing. It just shows the mess you can get into when you are not properly brought up.

There were a number of trips around the island. We went up to see the extinct volcanic crater, which was superb. We did a toboggan ride down the streets with men in immaculate white flannels, jumping on either side of the sledge to stop us bumping into the walls. We saw the woods, and on the far side the massive waterfalls which provided Madeira with its hydro-electricity.

There were little sheds that held cows, not for milk, but purely as producers of manure: all dairy products were imported. The cows were fed on any old rubbish and usually spent a lifetime in the shed, becoming blind. There was just not sufficient land for grazing, and I did feel rather sorry for the poor old cows.

On one of our trips round the island the guide told us the various theories of how Madeira had originated. One theory was that it was part of the lost island of Atlantis that was still sticking above the water. Another was that it was part of a volcanic eruption and one of a series of islands including the Canaries. The third theory was that when God made the world, he was so pleased with what he had done that he bent down and kissed the sea. Where he kissed the sea Madeira was formed. I must say I went along with that.

Most of the hotels had nightclubs, not sophisticated hot-spots, but pleasant genteel places where middle-aged couples, like ourselves, could waltz to *Who's Taking You Home Tonight?* and other tunes of our vintage.

One of the main problems was that every time we went out to a nightclub it seemed to coincide with the night starring the

Portuguese dancers, who pulled out members of the audience to join in their very vigorous dancing. I almost carried a notice saying, 'Beware Portugese dancers'.

By sheer chance, we had chosen carnival week in Madeira, the island's most important week of the year.

We were treated to the spectacle of mile after mile of beautifully clad young men and women dancing to bands that bobbed up about every fifth or sixth group. They wore the most exotic and bizarre costumes: giraffes, swans, toadstools, bananas and apples. Our own hotel's group, dressed as shellfish — lobsters, prawns and crabs — won first prize. It was a magic night with bonfires lighting up this procession of happy, beautifully-dressed young people and cheering crowds.

The carnival lasted all week and the main hotels were visited each evening by the carnival dancers. The judging of costumes took place in our hotel in the massive dining room which was cleared of all the tables. There was dancing all night, or at least there was moving about to music on the packed floor.

The hotel doors were flung wide open, at least five thousand strangers poured into the hotel, and although quite a number of people had had a few drinks, I didn't see a single drunk.

Nothing was stolen from the hotel, nothing was damaged. Even stranger still, there wasn't a single policeman in sight. It was a tremendous tribute to how things can be, and I hope it never changes. It was a place where ladies could safely go on holiday on their own, could walk the streets safely at night. Madeira is a small island, admittedly, and there is nowhere for a robber to run to, but it was very refreshing to spend just a short time in this unsophisticated atmosphere.

There was just one incident that cast a gloom on the holiday. The lady sitting next to me on the plane coming over was confused about her papers. She was a lady in her late seventies. I asked if I could help, and it came out that I was a doctor.

'I'm so pleased to know that there's a doctor,' she said, and she was even more pleased to know that I was going to her hotel.

I asked how much she had travelled in the past.

'I've never travelled alone on my own before. This is my first flight and my first trip abroad.'

She then gave me an account of the medication she was on. She suffered from severe heart disease and was diabetic. My heart sank. It looked as if I was going to have a patient for the whole week, but she was such a nice person and it had been her life's ambition to come to Madeira to see the orchids.

She was part of a singles group and we were pleased to see, on the first evening at dinner, that she was at a table with about thirty other people, all chatting. We didn't see her at all the next day but on the following day Pam and I found her sitting looking rather exhausted in the hall. We chatted to her briefly. She had seen her orchids and was rather tired, just taking a rest before going up to her room.

At dinner, she came in halfway through the meal and sat down alone. We determined to take her under our wing, so Jean Davis, her friend Marjorie, Pam and I went over and asked her to join us for coffee. We had a lovely evening with her, and she told us all about her family: how her daughter hadn't wanted her to go on her own, and how they were all worried about her.

51

In spite of us seeing her with about thirty people on the first night, she had been having a pretty lonely time. She had walked up the hill by herself from Funchal, and that had nearly killed her, but she had seen her Madeira orchids and fulfilled her lifelong ambition.

She was good company. What she hadn't seen was the hotel, so Jean Davis, who was the best of good souls, said she would pick her up from her room in the morning to show her around, and she would travel with us in future.

Next morning Jean came to me by the pool and said, 'It's very strange, there's a notice saying "Do Not Disturb" outside the old lady's room and they won't let me in. It's all very mysterious.'

I went down to the manager and told him that we were looking for our friend and couldn't understand why there was no reply. He looked at me and asked me into his office.

'Excuse me, sir, but did you know the lady in No 10?'

'Yes,' I said. 'Quite well. We spent yesterday evening with her.'

'I'm afraid I have some very bad news for you,' he said. 'She died in her sleep last night.'

This was absolutely staggering. We had had such a happy time the previous evening. She had told us about seeing the marvellous orchids which had fulfilled a life's ambition. I was able to ring her daughter who was absolutely distraught. She had obviously been a mum who was adored by her family. They were worried to death about her going in the physical state she was in but, she had insisted that before she died she would see her Madeira orchids.

Her condition was such that she could have gone at any time. Similarly she could have staggered on for a few years, but there must have been some instinct which told her that her time was short and unless she did the thing she had always wanted to do, she might never do it. In spite of her poor health, and in spite of never travelling by air before, she had the courage to get up and go. Suddenly I wasn't sad any more, just proud to have known this most courageous little lady who had achieved her lifetime's ambition.

CHAPTER 6

Clanger Bartlett

Clanger Bartlett arrived suddenly out of the blue. We had a phone call to say that he was in Plymouth. Could he come and see us?

I hadn't seen Clanger since my student days when he had been one of my closest friends, completing a trio with Taffy Williams, now a very distinguished physician in Scotland. Somehow, although we were very different characters, we stuck together all through our student years.

Taffy was brilliant: as well as qualifying in medicine he took an Honours Physiology Degree, topping the pass list at London University. Clanger was a mature student and had been doing some laboratory work before taking up medicine, and was more sophisticated and worldly-wise than Taffy or myself. He had easily assumed the name 'Clanger' because he could put his foot in it more times than any other six people put together. He was accident-prone but a good and loyal friend.

Without Taffy and Clanger I would have never survived or even qualified in medicine. Clanger and I both failed our second MB . . . mine through spending too much time at rugby and not being very bright, and Clanger through his variety of interests. He always had several different hobbies on the go and now, true to form, he flew his own plane and collected vintage Rolls-Royces.

He and I, after failing our second MB together, sweated through the whole of one summer in my mother's flat in Chelsea, being coached by Taffy. Taffy, as London's star physiology student, somehow managed to help his two mates scramble through at their second attempt.

We both qualified eventually, Clanger staying on at our teaching hospital to work in the pathology laboratories, then spending some years in Canada before returning to work in the midlands, and more recently doing some work with the Armed Forces.

The memory of two occasions with Clanger still brings me out in a cold sweat. One weekend the three of us took my mother's boat out on the Thames. The boat was called *Avise* and it had the special characteristic of having two lots of controls, that is to say two throttles. One was near the steering wheel and the other, which controlled the reversing mechanism only, at the back.

With Clanger steering, we were coming up to a lock somewhere near Hampton Court. A whole row of boats was queuing to go in, but Clanger thought he saw an empty space at the head of the queue. He throttled forward and the boat shot past the waiting line. Seeing the danger from my post at the back, I put the boat full astern. Astern won; we crashed into the lock approach wall and smashed our rudder in half, to the delight of the several hundred spectators who were coming out of Sandown Park races.

Somehow we managed to patch the boat up and limp back to its moorings. Taffy, who had nothing at all to do with the disaster, followed it by a week in bed with severe sunstroke. 'There just isn't any justice,' he groaned.

The *Avise* had a very strange history. It was reported to have crossed the Channel, which I can't believe. My mother had bought it ostensibly to hire it out but it was a pretty scruffy old boat. She did have one reply to her advertisement. A young, very unmarried-looking, couple wanted to hire the boat for a week. My mother was explaining how they should approach locks, what they did in locks, and what they did after locks, but they didn't seem to take much notice. She repeated her instructions and then said, 'You do understand about locks?'

'Don't worry,' they said confidently. 'We're not going to bother with locks – we're going to go round them.'

There was a panic call from them after they had been out for three days to say that they had broken down in front of an oncoming steamer and had abandoned the boat way up river. My mother and I had to go up and fetch it back.

Another fine mess Clanger got me into, or one I got him into, was a boxing match against Cambridge University. By failing to attend a meeting I came down one day to find I was the secretary of the boxing club and responsible for organising boxing fixtures. Failing to attend another meeting of boxing secretaries, I found I had been appointed vice-captain of the United Hospital Boxing Club, and my first job was to organise a match.

I was quite inexperienced with these things and had difficulty in finding a hall, particularly one with seats in. I eventually found one at the Elephant and Castle that had no seats. Full of resource, I borrowed some folding chairs from a nearby church hall, but had to erect them all as well as pick up and return them.

We had been sent the team list of the Cambridge boxers. I was selected to fight the Cambridge secretary and to my horror I found I was two pounds above the lightweight limit. (It is a very sobering thought to think that nowadays I would be fighting as a heavyweight.) In spite of all the rushing about and preparations for the match, I still had to spend the afternoon in a Turkish bath to lose the two surplus pounds.

I got to the hall to find that my opponent had been unable to come. We were very short of bouts, so to make up numbers I agreed reluctantly to fight their middleweight boxing blue. It was not an over-long bout. He knocked me out in the first round as well as knocking a piece off one of my teeth. My bank

manager, who was an old family friend, had come out to the Elephant and Castle to watch all this. He was very impressed. As he told my mother: 'Bob was fighting very well until he got knocked out.'

We just managed to scramble enough bouts together to provide the local, very roughnecked, crowd with an evening's entertainment. I showered after my knockout, dressed and came into the hall to find a man in a dark suit waiting for me. He was from the Customs and Excise, for which I should apparently have made some provision, and he assured me they would summons me after the match was over.

We had to wait until everybody had gone to clear the hall and take the chairs in Clanger's mother's brand-new car back to the church hall. At last we set off home. Clanger was a man of sudden impulses. We were driving back though London at the head of a queue of traffic when, within about two feet of a pedestrian crossing, Clanger decided to stop to let an old lady cross. Without any warning he jammed on his brakes. A lorry ran into the back of him and a car ran into the back of the lorry. It was the end of a perfect day.

I went with Clanger to explain to his mother the crumpled appearance of the back of her brand-new car. She was very good about it. This was at the time when getting any sort of car was a premium and a new one was like gold dust.

Before Clanger's visit to us at Tadchester, he had been involved in the setting up of a specialised blood unit, of which there was only one in England and one in America. He had travelled down to London for a course of instruction due to start on a Friday, only to find that the specialist had gone to America for the weekend, and that the lecture would not be until Monday. The lecturer appeared on Monday dishevelled, exhausted and unshaven, but somehow got through the lecture. Clanger tackled him on his absence the previous Friday and was given the following explanation:

A Saudi Arabian businessman, said the lecturer, had come to him with a blood disorder. He examined the businessman's blood and said he would need some special type of blood replacement which was only done at one place in England.

'Good,' said the Saudi. 'Ring them and fix it up.'

The specialist rang to find that the only six private beds in this hospital were full. The only way the Saudi could go in was as a National Health patient. The hospital, like many old English hospitals was archaic, just about falling down and desperately in need of funds.

'Right,' said the Saudi. 'Ring them back and say that I will donate a million dollars to the hospital if a private bed can be found for me.'

The consultant rang back. Whoever was in charge of beds there said the money would not make the slightest difference. The Saudi Arabian could come in as a National Health patient or not at all. He was quite happy to let a million dollars slip through the hospital's fingers.

57

'Where else could I get this done?' asked the Saudi.

'There's only one other place, and that's in North America,' said our consultant.

'Right,' said the Saudi. 'Fix it up there.'

This was done in a few minutes with a transatlantic phone call.

'There's only one condition that I insist on before agreeing to go there,' said the Saudi. 'And that is that you accompany me. I am of course prepared to donate a large sum to your research unit here for this service.'

So the bedraggled physician had to commute to North America once a week to attend his wealthy patient, who happily made a good recovery.

I told this story to a prominent London businessman who was holidaying in Tadchester. He had come across the same kind of situation. A multi-million pound deal had been arranged at government level with some Middle Eastern potentate. Almost as they sat down to sign the agreement, as an afterthought the Middle Eastern gentleman said, 'By the way, I would like my son to be found a place,' naming a well known British university. The university was consulted but were unable to offer a place other than through the usual academic channels. However, Harvard University in the States, acted quite differently when approached. They were only too delighted to give a place to the son, and both the boy and the multi-million dollar contract went to America.

There are two morals to be drawn from these stories. I have never ever been able to work out which is the right one.

CHAPTER 7

Dimming Lights

I am always saddened to note the onset of senility in my older patients. Usually the process is a gradual one, but sometimes it can strike with startling rapidity and within a few months turn an intelligent, lucid and responsible person into a shambling, incoherent baby.

Geordie Napier was one who changed quickly. He was a retired miner, whippety but strong as an ox, whose great delight was to tell of the famous fight he had underground long ago with four other miners.

'Whipped the lot of 'em,' he'd boast, crouching into a boxer's stance and jabbing at the air with his fists. 'One after the other.'

When senility set in, the story became confused and rambling, and the number of his opponents expanded into dozens. Sometimes he would revert right back to childhood and sing nursery songs, or tell schoolkid jokes and snigger at the more risqué ones.

Geordie's wife, Rose, had the patience of a saint. She washed him, dressed him, fed him and tolerated calmly all his silly ways. 'He's been a good husband to me,' she'd say. 'Never drank. Always brought his pay packet home unopened. The least I can do is look after him now.'

But the strain on Rose began to tell. Geordie didn't sleep a lot, so the poor woman was on the go practically twenty hours a day. To give her a break, I pulled strings to get Geordie into the old people's home for a fortnight.

It was a great weight off Rose's mind for a couple of weeks, but a great trial for the staff at the old folks' home. Every day, Geordie caused ructions, usually finishing by putting up his fists and challenging all comers to a re-enactment of his famous victory down the pit.

One day there was a special treat for the old people — a mystery tour by coach, with a pub lunch at the destination, a market town about forty miles from Tadchester. Geordie was included on the trip; not the wisest decision the home's administrators ever made.

He behaved himself on the trip out, and through the pub lunch. Then he had a half pint of beer ... the first alcoholic drink of his life at nearly eighty. He found it very much to his liking, so much so that he sidled off into another bar and bought himself a whole pint from the spending money the home had provided.

When the time came to leave, Geordie was nowhere to be found. Panic set in among the organisers of the trip, and they went in search of him. They didn't have far to look.

Under a bridge over the river in the centre of the town, a bunch of down-and-outs spent their days drinking cider mixed with meths. They generally followed their pursuit quietly, and the police let them get on with it. But when the searchers arrived there was a huge commotion going on, with a policeman trying to restore order among the brawling drunks.

In the centre of the melée was Geordie, prancing about on his toes and squaring up to the enormous bobby.

'He's harmless!' shouted one of the search party. 'We'll take him home!'

'Harmless?' said the copper. 'Look what he's done to *them*!'

There, on the ground, lay two of the drunks — out to the wide, laid low in Geordie's Last Stand.

It turned out that Geordie had left the pub, roaring drunk

60

on the small amount of beer, and entertained the methies with a couple of songs and some jokes. They had rewarded him with swigs from their cider bottles, which led to a garbled account — with actions — of the fight underground. A couple of drunks had misunderstood and had gone for Geordie. That was a mistake, as the prostrate forms on the ground testified. The other drunks had taken sides, and within seconds a general free-for-all had broken out, alarming enough for the police to be called.

'OK then,' said the policeman, grabbing Geordie by the shoulders and lifting him clear off the ground, 'Take him away – but for God's sake, never bring him back ...'

*   *   *

Tommy Butcher was a self-educated former trade union leader, a highly intelligent man, and in his day a tough and

61

shrewd negotiator, feared by management. His senility was strangely intermittent: he'd be speaking quite lucidly and logically one minute, then suddenly lapse into gibberish. He'd return to normality and realise that his mind had been wandering. This happened during one of my visits: after three or four minutes of talking pure nonsense, Tommy snapped back into his normal state of mind and suddenly burst into tears.

'Excuse that, Doctor,' he said, blowing into his handkerchief. 'It's not often I've cried in my life. But it's one thing to be going barmy, and quite another to know it. I just wish now I could stay potty all the time ... '

* * *

The most startling change was in old Winnie Parsons. She'd had a hard life bringing up five children on her fisherman husband's small income. She'd always kept them, her house, and herself spotless. She was a neat, tidy woman, very reserved, highly respectable and a keen churchgoer.

In her late seventies, and within the space of a few months, she changed completely. She became slovenly and foulmouthed, even to the extent of bawling obscenities in church. She was suspicious of everyone around her, including her devoted husband, whom she accused of all kinds of infidelities and foul practices. She failed to recognise her grandchildren, and finally failed to recognise her husband.

'Who *is* this man?' she'd yell when he came into the room. 'Take him away! Dirty bastard! Don't let him touch me!'

Within nine months from the onset, Winnie was dead.

I hate losing a patient, and take the deaths of even the old ones to heart, but in Winnie's case I made an exception. Without putting any finer point on it she was, poor old thing, better off dead.

* * *

And yet other patients moved into old age with dignity, even with zest. Nellie Walters was one. After the death of her husband, Nellie emigrated to Australia to join her daughter and son-in-law. Lots of people emigrate to Australia, but few at the age of eighty-two.

Within two years, Winnie was back.

'What was the matter?' I asked, when she called at the surgery. 'Didn't things work out?'

'Oh, I got on well enough with my daughter and her family,' said Winnie. 'Always did. They made me very welcome, and bought a mobile home for me with all mod cons and set it up in their garden so that I could have my own place.

'But Australia takes some getting used to. Their garden for a start – huge, it was. Seemed like acres and acres. But it had acres and acres of *dust*. For nine months of the year there wasn't a blade of grass in sight.

'And creepy-crawlies! Spiders, centipedes, horrible big beetles – they had the lot. Never could stand creepy-crawlies of any kind, let alone giant ones.

'The heat, too. Most of the time I was either in the shower or lying on my bed with the electric fan full on, trying to keep cool. Too much at my time of life.'

'I can see why you came back, Nellie,' I said. 'Don't think I'd fancy that very much!'

'No, I don't think you would. Take my word for it. But what finally did it was Danish bacon!'

'Danish bacon? Didn't you like it?'

'Love it. But that was the trouble – in Australia you couldn't get it, and Australian bacon isn't a patch on it. I was like that old man in *Treasure Island* – or was it *Robinson Crusoe*? – the one who dreamt of cheese all the time. I'd lie awake at nights thinking of Danish bacon, sizzling away in the pan. In the end, I'd had enough and got the boat back home. And the first thing I had when I got off at Southampton was a huge plate of Danish bacon.'

'Great, Nellie,' I said. 'And now what can I do for you?'

'Indigestion mixture, Doctor,' she said. 'The kind you used to give me. Since I've been back I've been over-eating. And do you remember that anything fatty used to bring on my acid?'

'Ah yes,' I said. 'Anything fatty used to do that. Such as – '

'You don't need to tell me,' said Nellie. 'Such as Danish bacon ...'

* * *

I worried about the health of Ida Allsopp, though she brought many of her ailments upon herself. She lived in a small cottage near the river and refused to leave it. She and her husband had spent long and happy years there and after his death she felt it would be a disloyalty to give up their old home.

But the place had stone-flagged floors, no proper damp course, and was consequently cold and wet. It was draughty too, as Ida's old landlord didn't have the funds to keep the place in good order.

Ida was bronchitic, and there was no hope of her ever getting better so long as she lived in that cottage. But all my pleas for her to move, all my offers to help get her an old people's flat, had no effect whatsoever.

Then the council bought the cottage for modernisation. The renovation was to be so extensive that there was no way Ida could stay while work was in progress. She was moved out, protesting loudly, to a purpose-built block of old people's council flats near the parish church. 'Just for a few weeks, love,' the social worker explained. 'And when your cottage is done up, you can move back in.'

'Oh, all right,' said Ida, grumpily. 'But I'm not staying in that new place a day longer than I have to.'

The flats were marvellous. Centrally heated, lifts to every floor, ultra-modern kitchens and, best of all, a series of alarm bells on the walls at different heights, so that any old person in trouble could ring for the warden who looked after the flats.

After a few days grumbling, Ida got accustomed to her new surroundings and began to take an interest in them. One window overlooked the grounds of the parish church, a blaze of colour in summer with the well-tended rose beds. Another overlooked a shopping precinct and several pubs, so that there was always human activity for Ida to look out at. The precinct meant, too, that many of Ida's old friends would call on her when they'd done their day's shopping, so she was never short of company.

One day Ida collapsed with a heart attack. As she lay on the floor she had the presence of mind to press the alarm button in the skirting board. In less than a minute the warden was up in the lift and opening the flat door with his pass-key. A quick 999 call, and the ambulance was round.

Ida recovered, and eventually the time came for her to move back into her old cottage.

'If it's all the same to you,' she told the social worker, 'I'd rather stay here.'

'That's all right, love,' said the social worker. 'No problem. But you do surprise me, especially now that the old place is snug and warm.'

'Right,' said Ida. 'But I used to sit there for weeks and never see a soul. Here I see people every day – with a free show every night, too, when the pubs turn out.

'And I'm not daft enough to think I may never have another heart attack. Just think – if I was still living in that cottage I'd be dead.'

'Half a minute,' said the social worker, dazed by Ida's logic. 'I'll need time to work that one out ...'

CHAPTER 8

Fishing Lessons

I don't number fishing among my more highly developed skills, but I do enjoy it, especially when I can get out with John Denton for a day and learn a bit more about it.

Enjoyment is a big part of John's philosophy.

'We're only here once, lad,' he'd say. 'Se we'd best make the most of it. That cemetery over there is full of miserable buggers wishing they'd laughed a bit more when they had the chance.'

Which was one reason John didn't have much time for the matchmen who crowded the banks of the Tad during the coarse fishing season, at least not for the obsessive ace matchmen whose only aim was to win at all costs.

'The lads themselves are all right,' he said. 'They don't take it too seriously, have a few laughs, and look forward to wetting their whistles and telling lies in the pub afterwards. There's more to fishing than catching fish. But some of the top rankers in the Tadchester A Team make your hair stand on end.

'Winning is all they're bothered about. They've got tackle that cost a king's ransom. Secret baits that twenty-four hours on the rack wouldn't get out of them. They're snooping round the club, earwigging in the pubs, in the hope of picking up any scraps of information about the water that would help them win a prize. They play merry hell about the peg draw if they've been given a bad swim to fish. And if they don't come first at the weigh-in they're jumping up and down and demanding a re-weigh.

'They're skilled all right: you've got to give them that. Snatching tiddlers at a rate you wouldn't believe. But they don't need *fish* – they'd be just as happy being let loose with a swatter in a room full of flies and seeing who could swat the most. Aye, it might be clever, but I'm buggered if it's fishing.'

Certainly the matchmen weren't happy during August. The weather had been hot and dry for several weeks, the river was low and de-oxygenated, and the fish were refusing to co-operate.

'Not much chance for me, then, John,' I said.

'I don't know, lad. If you fancy it, we can try tomorrow away from the match stretches. Apart from anything else, those match lengths are so soured by untouched groundbait that they'll be fit for nothing until the water starts moving again. We'll have a go for gudgeon.'

'Gudgeon, John? But that's tiddler-snatching, surely?'

'Don't you believe it. Get a gudgeon on light tackle and you'll feel him all right. No Moby Dick, I grant you, but for his size he's the best scrapper in the river. There's a bloke in Ireland, runs fishing holidays on the River Blackwater, who actually advertises gudgeon among the attractions – and that's in Ireland, where fishing really *is* fishing.'

The gudgeon is a small fish – though it has been known to grow to half a pound, the British rod-caught record is only 4 oz 4 drams – and it's not very pretty. It's a speckled grey or greeny-brown, and grubs around the bottom feeling for food with two little barbels that hang down from either side of its mouth like a droopy moustache. I'd heard no end of jokes about it among anglers in the Tadchester Arms, ribbing each other about gudgeon which fought like tigers.

'Aye, they're a joke when there are bigger fish stirring,' said John. 'But in weather like this, when other fish are off their grub, the gudgeon will go on feeding. And not only will they give you a run for your money on light tackle: if you hit a decent-sized shoal you could pull in fifty-odd fish in a morning. It's all right those blokes pretending to look down on the gudgeon, but they're bloody glad of them when there's nowt else about.'

Next morning we got down to the river just as the sun was lifting the mist from the water. John led the way to a long, gentle bay which cut into clear bank between two stretches of trees.

He pegged out two keepnets in the shallow water, supporting the end of each with a couple of old rod rests to make sure the mesh would not fold back to trap the fish, should we be lucky enough to catch any. Then he walked to the nearest clump of trees and returned with an armful of leafy twigs.

'What are those for, John? Camouflage?'

'Nay, lad. Shade,' he said, poking the ends of the twigs under the wire frames of the keepnets. 'They'll keep the sun off the nets. Strong sunshine in shallow water doesn't do the fish a lot of good. And once they're in the net, there's nowhere they can go to find shade.'

We then set our landing nets.

'A bit ambitious, aren't we, John?'

'Not really. We could just swing the fish in without a net, but it doesn't do them a lot of good. May as well do the job properly from the start, even if it does look a bit daft.'

We each tackled up with a fragile-looking nine-foot rod, a reel holding almost invisible nylon line with a breaking strain of only one pound, a No 14 hook and a float of the tiniest quill.

From his rod holdall, John produced a garden rake.

'I didn't like to ask before,' I said. 'But what the hell's that for? You're not doing a bit of gardening on the side?'

'You'll see,' said John. 'Tried and trusted is this.'

He waded out slowly into the shallow, slow-running water, taking care not to splash, and raked the bottom in two patches, about twenty feet apart, back towards the bank. Mud and bits of debris swirled to the surface and turned the water into the colour and consistency of thick cocoa.

'That'll attract 'em' he said. 'Nothing they like better than a pea-souper, full of creepy-crawlies from out of the mud.'

We each baited up with a tiny red worm, of which John had brought along a tinful, harvested from his compost heap, cast out and waited for the first twitch on the floats. We made our usual bets: 5p on the first fish, 5p on the biggest and 5p on the most. Beauregard Denton and Ace-High Clifford, last of the Mississippi gamblers.

We sat there for fifteen minutes or so without a tremble on the quills. John walked over to throw some chopped meat and bits of worm around my float.

'What's up, John? Reckon even the gudgeon are giving it a miss today?'

'No. They'll be around all right. Almost certainly rooting around there now. A bit of extra grub will encourage them to – Hey up!'

He strode swiftly back to his own rod and struck with a quick turn of the wrist. The top of the light rod jagged wildly as the fish plunged this way and that. Within a few seconds he had drawn the fish over the top of his landing net and was lifting it clear of the water.

He unhooked it, first wetting his hand so as not to strip it of its slime, and brought it over to show me: a muddy-looking, unprepossessing little thing, but a fish, nevertheless. He put it into the keepnet with as much care as if it were a prizewinning Japanese ornamental carp.

'You're a witness, Bob,' he said. 'Fought like a tiger. That's 5p to me then. *We're in the money . . .*'

As I was laughing at John, my own float trembled violently and shot under the surface. I struck, a little late but still in time, and was rewarded by a fierce thrumming on the rod. I was sure I'd hooked the world's record, and was disappointed at the size of the tiny fish which had caused all the excitement.

'Told you, didn't I?' said John. 'If these grew bigger, nobody would fish for anything else.'

The morning progressed very pleasantly in a drowsy hum of insects. It was reasonably cool on the bank, although the sun beat down relentlessly from a cloudless sky. Every five minutes or so, one or both of us would have a bite. Each time there was that amazingly fierce throbbing on the light rod; each time the appearance of a fish four or five inches long that looked as if it shouldn't have been parted from its mother.

When things got slack, John would wade gently out, give the bottom another rake, and throw in more chopped meat and bits of worm around the floats. Before long, back came the fish; usually when I wasn't ready for them.

They had an uncanny knack of taking my float under just as I was in the middle of taking the top off the thermos flask or opening a packet of sandwiches. This resulted in a few missed strikes and some muttered curses. (Non-gambler though I am, 5p is 5p.) One sure way of getting a bite was to leave the rod to answer a call of nature. When I got back, there was the float diving underwater and surfacing again as the fish dropped the bait.

Eventually, along came twelve noon.

'Right, lad. That's it,' said John. 'They've stopped biting now.'

'Never on your life. Hang on. I had a twitch then.'

'You know the rules, Bob,' said John. 'At twelve noon they stop biting. Go dead off their feed. Any twitches on the float are purely an optical illusion.'

I knew the rules. At twelve noon John packed up, giving himself plenty of time to get over to the Tadchester Arms for his one o'clock pint. A creature of habit, our John.

We lifted out the keepnets and counted the fish. I'd done well with forty-four; John had done better with sixty-three.

'Another 5p to me,' said John. 'But I've got to give you best for the biggest fish. Look at that little beauty of yours.'

The little beauty was three ounces if it were a dram; a giant among gudgeon. So even though my feckless gambling had left me 5p down, I could still boast of having caught the biggest fish of the day – and that fishing against the bailiff himself.

'Make a nice fry-up' said John, as he carefully slid the fish back into the water.

'I wouldn't fancy them,' I said, looking at the mud-coloured backs wriggling swiftly beneath the surface.

'You would,' said John. 'Great Victorian delicacy, these. They used to have punt parties, with everybody – women and all – fishing for gudgeon. And then they'd have big fry–ups on the bank. Butter, flour, few herbs, salt and pepper, squeeze of lemon: delicious. Only trouble is you need a lot of them for a plateful. Poor little buggers.'

In the Tadchester Arms we met another angler, hunched gloomily over the bar.

'Any luck?' asked John.

'Not a sausage. Not a nibble. You two?'

'Sixty-three for me,' said John. 'And forty-four for Bob here.'

'Give over. Sixty-three what?'

'Gudgeon.'

'Gudgeon? *Gudgeon*? Who wants bloody gudgeon?'

'Better than nowt,' said John, slurping gratefully into his pint. 'At least we've not come back looking as if we've been to a bloody funeral.'

'There's more to fishing than catching fish,' said the angler.

'You never said a truer word,' said John. 'Cheers.'

* * *

'Remember the gudgeon?' asked John, one October evening.

'I ought to,' I said. 'Who was it won 5p on the biggest fish?'

'Aye, well, there's another fish that's despised by some. The grayling, one of the most beautiful fish that swims. We'll try for some tomorrow, if you like.'

'You're on. But how come it's despised if it's so beautiful?'

'Strictly speaking it's a game fish, a member of the salmon family just like the salmon and trout. But a lot of upmarket game fishermen look down on it because it spawns at the same time as the coarse fish. Bit *infra dig*, dontcha know. To protect it, it's covered by the coarse close season rather than the game close season. And that puts it right outside the pale for the old pukka sahibs.

'Anyway, we'll try for some tomorrow. Bring some float trotting gear and a fly rod as well.'

The next morning was a glorious start to the day, with the leaves taking on their first flush of autumnal red and gold.

'Best time of the year for me, is autumn,' said John. 'And it's the best time for coarse fish – begging the grayling's pardon. They're well over spawning, they've muscled up and they're in good fighting trim.'

John stopped on the river at a smooth, fast run, and cast an eye over the water.

'Now then, we could trot down with worm. We'll have to do that to find the fish if they're feeding below the surface. But – Aye, there we go – ' John broke off at a splash and a swirl downstream – 'they're taking at the surface, so we'll try dry fly. Do you no harm, anyway: you've not done much fly work this year.'

We both assembled our nine-foot trout rods and put a flashy dry fly on the point of the line.

'The trick is,' said John, 'to cast downstream and across. With a dry fly you'd normally cast upstream, but the grayling has very keen eyesight, so we want the fly to reach it before it spots the line. Make sure you give line once you've cast; you don't want the fly to be affected by the drag. Go on – after you.'

I cast to land just upstream of where the splash had been. The fly floated down and then – whoosh! – another splash, and a swirl. But the fly went drifting on, untouched.

'Reel in and cast again at the same spot,' said John. 'Grayling are messy risers, another reason the game wallahs aren't always keen on them. They sometimes shoot straight from the bottom and miss the fly altogether.'

I cast out again. Another swirl and – Strike!

'Missed!' I howled as the fly was flicked clear of the water.

'No panic,' said John. 'The grayling is accused of having a soft mouth which allows the hook to come out easily. But it hasn't: it's got a small mouth and it nips rather than swallows. This time let it take the fly and turn under, then strike with just a turn of the wrist.'

I followed John's instructions and – Gottim!

'By heck, John, this is a scrapper,' I stuttered as my rod bucked and curved.

'Aye, well, you're taking her back against the current and she's got a dorsal fin like a sail to take full advantage of it. You'll see when you get her out.'

I played the fish upstream back almost to the bank. John slid the landing net into the water.

'Gently does it now, Bob,' he whispered. 'These things have a habit of kicking as they come to the net. Shame to lose her after all this.'

I lifted the rod tip so that the fish's head just cleared the surface, and slid it sideways over the net.

'Hup!' grunted John. And there was my first grayling.

What a fish! What a beauty!

The silver of its flanks was shot through with iridescent tones of purple, indigo, green and yellow, making it shimmer like watered silk. Its fins were tinged with purple. And most magnificent of all was its stately dorsal fin, shaped like an artist's palette, an impression which was heightened by its shimmering purple tones and the dark horizontal bands which ran across it.

I looked at the fish in the net for a full minute before starting to take the hook out.

'I don't think I've seen anything quite so beautiful,' I said.

'No, you'd go a long way to beat that,' said John.

'But if you don't take that hook out soon, you'll have nowt to look at. Those colours fade once the fish dies. Straight back in the water, lad: we don't want to risk that fin a keepnet. We could eat her, of course, but if you saw those colours fade it'd put you right off your grub.'

I wetted my hands, took the hook out, and turned to the water.

'One second, Bob,' said John. 'Smell her.'

'What for?'

'Just smell her.'

I sniffed.

What does she smell like?'

'Fish.'

'Good. She's supposed to smell of thyme. In fact her Latin name is *Thymallus thymallus*. But to me she's always smelled like fish. For years I thought I was missing something.'

'There she goes,' I said as I slid the fish back into the water. 'Little beauty, wasn't she? You've got me at it now, John, calling the thing "she".'

'Only seems right with a thing as beautiful as that,' said John. 'You couldn't imagine her being called Fred or Sid, could you? Old names for her were *Silver Lady* and *Lady of the Stream*, so I'm not on my own.'

We fished happily away until the fateful High Noon. I took three grayling and John took four, all a respectable two to three pounds. All went back unharmed.

The slanting October sun, the green-red-and-gold dappling of the trees, the autumn smells of the river, the glint and sparkle of the swift run we were fishing, all complemented the beauty of the fish we were taking out. It was one of those mornings you remember forever.

'That was magic, John, the whole thing,' I said back at the Tadchester Arms. 'You were right, you know. There *is* more to fishing than catching fish.'

'Aye,' said John, blowing the froth off his pint. 'I think this is where we came in ...'

CHAPTER 9

Tooth for a Tooth

'If it's not one bloody thing,' said John Denton, 'it's another.'

'I couldn't agree more, John,' I said. 'But go on.'

'Bloody poachers, bloody pollution, bloody pesticides, bloody swans. And now bloody silage.'

We were in the Tadchester Arms, putting back a bit of what the day had taken out. I was taking it steadily, sipping at my Dubonnet and lemonade. John was whopping back the pints of bitter and whisky chasers as if he'd had a hotline call about the imminent end of the world.

'Have another,' he said.

'No thanks, John. I'm not officially on call tonight, but there's bound to be some old love who thinks I'm the only answer to her problems. I was out again this morning at three o'clock. Didn't get back till five. A surgery at eight. Thank God I can't climb trees: they'd be calling me instead of the fire brigade next time a cat goes missing.'

'Too bloody soft, that's your trouble.'

'Soft? That's a hard word, John. Compassion, it's known as in the trade. Caring. Being worried about somebody old, tired and confused. Older, tireder and more confused than I am. That's all it boils down to.'

'Daft I call it.'

'Be fair, John. Was I daft when I came out to look at your dog Biddy when the poachers kicked and broke her leg? Was I daft when you'd followed up a session on the home brew with a lethal dose of time-expired black pudding and thought you were going to die? Was I daft when...'

'All right,' said John. 'I submit. Best of three falls. Give in. Apart from Biddy, you should have told me to bugger off. People take advantage of your good nature.'

'An occupational hazard. A couple of nights ago, in the Gents of this very pub, I had a pillar of society dropping his trousers and begging me to look at his piles. I pleaded bad light and asked him to call in the surgery the next day. I may be soft, John, but what can you do without insulting people or leaving them fretting unnecessarily?'

'You're right lad,' said John. 'So I won't burden you with my troubles. I'm killing the pain, that's all. Wouldn't want to inflict it on anybody else ...'

He stared moodily into his pint pot.

'Come on then, you silly old sod. What's up?'

'No,' said John firmly. 'I couldn't.'

He caught the barmaid's eye, never an easy feat in the Tadchester Arms, but trickier when she was picking her nose.

'Another pint please, love, when you've finished the excavations. Any road ...'

John Denton was the water bailiff on the River Tad. He came as a bit of a shock to upmarket game fishers, down for the weekend, who expected to hear a soft Somerset burr and see a knuckle to the forehead as a sign of respect. What they heard were some flat northcountry vowels and a spade being called a bloody shovel. John's forthright manner and blunt Mancunian speech didn't endear him to some of the snootier elements in Tadchester, but he was a dedicated and highly respected bailiff, especially good at teaching young anglers respect for the water and the wildlife in and around it.

'I've had a bellyful lately,' said John, picking up his pint from the wet patch caused when the barmaid slammed it down on the bar. 'It's a wonder there are any fish left in that river.'

'Poachers again, John?'

'Up to a point. I've cracked most of the organised poaching now with this walkie-talkie.' He pulled a little two-way radio from his pocket. 'I've given up tackling poachers on my own since they did for me and Nellie.' (Both John and his dog had been badly knocked about by a gang several years before). 'So now if I spot 'em, I radio back to Tadchester nick and guide the coppers to the spot. Yes, it's worked well. But there was one bugger I didn't spot the other week and he was using Cymag.'

'I've heard of that somewhere.'

'Quite common around here. Agricultural poison. Cyanide based. Destroys the oxygen in the water. Brings the old salmon up like nothing else. Quieter than gelignite and doesn't blow 'em into fish fingers. But when the poacher's cleared off, the poison's still in the river, floating downstream and killing everything in its path until it gets diluted enough to be harmless. There's a stretch of the Tad now with not a living thing in it. Breaks your heart.'

He took a swig of his pint and a deep breath before starting again.

'As if I hadn't got enough trouble with pollution already. We've had untreated sewage, factory outfall, seepage from the old colliery workings, pesticides from the fields – and now, on top of everything else, there's bloody silage.'

'Silage?'

'Aye. Would you credit it?'

'Surely that's only cattle feed, John?'

'That's right. Green stuff. Grass and kale and the like, fermented in pits and silos with crude molasses. Sounds harmless enough, but the Water Authority boffins tracked down a leakage from that bloody prairie farm – the one where they dug up the hedgerows a few years back – that had seen off some prime fish. Even worse, it was getting into the side streams where the salmon and trout go to spawn. So it not only killed off adult fish, it saw off the whole next generation. What with one thing and another, it's a wonder there's anything left in that river at all.'

'You mentioned swans, John. What's the problem with them?'

'Aye, the swans. The population's right down, and anglers are being blamed for leaving lead shot in the water. I don't deny that happens, nor that some of the swans have gone down with lead poisoning, though I do my best to educate anglers not to leave the stuff about. A couple of the swans have been found dead with spinners down their gullets, too. They'd broken off on snags and the swans had swallowed them. There's not a lot you can do when a swan's swallowed a spinner with a bloody great treble hook on the end.

'But I'm not letting anglers take all the blame. There's more lead gets in the water from the shooting syndicates than from anglers – you should see the pellets spattering down when the shortsighted old buggers blast away at birds near the water. It's a wonder we haven't had fishermen carted off with perforated arses.

'And I'm sure it's not just lead. Apart from pesticides and such in the water, look at the oil and diesel fuel on the surface after the pleasure boats have been charging up and down. The swans are swallowing that day in, day out. Not to mention their nesting being disturbed by all the river traffic.

'And the farmers are glad to have anglers blamed. Smoke screen. Takes the attention off them.'

'What have the farmers got to do with it?'

'Egg-pricking. That's what they've been up to. The swans are partial to young green stuff, and they've learned there's rich pickings away from the water in those kale fields. The farmers daren't shoot the swans, but it doesn't stop them pricking the eggs on the nest. I've found half a dozen nests with the eggs cold and rotten, and each egg with a tiny hole in it. I can't prove anything until I catch somebody at it, but those holes didn't get there on their own. Bloody farmers. Another pint please, love, when you're ready. Christ! She's picking her nose again! Bloody ... '

Another of John's problems was an outbreak of thefts of nightfishers' tackle. Drug-taking and glue-sniffing had finally come to Tadchester and Winchcombe, and gangs of junkies had taken to roaming the river at night, beating up or trussing up anglers, stealing their tackle, and selling it for a few pounds to pay for their next fix.

After one particularly horrific incident, John was forced to ban nightfishing altogether for the anglers' own sakes.

It was 2.30 in the morning when my phone rang.

'Sorry to get you up, Bob,' said John. 'I'm in the phone box by the bridge. Got a patient for you. Casualty. Lost a few teeth and bleeding a lot. Can I bring him over?'

'All right, John. As it's you. Too bloody soft, that's my trouble.'

'Sorry about that, Bob. I'll be there in five minutes.'

The Land Rover pulled up outside. I opened the door to find John helping out a shivering, middle-aged man with a blood-soaked handkerchief clamped over his mouth. When I got him into the light of the surgery, I could see that he was also badly bruised about the face.

I checked to make sure there were no bones broken and then said, 'Right. So far, so good. Let's look at your mouth.'

He took away the handkerchief and opened his mouth with a wince of pain. What I saw was horrifying.

Four or five of his teeth were missing, wrenched out as if some drunken dentist had gone berserk, leaving here and there bits of shattered stump and torn and bleeding gums.

'My God!' I said. 'Who did this?'

'Glue-sniffers or some such,' said John. 'This is Charlie Green, by the way, old mate of mine. They tried to nick Charlie's tackle and he made the mistake of having a go. They knocked him out and cleared off with the lot.

'I found Charlie spark out on the bank, with his tackle missing. All except a pair of pliers the buggers had found in his tackle box. They were on his chest along with bits of teeth. While he was unconscious they'd pulled his bloody teeth out.'

I gave Charlie a couple of local injections and cleaned up the

mess inside his mouth as best I could. The rest of the job would have to be done by a dentist.

'He can stay the night with me,' said John. 'I'll take him round to the dentist in the morning. I tell you one thing, though: I'm going to keep a sharp eye out tomorrow for anybody trying to flog fishing tackle in the town. And if I do find anybody, I'll put some extra business your way. There'll be a few more teeth flying around Tadchester ...'

I crawled back into bed, trying not to disturb Pam, who was just drifting back to sleep.

'You're getting too old for this kind of thing, Bob,' she murmured drowsily. 'What is it this time?'

'John Denton with somebody he found hurt on the bank,' I said.

'Oh dear. I hope he wasn't too bad. But I'd give my eye teeth for you not to be woken up like this.'

'That's nice of you, love,' I said. 'But poor Charlie Green's beaten you to it ...'

CHAPTER 10

Unquenchable Thirsts

One of the early signs of sugar diabetes is an unquenchable thirst. I have had patients coming in to see me in the early stages of diabetes reporting they had been so thirsty that they had even drunk the contents of their hot water bottles during the night. The trouble is that so many of my friends seem to have unquenchable thirsts that sometimes it is difficult not to think of them all as potential diabetics.

The thirstiest of my friends without any doubt was Chris Parfitt, known to everyone as C.P., Editor of the *Tadchester Gazette*, who had the journalist's occupational taste for a pint of beer or three, and he was a connoisseur of its finer points. He and his wife Joyce once disappeared for a week and when they came back he was full of enthusiasm.

'Sorry I didn't let you know about my sudden disappearance,' he said, 'but I didn't want to let anyone know. I'm not desperately sure about the future of the *Tadchester Gazette* so we thought we'd go up north and have a look around. We've been exploring the Pennines. I reckon if I sell my house here and buy a similar house up there for much less money, with a bit of freelancing I could make a reasonable living.'

'And there's another attraction. You'll hardly believe this,'

he said, and his eyes lit up like a man who has just stumbled across the Holy Grail. 'Do you know that up there, a pint of Barnsley Best from the wood, in good condition, costs less than two-thirds the price of an indifferent pint down here?'

'Good God,' I said, 'then I shall have to abandon my practice in Tadchester and look for one in the Pennines.'

Five or six years earlier C.P. had had an operation to restore the power of his voice damaged in a previous throat operation when a nerve was severed and his left vocal cord paralysed. The voice was restored by the injection of Teflon suspension into the paralysed vocal cord which brought the cord back to the midline and stopped the air escaping.

It was a simple but delicate operation and was carried out in Liverpool where the technique, pioneered in the States, was first being carried out in Britain.

C.P. always remembered the day he arrived in hospital,

December 9th, 1980, the day after John Lennon was murdered in New York.

'I thought there'd been a mass local disaster, plane crash or something,' said C.P. 'Nurses, sisters, even matrons were walking about white-faced and sniffling or with tears rolling down their cheeks. All the outpatients looked as if they had had a family bereavement. It wasn't until I went into the TV lounge that I heard the news that John Lennon had been shot. It shook me. I had always been a fan of his but what it did to those Liverpudlian girls who had grown up with the Beatles as their local heroes, was cataclysmic. From the look of them the whole city must have been in mourning.'

The operation was a complete success but C.P. was lucky to come home alive. Though his stay at hospital was short, it was fraught with temptation. The window of his ward overlooked a little pub on the other side of the main road. Lunchtime and evening he watched with growing frustration, the locals walking to the pub and reeling out happily two or three hours later. Before his operation he was on a no-liquids diet which made his torment even worse. After the operation he was to have neither food nor drink for a while.

'I felt great after the operation Bob,' he said. 'It was done under a local anaesthetic so I had no after effects at all and I could have murdered a pint. I thought the no-liquids rule was just a bit of hospital bureaucracy – you know, like waking you up to give you a sleeping pill. In the end I decided to throw a few clothes on and sneak out for a swift one, but I couldn't find my clothes. They had been moved to a cupboard in the sister's office.'

'Perhaps to keep them safe while you were out of the ward,' I said. 'Or perhaps they didn't want to lose a patient after all the trouble they'd gone to.'

'Why? One pint couldn't have done me any harm.'

'It could have drowned you.'

'Get away.'

'I'm serious,' I said. 'The local anaesthetic would have paralysed your epiglottis, leaving you no control over your swallowing until it wore off. If you had swigged a pint it would have gone straight into your lungs.'

'By heck!' said C.P. 'What a story – Patient Dies in Mercy Dash–Dry Land Drowning Drama!'

'Front page news if ever there was,' I said. 'But you wouldn't have been around to write it.'

'That's true,' said C.P. 'No use going to all that bother if somebody else was going to get the byline.'

The pub was the first place C.P. made for on his discharge. Not only did he fancy a pint, he also had a morbid fear and dislike of hospitals. He had bad memories of when, as a child, he had contracted mumps and scarlet fever and had spent a month in a hospital where the food was atrocious. The memory had lingered on.

C.P. was driving back from Liverpool by car so he stuck to the limit of two pints, not enough to get the flavour of the place. But he had to go back to Liverpool at intervals of two or three months for check-ups and then he made sure he went by train. His check-ups generally took place around noon, leaving him plenty of time for a lunchtime pint afterwards.

After one examination, which confirmed that all was well, C.P. nipped over the road for his customary swig of local atmosphere. There he found himself a charitable mission which gave his visits to the pub even more of a point. Towards closing time, as the landlady was poised to ring the bell, C.P. glanced at the door and noticed a man across the road halted by the traffic lights. A big man in a donkey jacket, he had one leg in plaster up to the thigh, was balancing on a crutch, and was waving another in the air, shouting hoarsely in the direction of the pub.

C.P. could not make out what the man was shouting because of the din of the traffic, but he recognised the gestures of desperation.

'Could you hold the bell please, love?' he asked the landlady. 'Disabled customer in distress on his way over.'

The landlady stayed her hand, the traffic lights changed and the big man made record time across the road in the

Multiple Fracture, Full-Length Cast and Two Crutches Handicap Sprint.

'Bless you, pal,' the man gasped as he crashed through the doorway. 'Saved my life. Pint of bitter please, love.'

On his next visit C.P. made it his business to look across the road towards closing time. Sure enough there was another thirsty outpatient trapped by the lights.

'Hold it please, love,' he said again, and another distressed customer's life was saved.

He got his reward a couple of visits later when his examination was deferred until the early afternoon. Still living in hopes of a pint later he was dismayed to find the consulting room packed with medical students, all of whom were there to have a look at the successful result of his operation. One by one the students peered down his throat through an orinascope. It was a lengthy process, with the consultant holding down C.P.'s tongue with a spatula. It was a ticklish process too, which caused C.P. now and again to gag on the spatula and hold things up further still. As the last student finished, C.P. glanced at his watch. Two-forty, only twenty minutes to get out and across the road for a flying pint. Still, it was all over now.

'Thank you gentlemen,' said the consultant. 'A very successful operation as you've seen for yourselves. Everybody *was* able to see it I take it?'

The students nodded and murmured assent, except for one student from Hong Kong at the back of the group.

'Sorry,' he said. 'Many apologies. I did not see very well at all.'

'In that case, you had better take another look,' said the consultant.

C.P. prided himself on his complete lack of racial prejudice. But with dreams of a pint evaporating before his eyes, he allowed himself just one lapse.

'Chinese twit!' he hissed.

It was all over in a few minutes, but to C.P. it seemed to take hours. He thanked the consultant, made hurried farewells to the room, scuttled to the reception desk to get the date for his next appointment, then flew down the stairs and out of the hospital. The traffic lights were against him and it was now two minutes to three.

'Hold it!' he yelled, hopping up and down waving his arms towards the pub door.

After an eternity the lights turned green and he was off from a standing start that would have left Zola Budd still on the starting blocks. He fell through the pub door just as the bell for time gave a brassy and unfeeling clang.

'Sod it!' he wailed.

'It's all right, love,' said the landlady placing a foaming pint of bitter on the bar. 'We saw you coming.'

'You're an angel,' said C.P. taking a long swig and fishing for his money.

'Paid for,' said the landlady. 'Chap by the door.'

The big man by the door raised his pint.

'All the best, Whack,' he said. 'Good health.'

'What do I owe you?' said C.P.

'Nothing,' said the big man. 'You saved me life once, remember?'

C.P. thought for a second. 'Oh yes,' he said 'it all comes back to me now. I didn't recognise you without your leg in plaster.'

*   *   *

I thought it would be sensible to test C.P.'s urine just in case he had developed a tendency to diabetes, a condition his grandmother and a couple of aunts had suffered from. (It is family and friends who get least noticed when they are ill. Gladys had once said that if she had walked into the surgery with an arrow through her head, nobody would have asked her what was wrong with her).

I gave C.P. a little stick, a clinistic. This has two little coloured plaques which give clear indications of whether there is any sugar in the water. If there is, the little blue patch on the stick will turn to brown.

'Come on,' I said to C.P. in the Tadchester Arms one evening. 'There's no time like the present. Go and wee on your stick.'

He went off the the Gents and returned in a few minutes looking a bit shamefaced and handed me back the little stick. The portion of the stick with the indicators on was completely burnt away.

'Good God!' I said. 'This is a new one on me. You've made medical history. What have you been drinking – firewater?'

'Sorry Bob,' said C.P. 'My mistake. I had the thing in my hand as I went out and I accidentally tamped my pipe with it. Give us another stick and I'll have another go.'

I produced another stick which C.P. was careful not to set fire to. Happily, the indicator showed he was clear. I raised my glass.

'Here's a toast to prolonged good health and this move to the Pennines,' I said. 'Just think, C.P., if Barnsley Best is as cheap as that, you could afford to have a bath in the stuff.'

C.P.'s eyes lit up for a second, then a look of horror crept in. 'Bath in it? he said. 'In Barnsley Best? Good God, Bob – have you no *respect*?'

CHAPTER 11

Sabbatical Leave

It had been decided in the practice that we each in turn, once every seven years, should have a three-month sabbatical holiday. The idea had been sprung from a couple of five-week Saharan trips I made when my ever-patient partners had allowed me to pay for a locum. Paying for a locum sounds like a luxury – and so it was – but I had earned some money from writing.

One expedition had been as a paying member on a 4,000-mile circuit through Algeria, Niger, up to the Tassili Plateau in Niger to look at rock and cave drawings. I went again as a paid medical officer for the same company, escorting some rich but delightful Americans along the same route.

The first to go on his sabbatical was Steve Maxwell our senior partner who went to Nepal for three months. He spent two months working in a mission hospital, then a month exploring some remoter parts of Nepal. Being Steve, he hardly mentioned it when he came back. It was very difficult to wheedle out of him what had happened, but he had seen a whole array of medical cases: diseases like tuberculosis which have almost disappeared from Britain, but which are still rife in Nepal. There was one small change when he came back. At the reception hatch there was a collection tin towards a new roof for the mission hospital he had worked in.

Henry Johnson's sabbatical was in Kenya. He had relatives there and some connection with the flying doctor service. He balanced his sabbatical with a more normal holiday, spending half his time sunbathing in Mombasa and in safari parks, and the other half flying around doing emergency surgery in the remotest parts.

Jack Hart's sabbatical was the simplest of all. He and his wife Joan just went to Southern Italy and lay in the sun for three months, coming back with absolutely the darkest sunburns that we had ever seen.

My sabbatical came about six months after Pam's hip operation and eighteen months after my coronary bypass. We decided to use it to continue our love affair with France and really to get progressively fit and well.

One of the problems of general practice is that you never seem to have enough time to enjoy the place where you live, and we were determined to spend some time doing that. But to make symbolically sure that we were starting doing something different, we booked a three-day holiday in Boulogne at the beginning of our three months off.

We went by boat-train. Having travelled many times on spruce inter-city trains to London, we were surprised at the shabby boat train down to Folkestone. But Boulogne was a lovely city and we had a good hotel. We did a lot of walking. The market was colourful, food inexpensive, the cathedral on top of the hill a good test for both my heart and Pam's hip. The only things that marred the trip were the eternal busloads of our fellow countrymen arriving on day trips, principally to go shopping in the supermarket.

I'm sure that the vast majority behaved themselves. Crocodiles of English schoolchildren with harassed-looking teachers wound their way demurely around most of the major sights. But wandering down the main streets and in the restaurants where we ate were ill-behaved louts, at twelve noon already much the worse for drink, supporting inebriated and almost unconscious girls. Half a dozen young Britishers made awful scenes, then staggered off to the supermarket which, when we visited it in the afternoon, was again full of our countrymen buying vast amounts of liquor to take back home. Many were behaving very badly and buying such quantities of alcohol – trays and trays of beer – quite beyond their ability to carry. I am sure these were the unrepresentative few, but I certainly wasn't proud of being British.

After a spell at home again we set off for a long holiday in France, crossing this time by the Dover-to-Calais route. Again, the train and boat were dirty and the crews sloppy. Things could have been better.

This planned holiday was an exciting one. We were to travel by sleeper on the famous Blue Train to the South of France and stay in Carnon in the Camargue about six miles west of the great French resort of La Grande Motte which is characterised by its spectacular and well-planned modern buildings. We had a compartment to ourselves with two bunks, toilet and wash-basin. A hot meal with some wine was served to us: it was a home of our own, a genuine wagonlit. The only difficulty was trying to sleep with the train going at 150 miles an hour, swaying and banging along the tracks and occasionally stopping at stations.

The final destination of the train was Menton, by the border with Italy, but we got off at Arles, the lovely old Roman town that used to be the capital of the Languedoc area.

After breakfast in the local restaurant we were taken by coach to Carnon. As we drove through the Camargue I saw for the first time wind-ruffled fields of rice, flamingos wading in pink flocks, the famous white horses splashing through the water. There were great shallow lakes on one side, the Canal du Midi following the road for much of the way, and the sea on the other side. There was an incredible feeling of space and suddenly we passed acres and acres of close-planted vines. The single biggest vineyard in France is in this area. We visited it on one of our day trips. In the height of the picking season 10,000 tons of grapes, most of which are picked by machine, are crushed to be made into wine. The machines spoiled my romantic images of grape picking, and the wine they offered us for tasting spoiled any thought we had of buying wine from this particular vineyard.

Carnon is little more than a new marina with shops, restaurants and apartments shooting up all over the place. It had been beautifully planned so that our main hotel room was only about 20 yards from the harbour and we could sit and watch people messing about with boats. I don't know how many serious sailors there were there; it seemed much more important to the owners that the boats were polished and shining and well provided with food and drink, rather than they should be sailed.

We explored many of the areas and towns round about. Montpellier is a lovely old town, with one of France's oldest if not most important medical schools. As we sat down for lunch in a restaurant the man next to us spoke to his companion in perfect English. The conversation was about the various aspects of sputum. It all sounded vaguely familiar but it didn't go too well with the food. They were two physicians from Barts Hospital in London, who were on some course at Montpellier. They were moved on to another table, as ours could accommodate four more people, and the food tasted much better after that.

Montpellier was a lovely old town with views from avenues of trees leading to a monument at the end of the town. To my surprise, as in many other French towns, there were a number of beggars.

To show how fit we were we walked seven miles to Las Pavalos, the next port along the coast, and back.

Another magical place we visited was Sete. It was almost another Venice, interlaced with rivers and canals. The town was obstructed by public works. The canal in one area of the town was blocked off to build an underground car park. It seemed funny parking under water.

We had a day going through the Camargue by boat seeing much of the wild life: the bulls of the Camargue, the white horses, the flamingos and a host of other birds. It was all over too quickly and before we knew where we were, we were standing on the station at Arles being stung unmercifully by mosquitoes, waiting for our wagon-lit to take us back to England.

The next part of our holiday, back in England, was concentrated on our other love: the Thames. With our friends Joe and Lynne Church, we were hiring a boat from Wallingford, Oxfordshire, down to Chertsey in Surrey, then along the riverway and canals up to Guildford.

The river was running very high when we picked up our boat and it was raining heavily. The first lock keeper thought the whole thing would be over by the weekend, so we pushed on through the most glorious countryside to Goring and Streatley and moored near the Child Beale Trust on the stretch of river running up to Pangbourne.

It was strange at night, lying in the boat and hearing cries of the various birds from this Trust, set up by an old gentleman, for children. With the noise of hundreds of different birds, many of them protected, it was like being in the African jungle.

Next day it was still raining and the river was still rising, we debated all day whether to go on, as there was a big weir to negotiate at Pangbourne. Things appeared a little better in the afternoon so we set off, negotiated the lock comfortably, and made for the next stretch.

Our next lock was at Mapledurham. There we found the whole lock under water, with men in red armbands directing the traffic.

'Head into the weir stream as you go out of the lock,' said one of the officials. 'Otherwise the current will take you into the bank.'

We did as he instructed, headed into the weir stream, and bobbed around like a cork. It was all very exciting although my crew were looking a bit apprehensive. We bowled along with the current down safely through Caversham Lock in Reading, then even faster still towards Sonning Lock. It was still raining and the river was still rising. When we arrived at Sonning Lock we asked for some advice about where to moor.

'You're better mooring above the lock,' said the lock keeper, 'it's a bit rough down below. The water is still rising. But now you are here, go through the bridge and then try to moor in the bank. Get in behind some trees or any other shelter.'

It was a sad relection on our times that there was a large warning notice on Sonning Lock saying 'Beware of Vandals who Jump on the Boat as You Go Through Sonning Bridge'. It was unlikely that we would have trouble today, but Joe and I had a couple of mooring stakes handy to repel boarders. Who would ever have imagined piracy on the River Thames?

Going through the weir stream before Sonning Lock was much like our experiences at Mapledurham. The River Thames was showing how strong it could be and we were thankful to get out of the turbulent waters. We looked for a spot to pull into the bank and moor safely for the night. We spotted a likely place and went about a hundred yards past to see if there was a better one and then turned round and went back upstream with the throttle full open. There was a great bow wave and when I looked at the bank I realised we weren't moving forward. The hundred yards to get back to the secluded mooring spot took us three-quarters of an hour. We obviously weren't going to go anywhere until the Thames settled down.

We tied the boat up with about five lots of lines and were stuck there for three days. Occasionally boats would move past us but they were much more powerful than ours. We saw hired boats going up in convoy, often being pulled by tugs.

Sonning Lock was our nearest water supply and as we were running short of water, it meant repeated journeys to and fro with our two gallon can. After three days we rang home to tell them that we were all right, to find that they had desperately been trying to get in touch with us. The bad news was that my elder son Trevor, who had been filming on Sark, had fallen and broken his hip, and was now in hospital in Guernsey. Could we get over there as soon as possible?

We set off in the turbulent stream down to the next lock,

Shiplake Lock. We just managed to get into the boatyard below the lock. Then we took a taxi back to Wallingford and explained our problem at the Wallingford Travel Agency.

They couldn't have been more helpful. The local manager was being visited by the area manager, who had a friend in Guernsey who ran the Old Government House Hotel. He rang him and booked us in, then booked us a plane and a car to meet us at Guernsey Airport. From calling at the Wallingford travel agency at 11 a.m., we were in Guernsey by six o'clock that evening. Back on the Thames, our boat was later picked up by some friends who lived in the Berkshire village of Woolhampton, Bernard and Joyce Walter. They brought it back to Wallingford when the floods had subsided.

In Guernsey we drove straight to the hospital. We found Trevor just coming round from his anaesthetic. Although his hip had been pinned by a urologist, it had been done expertly. It was a great relief to see him.

He had been acting in a television series, *Mr Pye*, for Channel Four, and this would have been his last day on the island. Taking a short cut, he had come to a sunken roadway. The bank had given way and Trevor fell almost in front of an oncoming tractor.

The crew sent for the doctor who came on his bicycle – cars aren't allowed on Sark – and for the ambulance, which is a caravan pulled by a tractor. Then via the hospital boat, the *Flying Christine*, he was whipped across the water to Guernsey to the Princess Elizabeth Hospital.

The hospital really was first class. They seemed to have many more nurses than we do in England. I think the National Health Service has a lot to learn from Guernsey; there always seemed to be somebody about and the nursing care was absolutely excellent.

Trevor's hospital stay cost him nothing; as a British National he was covered by a reciprocal arrangement with the NHS. This is not the same for Guernsey people. It costs them £10 every time they visit their general practitioner, £90 a day if they are in hospital. I felt certain that my appoint-

ment list would shorten at home if everybody was charged £10 a time.

We spent two weeks in Guernsey exploring the island, visiting Trevor every day until he was well enough to come home by plane.

The Old Government House Hotel took one back thirty years. The accommodation and food were superb. There were no extras. You still left your shoes outside your room to be cleaned at night. Instead of getting fit and lean on the river, I got fatter and fatter on the food of Guernsey.

They could only put us up for a couple of days at the Government House Hotel, but the manager booked us into a country club where again we were treated with the utmost kindness.

Trevor was checked by one of my orthopaedic consultant friends when we got back home and it was pronounced that a perfect job had been done on Guernsey.

The end of our sabbatical was drawing to a close. As a finale we had five days by car in Normandy and Brittany with two friends, Des and Joan. We travelled from Portsmouth to Cherbourg on a Townsend Thoreson boat which was a complete contrast to the boats on which we had crossed before. This boat was immaculate. Even the people who were cleaning the floors and clearing the tables had spotless linen coats and trousers on. The restaurants were immaculate, the food was absolutely first class, and there was plenty of room and accommodation.

We spent our first night at Barfleur, the little port on the top of the Cherbourg peninsula from where William the Conqueror set sail for England. We travelled down to see the Bayeux Tapestry, on for a couple of nights in Dinan, a fascinating town with a huge castle wall overlooking the River Rance. We had a marvellous meal in a restaurant where the madame seemed to cook, do the bills, the wine, everything. Its popularity was confirmed by the queue of people outside.

Our last two days were spent in Dinard, the seaside resort. We went round looking at properties, we always do, I cannot think of holidays when we haven't said, 'We must come back and get an apartment here.' Perhaps, who knows, one day we will.

A trip back on the Townsend Thoreson ferry, and our sabbatical was over. We had crammed a lot into it, three trips to France, our abortive river trip and a fortnight in Guernsey. I was quite exhausted.

When I went back to the surgery I felt I had been away a hundred years.

'A good sabbatical?' said Steve. 'How are you feeling?'

'To be quite honest,' I said, 'I feel just like a holiday to get over it all.'

*　　*　　*

I wasn't the only one to benefit from a sabbatical that year.

Chris Parfitt, the man with a fondness for Barnsley Best, came into the surgery one day with his symptoms typed out on a piece of paper.

'Don't want to waste your time, Bob,' he said. 'And it saves me forgetting anything.'

The paper read:

'For the past few weeks I've been waking up in the middle of the night for no apparent reason. My heart has been working faster than usual, and I've had this strange feeling of fear.

'Once I'm awake, I start fretting about all sorts of things, mainly the future: how the wife and I will survive on my measly pension after my retirement from the *Gazette*; whether the kids (he had two grown-up children, both living and working away from home) will survive the pressures on them and live happy and fulfilled lives; whether I ought to get the chimney stack re-pointed before the thing falls through the roof; whether that stain on the garage beams really is the start of dry rot – all sorts of silly things which normally I'd dismiss or do something about.

'Last night I was sitting in the Tadchester Arms, enjoying a quiet pint and quite relaxed, as I thought, when all of a sudden my heart started pumping. It was going so fast I thought something was going to blow. I left the pub and, during the walk home, had to make a conscious effort, by deep breathing and what willpower I could summon, to get my heart back to something like a normal beat.

'Even so, I woke up during the night with the damn thing racing and all the fears crowding in again. In a word, Bob – *HELP!*'

'I think you've diagnosed yourself here, C.P.,' I said. 'Sounds like stress if anything did.'

'But I've nothing to be stressed about. I'm on top of my job, the kids are off our hands and the bank has stopped sending me threatening letters. Where's the stress?'

'Don't forget you've been living on adrenalin all your life,' I said. 'You're meeting deadlines all the time and the old fight-or-flight mechanism is what gives you the speed to meet them. You're not switching off. And you do tend to burn the candle at both ends, old lad.'

C.P., as I have already related, liked his ale and enjoyed the company in the local pubs. He also hated inactivity. The days were too short for him and he'd sit up into the small hours, talking or reading, and be up early the following morning.

Nor was his job either a routine or peaceful one. Jackson Wilder, the hardnosed and tight-fisted proprietor of the *Gazette*, made sure he got his money's worth.

I sounded C.P.'s heart, which seemed strong enough; checked his pulse, which was too fast for my liking; and took his blood pressure, which was high.

'What you could do with,' I said, writing out a prescription for beta-blockers which would inhibit the flow of adrenalin, 'is a good long holiday with plenty of fresh air and exercise. Get yourself away from that desk and the telephone for a while. A sabbatical wouldn't come amiss; I've just had one myself and I can thoroughly recommend it.'

'Great, Bob,' he said. 'I'll try for one.'

He was back the following week for a blood pressure check, looking very down.

'That miserable old bugger Wilder says that no way is he letting me go gallivanting in the firm's time and on his money,' he said. 'If I want time out of the office I've got to justify it by producing some copy for the paper. A right busman's holiday that'd be.'

But he was back the following week, waving a copy of the *Gazette*.

'I've cracked it, Bob,' he said, pointing to a front page story. 'That's me – the *Gazette*'s Man of the Woods!'

There was a picture of C.P. looking ridiculous in a camouflage jacket and a Davy Crockett hat, brandishing a large axe and grinning menacingly at a tree.

'For God's sake, C.P.!' I said. 'When I said exercise I meant walking or digging the garden. You'll kill yourself waving that thing about!'

'That's only for the picture,' said C.P. 'And I wouldn't be seen dead with that former cat on my head. Just read the story.'

The story was about a group of conservation-minded Tadchester citizens who had banded together to take over Downhanger Wood, a large tract of beech and oak which had been allowed to run wild by absentee owners. Calling themselves The Men of the Woods, they had bought the land through public subscription and were now proposing to clear the dead and diseased trees and hack away the tangled undergrowth which was choking the place. They were appealing to local businessmen for funds and for volunteers to do the unskilled clearing work.

'They tapped up old Wilder for a subscription,' said C.P. 'He went white. Blood from a stone has nothing on getting him to part with his money. And that's where I saw my chance.

'"Give them publicity," I said to Wilder. "That'd be worth more to them than cash." And I offered to write a big feature every week for a month on the clearance operation, provided I could work in the woods myself as a volunteer. I'd be getting my sabbatical for the price of a couple of hours' writing a week and Wilder would get plenty of column inches for the *Gazette*. He'd save his cash, he'd get lots of public prestige from campaigning features about Saving our Heritage and – this is what clinched it – he could approach all the local firms sponsoring the operation to place ads with the *Gazette*. Even he saw that he couldn't lose on the deal – so I start on Monday as your friendly neighbourhood Man of the Woods.'

'Sounds OK,' I said. 'So long as you don't overdo it. What exactly is involved?'

'No axe work, for a start,' said C.P. 'Felling of the big trees is being done by paid professionals with chainsaws. I'm cutting down or pulling up all the sycamore and maple saplings which are infesting the wood and crowding out the native beech and oak. I'm using heavy duty secateurs and a log saw to cut them down, then painting the stumps with herbicide to stop them sprouting up again. While I'm in the woods, I'm also supposed to stop motorcyclists using the place for scramble practice, but I think I'll give that a miss: I've grown attached to my front teeth.'

Off he went, singing *I'm a lumberjack and I'm OK*, and that was the last I saw of him for four weeks, though I followed his progress in the *Gazette* and gathered from his articles that forestry work wasn't quite the idyllic pursuit he'd expected it to be.

On the last Saturday of his stint he called in for a check-up and a repeat prescription of the tablets. 'Called in' is perhaps not the best description. 'Crawled in' would be nearer the mark. Though he looked weatherbeaten, it would be incorrect to say he looked fit. He was limping, was bent forward from the waist in a Max Wall crouch, and blew his nose loudly every couple of minutes.

'How are you, then?' I asked.

'Knackered,' wheezed C.P.

'Yerss ... I have seen you looking more sprightly. Let's try the old blood pressure, shall we?'

His blood pressure was well down, still on the high side but a lot better than it was.

'Your sabbatical seems to have done the trick,' I said.

'It's bloody near done for me,' he croaked, and broke into a coughing fit.

'Not what you expected, I gather?'

'Not a bit. You can stick forestry work from now on. Give me a month in the abbatoir any time.'

'What was the problem?'

'What *wasn't* the problem? Aaaah – CHOO! Excuse me.

'First of all, I'd never appreciated the size of these woods. Probably because I'd never tried to hack my way through them before. And I'd never realised there were so many sycamores in the world. Millions of 'em, springing up like bamboo. A dog couldn't get through some of those thickets. I was shifting up to a thousand a day of the smaller saplings, sometimes more, and still only clearing a patch the size of a backyard.

'I used the saw to cut down the bigger ones, and to avoid leaving a tall stump I had to crouch and saw close to the ground. That did my back a lot of good, I can tell you.

'And wet! There is nothing wetter or colder than a wood first thing in the morning. On the first day I got soaked to the skin, so I bought myself a rubberised fisherman's outfit. I only used it twice, though. When I got down to the job I worked up such a sweat that I was getting soaked from the inside; my socks were squelching in my wellies. So I went back to getting wet from the outside.

'As the day warmed up, it brought out the midges. I had a bush hat to keep them off my head, but they bit everywhere else they could land on.'

'Still,' I said, 'you did have the consolation of knowing that you were doing a worthwhile job. People round here will be grateful for it.'

'Don't kid yourself,' said C.P. 'The first people I met were two ladies out for a walk. I rose from a thicket just as they were passing, and they ran off screaming. After that I wore a cyclist's fluorescent Sam Browne belt and whistled myself dry so that it wouldn't happen again.

'Another old lady came up to me and said she hoped that I'd tidy the place up after me. Never mind the fact that I was doing it all for nothing. She didn't want her woods — *her* woods! — looking a mess.

'Two yobbos on a motorbike came roaring down a bridle path near where I was working. I raised my hand to stop them and have a few gentle words, but the rider speeded up and skidded passed me, covering me in mud. His pillion rider stood up, gave me a V-sign and yelled things to the effect that I was a silly old pillock.

'Then, to top it all, a bloke came charging down from a big house on the edge of the wood — thinking I was nicking the trees for firewood — and set three bloody dogs on me. Three! If I hadn't got in first with the old power-packed welly I could have been coming here for a wooden leg.

'I gave him a piece of my mind, forgetting that I represented the finest traditions of the *Gazette* — whatever those may be — and he wasn't too pleased. Neither was I when I found out he was a masonic mate of old Wilder.'

'Never mind,' I said. 'There must have been some compensation from all the wildlife you saw while you were working.'

'Wildlife? There was one pigeon which shit on my head when I took my hat off for a scratch, one geriatric squirrel with

a bald tail, a frog which turned up twice, and a dog which cocked its leg over me as I was crouching down.

'Anyway, whatever wildlife is in that wood, I don't think I've done it any favours.'

'Why not?'

'They forgot to mention the bird sanctuary. A local ornithologist had pegged out a particularly overgrown patch to observe the numbers and habits of the birds in a given area of dense growth. By the time I'd stumbled upon the pegs, the place wasn't dense any more: I'd chopped the bloody lot down.'

'Oh dear,' I said. 'I suppose you're glad it's all over. Still, you're all the better for it.'

'I certainly don't feel it. I could do with a holiday to get over it all.'

'Steady on,' I said 'You're pinching my lines ...'

* * *

The sabbatical did do C.P. good, though, despite his moans. Apart from toning him up physically and lowering his blood pressure, it distanced him from his worries and allowed him to get things into perspective. He lived in a big old house with a fair bit of land, and its value had appreciated considerably over the years. On his retirement he could sell up, move into a smaller place, and have a decent sum to invest to supplement his pension. (As his wife, Joyce, said, if he'd gone on worrying about his pension, he wouldn't be around to collect it.) He realised too, that he could supplement his income in his retirement by writing the odd freelance article: his skills were portable, so it didn't really matter where he lived. Perhaps he would make it to the Pennines yet!

He had the chimney stack pointed and the garage timbers treated; two more worries less. And when his married son told him that he was shortly to become a grandfather, C.P. was left without a worry in the world.

CHAPTER 12

Auntie Kitty

I first met Pam's aunts, Kitty and Daisy, at our wedding. They were already legends in her family, both in their seventies: two delightful, contented ladies who had lived quiet, genteel lives and of whom I never heard a cross word.

Daisy once had a job of some sort, but Kitty had never gone out to work. She had spent most of what would have been a normal working life looking after her parents. They must have been of reasonably affluent means, as between the wars they regularly went abroad for their holidays. They were not rich, but they were obviously very comfortably off.

Daisy died when she was about eighty, leaving Kitty on her own in the family house they had shared. Though she now had only herself to look after, Kitty kept busy. She gave freely of her time to such worthy organisations as the local lifeboat fund and horticultural society, of which she was president for many years.

She once came to stay with Gerry, Pam's late father, when he lived in an annex to our house. I cooked a Chinese meal for us all, and Kitty tucked in with relish to these new and strange dishes. She was then in her mid eighties, mobile, active and spry.

We had no more real contact with her until Pam, on a trip up to London, called in to see her. The house that she remembered as a little girl as being grand and imposing was now a crumbling wreck, not so very big after all. Kitty, now in her early nineties, was living in a state of complete confusion.

She insisted on remaining independent, although it must have been a hazard every time she left her house. What had been her front garden had been compulsorily purchased, and what had been a quiet country lane was now a major road.

Finally, at ninety-five, she acknowledged she was no longer fit enough to manage on her own and elected to move into an Eventide Home in North Wembley. She liked it particularly because there was a pond by which she could sit and watch the birds and feed the ducks. It also had nice gardens and she was able to go and give a hand with the blooms. We used to visit her there once or twice a year. We would have tea with her and a little walk in the garden.

She had a hilarious holiday with us when she was about ninety-eight. She couldn't get up the stairs and so I had to carry her up with a fireman's lift on my shoulder. She came downstairs on her own, bumping down on her bottom and shouting, 'Look at my bloomers! I hope they can't see them in the street!'

She enjoyed everything. Her main complaint about the retirement home was that it was full of old people. She played whist regularly twice a week until she was 106. She always remembered her Chinese meal, and Pam's father saying: 'If you'll eat that, you'll eat anything.'

Kitty got progressively frailer and was eventually confined to travelling about in a wheelchair, but she still enjoyed her twice weekly games of whist and any other entertainment or trips put on by the home.

When we went to see her, she would wake up, a little tiny, frail figure on the bed, open her eyes and say, 'Hello, Pam. Hello, Bob,' and then would straightaway drop into conversations about things we had done together, ask questions about the children and reminisce about the Chinese meal. It was as if we'd seen her only the week before.

107

Her sight was beginning to fail and she was getting a bit arthritic, but her mind stayed clear. She couldn't read very well but she seemed to take memories out like transparencies and have a look and a chuckle at them. She never ever reprimanded us for not visiting her more often. The main load of taking care of her fell on Pam's brother, Theo, who managed all her legal and financial affairs.

She certainly wouldn't part with her money without a struggle. One day she had to have a new pair of glasses and the optician asked, 'Have you got a hundred pounds Miss Baynton?'

'Yes,' said Auntie Kitty, 'but you won't get it from me. Any dealings you have must be with my cousin.' At this stage all men were her cousins.

I used to pull her leg about her age.

'Come on Kitty, tell us about the Relief of Mafeking,' I said once.

'Oh, shut up, Bob,' she said. 'I had a lot of friends in Mafeking.'

Kitty had been born in 1877. She was twenty-three at the turn of the century and thirty-seven when the First World War broke out. At the age of 107, she said to me, 'You know, this Common Market business is sound politically but bad economically.' Who could argue with her, with all her experience?

In her last year, because of her failing sight and increasing arthritis, she was unable for the first time to send out her own Christmas cards. This was a great blow to her.

She died peacefully three weeks before her 108th birthday, a fine, lovely old lady. I never heard her criticise anyone, I never knew her anything but good-natured and entertaining, well informed and highly intellectual. I think that the secret of her great age was the fact that she took everything calmly as it came along. She had been fortunate in that she hadn't been pressed financially, but on the other hand she hadn't squandered her resources; there were still a few pennies left in the bank to go to some South African relative after her death.

I always wondered why she hadn't married. Theo, going through her papers afterwards, found some letters and pictures which gave away part of her secret. She had had a young man when she was in her early twenties and there was a postcard from him: a handsome dark-haired young man, sitting in a Victorian or Edwardian pose at a table, and on the back a note saying, 'I'll see you soon my dear. I'd love to come and bite your nose.' This was obviously some form of secret language between them.

So this was her love, the man to whom she was faithful for the next eighty-five years. He died sometime around about 1900. It was possibly tuberculosis, or he may had died in the South African war. Kitty never talked about him. It was only from the letters and photographs that we learned of the most beautiful, touching and loving relationship she had with the man she intended to marry. There was no trace anywhere of the sadness or bitterness she must have felt when she lost him.

She was lucky that she had found, for a time anyway, her one and only true love. Like all people who are remembered, he never completely died; for Kitty, always something of him remained. She had had this love and part of it had remained alive in her forever. Nothing had spoiled it, she had kept it to herself, hadn't had to share it with anybody, and it had helped to sustain her against all life's harassment.

Although we only saw her rarely, I miss her and I acknowledge that perhaps she had got closer to the real art of knowing how to live than anybody that I've ever met. God bless her.

* * *

Nurse Jones did not reach the great heights of Auntie Kitty's age, but did manage to reach a respectable ninety-six. Her life was quite different from Kitty's, and primarily devoted to nursing. There had been a husband some way back, but seemingly no children, and odd relatives somewhere in Kent that she used to visit.

She had been a nurse and midwife in Tadchester, presumably since her early twenties. She knew the inside story of every family in the district, about which she was not always too discreet. She kept on nursing into her nineties when she used to come into infant welfare clinics and help hand out vitamins and medicines. She almost had to be carried there and carried back but it did give her a feeling of some importance.

She lived in a small cluster of houses about two miles out of town which had been specially designed for the retired and elderly. There was one small shop, a garage and a pub there, but – with true forward-thinking municipal planning – there was no public transport.

From about her mid eighties to her death at ninety-six, Nurse Jones' health was indifferent. For the last five or six years it was awful, with repeated chest infections. She would be found by neighbours lying on the floor and I had to send her into hospital many times, always thinking she would not come out. Not that I thought she would die, but I thought that the hospital wouldn't let her return to live on her own.

Very recently arrived in the group of houses – and in Tadchester that meant about five or six years ago – was a lady, a Mrs St Clair. And by a lady I mean a lady.

She had been a companion at one of the big houses nearby and insisted on her independence. She had a furnished apartment which was always immaculate, and a dog, cat and budgerigar for company. She was always doing something: making curtains, gardening, knitting cardigans for somebody's baby, or sewing for the W.I. She was virtually a one-woman social service for the little community. Everybody expected Mrs St Clair to do things for them.

'Mrs St Clair, will you get my prescription?'

'Mrs St Clair, will you do my shopping?'

People visiting sick relatives in this little enclave went away happy with the thought that Mrs St Clair would be keeping an eye on their elderly kinfolk, although in some cases it was the last thing Mrs St Clair wanted to do. She had many interests of her own and hadn't really come here to look after other people, but somehow it became her lot. At Christmas she had about five or six people round to dinner. Nurse Jones always managed to get returned from hospital by declaring that Mrs St Clair would look after her.

Nurse Jones, game that she was, became slightly confused as she got older. She insisted on living alone, despite the great effort it took to reach and answer the front door. She used to go to bed at six o'clock in the evening which meant that she got up at three in the morning. She always used to tell me that I was the best doctor in the world, that she would never manage without me. When I'd gone, she would say the most scurrilous things about me. I was not alone; she said scurrilous things about everybody, especially her home helps, who tended not to stay long.

With one chest infection, she fell out of bed and was found there by Mrs St Clair who from then on, made an early morning visit every day. It reached the stage when Mrs St

111

Clair, apart from all her duties to her other neighbours, was providing all Nurse Jones' meals, tidying her flat and not getting too many thanks for it.

I think that I must have sent Nurse Jones into hospital at least twelve times, when she had become completely unmanageable at home and when it often looked as if she wouldn't last more than a few days. It was grossly unfair that Mrs St Clair should be burdened with Nurse Jones, and for years we tried to persuade her to go somewhere she could be looked after. Eventually after one particularly bad incident in hospital, she agreed to go to a special home for retired nurses.

Mrs St Clair kept in touch with Nurse Jones, visiting her in the home, writing to her and telephoning her regularly. It was she who broke the news to me of a sudden and vast improvement in Nurse Jones' health. What had happened was that this cantankerous and ailing lady of ninety-five had fallen in love. It was with another resident of the home, which must have been for retired nurses of both sexes. He was a mere lad of eighty-nine, but he obviously reciprocated her feelings. They got engaged and there was even talk of marriage.

Nurse Jones was completely revitalised. Alas she was perhaps over-vitalised. The excitement proved too much for her and she had a stroke. As soon as she was over the worst of it and could manage a wheelchair, Nurse Jones travelled round to see every patient in the nursing home, including her fiancé, to say goodbye to them. She didn't miss a single person and it was quite a physical effort to push herself round the whole place. Having said goodbye to everybody, she got into her bed and from then on refused any food, drink or medication and died within forty-eight hours.

The lives of the two old ladies, Auntie Kitty and Nurse Jones were almost opposites. Auntie Kitty was sustained for four score years by a love that was extinguished too soon. Nurse Jones was struck down by a sudden burst of love at the age of ninety-five which proved too much for her. But both were remarkable and unique old ladies.

*   *   *

Unfortunately not all my patients reached the great ages of Auntie Kitty and Nurse Jones. Death sometimes came like an epidemic and one seemed to be dealing more with death than life. It is a situation in any circumstance I have always found extremely difficult to deal with. I have never been able to detach myself from the emotions of the bereaved. I have always felt that I wanted to weep with them. And when it was people that I knew well, and particularly people that I worked with, it became almost too much to bear.

I had worked with Amazing Grace, our much beloved receptionist, for more than twelve years. She was always a source of laughter and warmth and reassurance, and the patients loved her. During the twelve years I knew her she had to bear the ordeal of losing two husbands, both war heroes who had lost limbs, and who both died of a cancer of the stomach. Somehow she survived these awful losses and kept going. Then Grace herself was taken ill and although she struggled on to work almost to the bitter end, in six short months she changed from a laughing, outgoing person, to one whose total energies were absorbed in fighting off pain.

She never lost her sense of humour. In hospital the day before she died, she winked at me, pointed across at the woman in the next bed, and said, 'She's a silly old bugger.' This was typically Grace, joking through the most awful pain.

There was a massive turnout for her funeral and a strange sort of quiet has remained in the surgery waiting room ever since. She was always prepared to listen to our troubles. She would always cheer us up. She always decorated the surgery at Christmas. She always put up the Christmas tree. She was a very special person and her loss shattered us all.

We bought a special armchair with a little plaque engraved in her memory which is kept in the waiting room for the more disabled patients. By doing that, we felt that part of Grace would always remain with us.

The same week that Grace died Jackie Dean, a woman doctor colleague I had visited every week for fifteen years, also – mercifully – died. Jackie had innumerable conditions which

113

had kept her virtually bedridden for about ten years. Her only trips from her bedroom were down an electric chair-lift. She was nursed by her devoted sister who somehow had kept her clear of bed sores. Always fresh and pink, Jackie would try and have her hair done the day before I did my weekly call. She never complained about her medical condition and she had a myriad of conditions; a collapsed spine, a fractured arm that hadn't healed, a malabsorption syndrome, a broken leg.

I had sent her to London to my teaching hospital to see whether they could offer her anything. Having given her the fullest scrutiny, they said there was no treatment they could possibly offer her and they thought that at the outside she could only manage to survive about another two years.

This news was broken to the family but, mainly through the support and care of her sister Marie, she managed to have ten fulfilled years; fulfilled in that lots of people came to see her, she was always interested in what was going on, she could watch the TV at the end of the bed. We always had a joke when I went in to see her. Sometimes she would be wearing a riding hat; she had been a great rider in the past. She used to bet in mythical millions of pounds for me on televised horse races.

It was only in her latter months that things became miserable, when her condition had really deteriorated. She could understand what I said to her but we couldn't understand what she was saying to us. It was like a man on the stage answering questions into a microphone on which the wires had been cut.

Grace and Jackie died in the same week and their funerals were in the same week. Grace's was an Anglican funeral and Jackie's a Roman Catholic funeral where the family asked me to be among those who sprinkled holy water on her grave.

In this very same week, I was invited to be a guest in London at a Jewish dinner, a charity dinner for a home for elderly Jewish people. It was a tremendous experience. The top British Jewish families were there and the entrance to the dining place was swarming with security men with walkie-talkies. There was a magnificent dinner. Three or four hundred people were there and pledge cards were placed in front of all the diners except for my host and me, as my host had made some large donation from a trust fund and was exempt from pledging. To my utter amazement it was announced at the end of the dinner that the amount of money pledged from the assembled company was more than a million pounds. This million pounds was to be used for the succour of their elderly dependents.

At the end of the dinner a grace was sung which was very similar to one of the addresses given by the Roman Catholic priest at Jackie Dean's funeral and both were in many ways similar to parts of the service for Grace. Exposed to three different branches of religion in the same week I was struck by their sameness.

When I pick up my daily newspaper and see the various conflicts raging round the world, the Middle East, Northern Ireland, Iran, the vast majority of them seem to be over some religious difference. What a great pity that mankind has not yet learnt to concentrate on the things that we have in common rather that fight over the things we differ about.

CHAPTER 13

Medical Advances

Henry Cooper was a mechanic at the Tadchester Garage; a wiry young man in his early twenties. His famous name, alas, brought him no favours, just liabilities. Hardly a day passed without somebody splashing him with Brut or shouting 'Give us your left hook, Henry!'

The witticisms he had to put up with were about as original as those of one of the nurse's husbands who, at each hospital Christmas party, would say inevitably, 'Is there a doctor in the house?' as if he were making a highly original joke.

Being the centre of attention upset Henry to the extent that he became quite withdrawn and mixed very little with his mates, spending all his time either fiddling with cars at home or going out with his fiancée, Alice who worked in the garage office. He was a most obliging and pleasant young man. If I got a puncture or a mechanical breakdown out of hours I knew I could always call for Henry and he would nip along and fix it.

I am sure his parents never knew the handicap that they were putting on him when they called him Henry. It was an even greater handicap than that of another patient called Down, whose parents christened her Ida, thus making sure that at least her school life was hell on earth.

Henry came to the surgery one day. He had been on holiday in Cornwall and had had to go to a doctor with a swelling on his neck. The doctor said it was a strained muscle, but when I saw him he had a large round swelling in his neck which was obviously not a muscle. I sent him off to see a specialist in Winchcombe and a diagnosis of Hodgkin's disease was made.

Hodgkin's is a disease of the lymph glands, and it brought back horrific memories of one of the first clinical cases I saw as a medical student. In outpatients was a most beautiful Swedish girl in her early twenties, and the consultant made us all go and feel some glands in her neck. This particular consultant was an unpleasant and tactless pontificator and, having asked us all what we thought it might be, he asked what was going to happen to the girl. We all put our various ideas forward and then, almost in triumph he said, 'Whatever treatment we give her she will be dead within two years at the most.'

This shattered me completely. I just could not believe that such an awful thing could happen. In those days there was no treatment for this condition. It was my first brush with the awful realities of life. That night I explored my own body and my hair stood on end when I found a large gland under my left arm.

For months I haunted my student friends, getting them to feel the gland. I was positive I had the same condition as this girl. I took out a life insurance policy that didn't require a medical to provide some benefit for my family and cover any debts I might have. I remember sitting down for a dinner at Christmas and looking round at the family thinking that this was probably going to be my last Christmas on earth.

I continued like this until one day after a rugby match. We had just beaten Coventry at home on the morning of an international, a great triumph for the hospital, and all the players were celebrating after the game, while I was sitting morosely fingering my gland. Taffy Williams, the fly half, came up to me without any warning and gave me a terrific kick on the behind.

He said, 'I've been wanting to do that for the last few months. Stop fingering that stupid gland. We've all got glands.'

And of course we have. If any of us examine ourselves we've got glands in our necks, under our arms and in our groins; it's quite normal for us to have them. Taffy's kick worked. As one of my colleagues reminded me thirty years later I was one of the few people to get over Hodgkin's disease without having any treatment.

The situation for Henry was quite different from the poor Swedish girl. Hodgkin's disease is now quite curable. It may mean a fairly prolonged course of treatment but I am able to tell patients that they are going to get better. The treatment would probably be a mixture of radiotherapy – that's X-rays – and chemotherapy, drugs.

Henry went off and had his treatment. He lost his hair for a time but it all grew again. He came back to work fit and well. He got married and actually did live happily ever after. I so wished that this treatment had been available for the beautiful girl of my student days.

It sometimes happens, when you see one particular type of case, that you get a whole run of similar cases. Then you may go many years or even forever, without seeing anything similar. Henry was the first case of Hodgkin's disease that I had seen since I had started in practice, but in the following six months I saw three similar conditions.

One was a free church minister who had suddenly become yellow. The reason that he had turned yellow was that he had developed a glandular disorder, not exactly the same as, but similar to, Henry's. He went off like Henry to the radiotherapy/chemotherapy clinic. He was cured, and after his treatment was promoted to one of the most senior positions in the church.

One of the sea captains coming into Tadchester also had a lump, again not quite the same as Henry's but similar. This was called a lymphoma. For this they had to try several treatments. At one stage, having almost given up, they tried one further drug which completely cured him. He made a complete recovery and went back to skippering his boat as if nothing had happened.

My last patient during this spell was our grocery delivery boy who had a swelling on his testicles which turned out to be malignant. He went off to the radiotherapy/chemotherapy department and they cured him too. The outlook for this particular condition now is excellent whereas twenty years ago it was very poor. Our grocery lad, like Henry, lost his hair during his treatment but it came back and I would see him riding his bike about, back at work, fit as a flea.

'No problems Jack?' I asked one day as he delivered our groceries from a basket in the front of an old-fashioned sit-up-and-beg bike.

'No, I'm fine, Doctor. They call me the Bob Champion of Tadchester nowadays.'

I think there was a distinct advantage in being called Bob Champion rather than Henry Cooper. Nobody squirted you with Brut.

I had played no part in the treatment of any of these four cases. They had all been treated by these new and thriving departments of radio and chemotherapy. It is likely that the management in the future of disease will lie much more along these lines and will rely less on surgery than it has done in the past.

When penicillin was discovered, five conditions that previously always had been fatal, became completely treatable. The equivalent progress is now being made in the radiotherapy/chemotherapy field. It means that there is rarely such a thing as a hopeless case, and a cure for a condition considered untreatable may be only days away from being discovered. There is no doubt that we are becoming increasingly expert at keeping people alive. What we do not know, of course, is what they will do with their lives.

I remember the Roald Dahl story of the obstetrician who, using all his skill, managed to deliver a live baby where perhaps nine out of ten other consultants would have failed. When all was tidied up, the consultant went to the mother and said, 'What are you going to call the baby?'

The beaming mother looked up and said, 'Adolf.'

'That's a fine name, Mrs Hitler,' said the obstetrician.

CHAPTER 14

Creatures Small and Small

My patients on the whole were a self-respecting lot, and even the poorest kept their little homes spick and span. There were a few exceptions, though, whose houses had never known the flick of a duster or the hum of a vacuum cleaner for years. I'd be called out to a home confinement now and again, and come back wondering how a baby could possibly survive among all the filth.

If I had time after such a call, my first job was to rush home, have a shower and a complete change of clothes in case I'd picked up any little strangers during my visit. Yes – fleas.

I'd read the occasional magazine article on the decline of the flea circus, complete with quotes from sideshow entrepreneurs bemoaning the fact that human fleas these days are almost impossible to come by. I could have given them a few addresses in Tadchester which would keep a dozen flea circuses fully staffed for twelve months of the year.

One tip I was given by an old country practitioner was to sprinkle flea powder into my trouser turn-ups before I called at a house known to harbour vermin. That took care of the dozier fleas who alighted on my trouser bottoms after a half-hearted hop from the carpet, but it could have no effect on the more energetic ones who leapt higher.

Often I'd be convinced I was hopping with fleas, when actually there wouldn't be a single one on me, but I reckon I'm entitled to get paranoid about things like that: patients would soon lose respect for a doctor who sat there scratching and swatting while they told him their symptoms.

The paranoia goes back some years, to when Jane was about four. I'd been on a visit to a particularly unsavoury house, and couldn't wait to get home and change. Unfortunately, my evening surgery was late, we had people coming to dinner, and I didn't have time to do more than have a wash and change my shirt.

I was about to come down and give a belated welcome to our guests when I felt a tickle on my chest. A flea? In my vest? Of all the times . . .

'Quick, Pam,' I said, taking off my shirt and vest. 'I'm sure I've picked up fleas at that house! Have a quick look, would you?'

Pam inspected me, pronounced me flea-free, but ran for a clean vest just in case.

I hadn't realised that Jane was sitting in a corner of the room, playing quietly with her doll. She left the bedroom after Pam, and wandered down into the lounge where Trevor was doing his best to entertain our friends on his trumpet.

'Daddy won't be long,' she announced. 'He'll be here as soon as Mummy's got rid of his fleas . . . '

Fleas weren't the only embarrassing condition that cropped up in general practice. Happily we managed to keep clear of most of the others. In the Sixties and Seventies, a scourge of every level of society was scabies. In the past it had been confined to groups of the unwashed, people with bad hygiene and people who shared a higher number of bedmates than normal. Something changed in the nature of the spread of this disease; it became no respecter of person or class, however good their hygiene, and turned up everywhere.

Scabies is a little mite that burrows under the skin – the burrowing can be seen under a large magnifying glass – and causes intense irritation. The irritation is worse when one is warm in bed at night and the most refined people used to appear in the surgery. One titled family, in which the grandfather, parents, children and grandchildren, including an eight-month-old baby, were all afflicted by this condition and came into the surgery looking as if they were all suffering from St Vitus' dance. My suggestion that they should all give each other wire brushes for Christmas wasn't well received.

The trouble with scabies is that it imitates many other skin conditions and is very similar to an allergy. However, the treatment, once the condition is proved, is very simple. It means having a hot bath, scrubbing yourself all over with a soft nailbrush and then being painted from head to foot with a liquid, keeping this liquid on for twenty-four hours. Follow this with a bath, a change of clean clothes and bed linen, and it's all over. In fact this is often the way in which the diagnosis is proved: if this treatment clears the widespread itchy skin condition, then you have had scabies. It's sometimes worth doing purely as a diagnostic measure, though it's not always a condition that people accept too well.

Other embarrassing conditions are worms, which most of us have had at some time. There are a great variety. Patients bring these rare delicacies to the surgery, wrapped in newspaper or in little jars, horrified that they may have a terminal illness. But, like scabies, most worms are easily eradicated. This is not so of a tapeworm which does take a real bit of shifting, but fortunately these are very rarely seen. I have only seen one in my whole medical life.

One of the most widespread of the embarrassing conditions is dysentry. The expression, 'It only hurts when I laugh,' is only topped by, 'You just don't know what happens when I sneeze'. Dysentry, like scabies and fleas, is no respecter of persons. With increased foreign travel, with people arriving from more and more different parts of the earth, not only do we get increases in outbursts of this condition, but we get an increase in variety. It's amazing how it can spread through close communities.

I had a friend whose misfortune was to be the medical officer to a leading British prep school. This prep school, whose pupils were children of really wealthy people, provided boys for the top public schools when they reached the magic age of thirteen. Among them would be some of the nation's future leaders: cabinet ministers, even prime ministers.

The school was struck by a particularly vicious dysentry bug that just wouldn't go away. It started with just one or two boys, then eventually the whole school was overwhelmed. This meant that stool specimens had to be obtained from every single boy in the school, every single person in the kitchens, all the indoor staff and all the outdoor staff. This was a major feat on its own. But when every possible suspect stool had been collected and examined the epidemic still didn't abate. The cook, who wasn't responsible but whom everyone thought might be, almost committed suicide. Then, because the epidemic showed no sign of dying down, investigations had to be made further afield.

After specimens from everybody in the school and its entourage had been examined, specimens from each member of the boys' families had to be obtained. There was the spectacle for a few days of streams of Rolls-Royces purring to a halt outside the school with embarrassed chauffeurs bringing in collections of little pots, perhaps feeling that their contracts of employment did not cover this end of the business.

In spite of these massive investigations, the condition still would not go away. Some mothers thought it was an Act of God. The school was persuaded to hold prayer meetings and a repressed mass hysteria set in.

Eventually the school was shut for half a term. When it reopened for the following term there was, thankfully, no sign of the disease. Its effects weren't entirely negative, however; many members of the upper crust had gained a wider experience of the fundamentals of life that might help to widen their understanding in the future.

One other, fairly recent, social leveller is ringworm. Children from the pony clubs and even people from the hunts came in with small patches of eczema to be cleared up. They were horrified to learn that they had contracted ringworm, almost certainly from their precious quadrupeds.

Once having got ringworm, it's very easy, like scabies to pass it round the family. It can be very stubborn and difficult to get rid of.

The most unfortunate member of the horsey set was a beautiful young lady in her early twenties who, the night before a special hunt ball, came to me desperately in need of help. She not only had ringworm, but scabies and dysentry as well. A holiday in Greece a few weeks before could easily have accounted for the additional problems. I had to tell her reluctantly that however much she was itching to, not to go to the ball. Not only would she be in danger of infecting fellow guests, she might even infect a few horses and I am sure the chauffeurs' union, or whoever represents these long-suffering gentlemen, would have objected to their queuing up with specimens from those large family pets, for inspection.

I was medical officer to Drake's College, a middle-ranking public school. It had a good, solid reputation and the boys came literally from all four corners of the earth.

We had our share of embarrassing parasites but ours had a touch of class about them. Boys with worms usually had them of the more exotic type, such as a Nigerian spearhead or bilharzia from the Middle East. We even had cases of malaria and once a case of typhoid. Specimens sent to the path lab from boys returning from outlandish places always caused a certain degree of excitement. Boys had worms, like most other people, but very rarely fleas. There was the odd case of dhobi's itch, which is a sort of athlete's foot of the groin. Altogether, we were rather proud of our overseas infestations; they gave us a slight edge over the local *hoi polloi*.

That is until one day when Matron came to me with a very long face.

'Doctor Bob,' she said, 'I'm afraid we have trouble.'

My thoughts immediately ran to diphtheria, meningitis, polio.

'What now?' I said, bracing myself for the worst.

'I'm afraid the whole school is down with nits.'

Unfortunately the news leaked out to the local grammar school. The pupils there, all being day boys, tended not to suffer from community diseases.

Nits, or head lice, once they get a hold in the school, take a great deal of shifting. It meant that whole forms of boys at a time had to have head inspections and special shampoos and lotions. The school never quite lived it down, and in clashes between local youths and boys at Drake's College the Drake's College boys were always referred to as 'nitwits'.

Taking the longer view, worms, fleas and nits are all part of growing up. However fastidious you are about your cleanliness and general hygiene you are lucky to pass through childhood and adolescence without at some time having at least one, if not all three.

A postcard dealing with the subject of worms was the second dirty story that I ever told, at a large family gathering. I was about four-and-a-half and could read. I had seen, on a postcard at the seaside a lady, looking down at a boy fishing in a river. The woman said to the little boy, 'Do you find it difficult fishing with worms young man?'

'No,' replied the boy. 'I've had them since I was three.'

This did not provoke quite the same hostile reaction that my first dirty story did, told at the age of three also to a large family gathering, when 'The same to you with knobs on' was the phrase of the moment.

'I have a story to tell,' I said.

'Yes Bobby,' said all the relatives, looking at this little golden-haired angel. 'What is it?'

'Well,' I said, 'Mae West went up to Primo Carnera and patted his chest and said "What a fine chest you've got"'.

'Yes Bobby,' said all the admiring relatives. 'And what did Carnera say to Mae West?'

'The same to you with knobs on,' said I, smiling in triumph.

It took me some years to understand why my uncle, who was sitting next to me, gave me a good clip round the ear and sent me straight up to bed.

* * *

Many people, have phobias about small creatures. At the top of the phobia list is spiders. And at the top of the spider phobia list was our slim, long-legged secretary-typist, Jean.

She said that the bravest thing that she ever did in her life was once when her husband was away and she found a spider in the bath. She nearly ran out of the house, but she plucked up courage, got the spider on a piece of paper, put one of her best teacups over the paper and flung both teacup and paper and spider out of the window. Unfortunately, this meant that from then on she could only have five people sitting down for tea at the same time.

Jean had inherited this phobia from her mother. Once, on holiday in Guernsey, with some sort of kamikaze instinct, they decided to visit a butterfly farm. They walked into a beautiful greenhouse with soft music playing in the background, beautiful flowers, fountains, peace and quiet. Walking towards them was a man with something on his hand. Jean's mother took a quick look. It was in fact a butterfly but, from where she looked she thought it was a spider. She screamed at the top of her voice, grabbing hold of Jean in one of her softer, tenderer parts which, for example, she wouldn't have been able to grab on Jean's brother Robert.

Her screams set loose a swarm which filled the whole of the huge greenhouse with a madly fluttering cloud. Mother and daughter, with eyes shut, had to be led out and revived with brandy. There was even talk of admitting them to hospital, but it was wonderful what fresh air and a couple of tots of brandy did for them. What was unfortunate was that Jean's husband had already bought a memento of the holiday – a butterfly brooch.

CHAPTER 15

Different Ways

There was an upsurge in physical activity in Tadchester.
There were more cricket teams, more football teams, athletic
teams, swimming teams, rowing teams than there had ever
been before. I think it reflected partly on the state of the
economy. Some of the unemployed swelled the ranks of the
various teams, of course, but what was more significant was
that a lot of men were taking early retirement in their mid-
fifties and early sixties. Any club is only as good as the committee running it. Now there were available a lot of middle-aged
men, past their own days of active sport, willing to give a hand
in running clubs.

It was most encouraging. Half the cricketers played Saturdays
and Sundays for two different teams and, the vast majority of
footballers played Saturday afternoon and Sunday morning.

Tadchester still boasted two semi-professional teams. One,
Tadchester United, played from the council stadium as usual
importing all its players except the odd one. The other team,
Tadchester Royals, played in a much superior sort of stadium
Up-the-Hill. The rugby club, who used to share the council
ground, had now built a ground of their own with first class
changing facilities, club house and bar, and flourished.

For the second time in the town's history one of the football clubs, Tadchester Royals, reached the first round of the F.A. Cup proper and played a third division side at home. However, they only managed to draw and lost the away fixture but there was great excitement in the town on the day of the cup tie.

The rugby club grew stronger and got better fixtures. They even entertained Cardiff Rugby Club on tour and gave them a very good game. The town, not very sports-minded before now, had two flourishing athletic clubs.

A girl came to see me in the surgery one night who was so thin I thought she must have anorexia nervosa, the slimmers' disease. She was in fact a champion three-thousand-metre runner on the verge of an international career and had pulled a muscle in her calf. Her calf seemed to be all sinew and bone; there was hardly room for muscle. Happily she soon responded to my treatment.

The best cricket club by far was Stowin, who often included in their Sunday games members of the Somerset county side. Sanford-on-Sea would strongly dispute this fact and games between the two clubs were battles royal. Sanford-on-Sea would raise their game to the height of their better opponents and usually came away with credit, if not as victors.

Regatta week was exciting. The number of crews competing gradually increased each year, but the fair that came for the week of the Regatta changed much in nature. The boxing booth went, there were no tents showing three-headed lambs, tattooed ladies or shows offering glimpses of partly clad ladies. These side shows were replaced by terrifying new types of roundabouts, whirligigs, rollercoasters that almost seemed to have entered the space age. It amazed me that they didn't take off and fly out to sea. Most people seemed to thoroughly enjoy them. I know all of them would have made me sick.

The carnival which in years gone by had been the highlight of the year, still tottered on. It was about half what it used to be but, it was still quite a creditable performance. Much of the trouble was that there were, as opposed to the number of people willing to help organise sporting activities, few people were prepared to give up their time for the carnival. Part of the reason for this was the fact that the carnival, in the past, had been a great help in financing Tadchester Hospital, the town's own hospital that belonged to the community. Now it belonged to the government. Although there were worthy causes like the new Cheshire Home and the new Hospice and they were raising money at Winchcombe for a body scanner, it wasn't quite the same.

This year there were a few more floats than usual and a lot of hard work had been put into them. The carnival queen looked gorgeous and was surrounded by pretty girls and boys all

dressed up in their finery with their proud parents watching. It was a fine day and it looked grand as it came round the corner for its main procession along the quay where most of the spectators were gathered.

It was at this point that things started to go wrong and probably made it the last carnival that Tadchester would hold. A few drunken youths started to pelt the floats with eggs, fruit and vegetables.

The Tadchester rugby club, who were all dressed as pirates and were doing the collecting, took immediate and vicious revenge on the hooligans and terrible fighting broke out all the way along the quay. Young children jumped terrified from the floats, looking for their parents. There were pirates and a few parents locked in fierce battle with the drunken louts. The rugby club made thirty-four citizens' arrests, three of the people arrested finishing up with broken arms. It brought the whole carnival to a halt. Gradually parents claimed their children or some neighbour took them away, and the beautiful float lorries that so much time had been spent on, went back home in tatters. Meanwhile, the snarling rugby pirates, backed by dozens of spectators, herded the bunch of arrested youths towards the police station.

There were only about half a dozen policemen on duty altogether, and they were quite beyond coping with all the melée down on the quay. It was all a terrible shame. There was a special court hearing. All those arrested were put on bail and, when their hearing came up, were fined £25 each and bound over to keep the peace. The ones with broken arms said they were going to sue the rugby club. Many of the parents said they were going to take private summonses out against the louts for damage to material and property, but of course nobody ever did.

On the night of the fracas, a few dozen leather-jacketed motorcyclists came over from Winchcombe and joined up with the remnants of the louts who had escaped being caught in the afternoon's activities. They must have been about sixty or seventy strong. They filled themselves up with beer, formed up in a column and marched towards the fairground singing, 'We stopped the carnival! We stopped the carnival'.

The fairground people seemed perfectly capable of dealing with the situation. As the mob got closer, getting braver as they sang, suddenly all the way along the footpath of the fairground appeared men in sweatshirts and overalls, each holding a huge monkey wrench or a piece of lead piping, saying nothing, doing nothing, just watching. The marching singers could see clearly that it would mean a broken skull rather than a broken arm if they came anywhere near this lot. Their singing gradually faltered as they walked past the fairground.

People attending the fair began to boo them, remembering the afternoon's chaos. A threatening crowd began to gather, the leather-jacketed toughs sobered up very quickly. A police car whizzed up and the local inspector got out and cooled the whole situation. He marched the motorcyclists and local boys, visibly displaying a truncheon in his hand, back to where their motorbikes were, saw them on their bikes then made the local youths queue up while a police constable took the names of each one.

Such incidents are sad reflections on our time. In Tadchester we're lucky: we suffer less from this sort of thing than most places. As yet nobody has found a proper answer ...

* * *

The health of Tadchester, like everywhere else, appeared to improve. People seemed to be living longer, the general health was good, and we got fewer night calls. I think this was mainly because we had better drugs.

One of the common night calls in the old days was for a condition called paroxysmal nocturnal dyspnoea, or cardiac asthma: in simple terms, some people suddenly had attacks of breathlessness at night. It meant that when they went to bed, the left side of their heart came under some strain. Now better drugs, particularly ones that make the body lose surplus water, have virtually eliminated this condition as a night call. And people who had good nights generally had better days.

However, there was one change in the world of medicine, doctors were no longer the only people to turn to when you became ill.

Tadchester, like most of the country was going through a time when alternative medicines of one sort or another were the vogue. All alternative medicines enjoy one of the same benefits that conventional medicine has: namely that the vast majority of people get better without any attention, and sometimes in spite of the attention they are receiving. When they are getting better, they tend to give credit either to the medicine they are taking or the person who is looking after them, whereas the healer is actually good old Mother Nature.

Some patients' attitudes changed. A patient you had known well, who had perhaps been attending for years, would come and say sneeringly, 'Thank goodness I've stopped taking the muck that you've been giving me all these years.' He would then outline his present treatment, which could be anything from carrot juice to yoga which had completely revitalised him, helped him to discover his inner self and completely stabilised him. The fact that usually, after a few months, at least ninety-five per cent of such patients were back with the same old problems, didn't seem to lessen their contempt for conventional medicine.

I was summoned to the bedside of one lady patient who was, as she said, in a complete state of exhaustion. Admittedly she had had a few games of tennis that morning and was hoping to go to a ball the following night. Apart from answering a few questions, she conducted the whole conversation as a monologue for an hour and a half. She had at last found the answer to her problems. She almost despised the medical profession; we just didn't understand things. Although she was completely exhausted she was going to seek no help from us any more and, by the way, would it be all right if she went up to London to a wedding on the Saturday?

I had to learn to take such things in my stride. This particular lady was back again in a month's time repeating that nobody in the medical profession understood her problems which had all come back again. I hadn't the heart to remind her that only four weeks earlier she had cured herself.

This lady personally explored several branches of medicine. On each occasion she came back triumphantly to say that her condition was not nervous, that some unqualified doctor had found that vitamin lack or hormone imbalance was her trouble. She refused to accept the fact that the source of her whole trouble was perhaps a basic depression which would have responded to the right drugs prescribed by a qualified psychiatrist. To accept her depression would have meant losing face with herself, and when she did see the psychiatrist she said he was a rude man who just didn't understand her complaint. There is no answer to this sort of patient. You have to accept that some patients will always be like this, and that you can't be all things to all men. Or women, either.

* * *

When I was a medical student I met, on a television programme, a taxi driver/writer/philosopher called Herbert Hodge. He became a great friend.

Herbert, one of the most honest men I have ever met, was ahead of his time. Among many other literary achievements, he wrote a weekly philosophical article in *John Bull* magazine. I always remember two things that he said to me. Once, after dealing with a particularly depressing bout of patients, I had thought of emigrating to Canada. Herbert wrote me a long letter saying that I should remember that, wherever I went, I would only be taking myself with me.

I think this was a major factor in my not uprooting the family and going to Canada. Going abroad would not make me a different person, and I would find the same problems that I was having to deal with now. And it certainly wouldn't be any easier three thousand miles away from familiar surroundings.

His other suggestion was that society should provide professional listeners. I think he had a point. They would be people whom you could go to and unashamedly pour out all your woes. The professional listener, having accepted his fee,

would have to listen, not necessarily make any comment but to give people an opportunity to get things off their chests.

Many of the branches of alternative medicine are very close to filling the suggestion that Herbert made twenty years ago. There are growing numbers of counsellors, often having links with psychiatrists or general practices. Many of them, alas, cannot be included in the scheme of the National Health Service but for £35 an hour, you can pour out your woes to them. You can approach them directly without being referred by your doctor. The counsellors are often a tremendous help, doing that most precious of all things, saving peoples' faces with themselves.

Other alternative branches are better known, such as chiropractic, osteopathy and the fast-growing one of acupuncture. None of these are completely divorced from conventional medicine, and many doctors have become qualified in these additional skills. There was a general practice in Winchcombe where two of the partners were excellent manipulative surgeons and achieved marvellous results with patients we sent to them.

Non-medically qualified chiropractors, osteopaths and acupuncturists vary from the very good to the very bad. I have known patients who have greatly benefited from these alternative forms of medicine. Similarly, I have known others lose a great deal of money with no benefit. Others still, by seeking such help without being conventionally assessed, delayed the diagnosis of more serious medical problems.

I remember at least two cases of patients in great pain being manipulated by an unqualified or non-medically qualified osteopath. They were discovered to have cancerous growths in their spines, and had not had this possibility excluded before the treatment.

Another change in medicine is the increasing availability of medicine under private schemes. This has a balance of good and bad. It means people can skip National Health hospital waiting lists for medical treatment. This sounds unfair, but it does make National Health waiting lists shorter and if a man has a one-man business he can't afford not to be there.

I accept that people have a right, if they want to, to spend money on their body. What is most irritating, and this really the fault of my consultant colleagues as opposed to the patients, is when my own patients announce that they have just changed their gynaecologist, or their new psychiatrist has put them on a new form of medication.

The consultants are breaking medical ethical rules in that they should only see patients who have been referred by general practitioners. Not that general practitioners are infallible, but there is a loss of continuity of care of patients; neither the general practitioner nor the consultant knows what the other is giving the patient.

The whole situation may become self-limiting as my consultant colleagues' fees become more and more expensive. The time may come when the private medical schemes are likely to founder because the doctors and the independent nursing homes they run, have priced themselves out of the market.

However, in spite of this recent growth of alternative medicine and private medicine, it made no difference to our medical load at Tadchester, which seemed to steadily increase year by year.

Two new areas of medical care that sprang up locally were of tremendous benefit to the community and I couldn't speak too highly of both organisations. One was a hospice at Stowin, which Steve Maxwell was very much involved with. He was concerned mainly with the care of the dying and terminally ill, but people with long illnesses also used to go there for periods of rest and recuperation and to give their families a break from looking after them.

Strangely, the hospices were happy places. Patients were well looked after, the staff were experts at keeping people free from pain, and patients were allowed to die with dignity in pleasant surroundings. What an advance from the days when there used to be hospitals with bold lettering on the gate announcing that this was St John's Hospital for the Dying.

Hospices seem to have found the right approach and to have attracted the right people to run them. They are beginning to solve the management of that most complicated aspect of life – namely, death.

A Cheshire Home opened halfway between Peargate and Sanford-on-Sea. It had good views of the sea and the bay and cared for the long-term ill and disabled.

Again, it attracted selfless people with the highest motivation to look after their less fortunate fellow men.

These two new establishments had a great influence over the whole of our area, and in general brought out the best in people. In fact it brought the best out of the whole community as fêtes, jumble sales and all kinds of fund-raising events were run to provide funds for both these places. It gave a sense of purpose and somehow I feel if they had been there before poor Tom Leatherbridge had been run out of St Peter's, he would probably have still been in Tadchester. But again that could well have been a mistake. His parish up north was the ideal place for him.

We used to make it a point that all five partners would meet for coffee every morning at eleven, and on the days Catherine worked she would join us as well. We then used to hand over cases of people we may have seen for a partner the night before or over the weekend. We also chatted generally about our problems. It was a great help to get things off one's chest, to talk about our worries and have our partners pat us on the back and say, 'Never mind, everything's going to be all right.'

I was always called on to give a thought for the day which usually meant telling a dirty story. With the coming of these many types of alternative medicine, I suggested that we knock nails upwards through the seats of the surgery chairs so that

patients could have instant acupuncture while they waited to see us. I also thought it might markedly cut down on the number of patients, as I am quite sure that a great number came just to snuggle in a comfortable chair in the warm. However, none of my partners would back me up, so we went on practising conventional western medicine as before.

CHAPTER 16

Going Home

Great changes were taking place in the surgery and in medical life in general. Soon after Grace's death, Gladys – our senior receptionist since long before I had arrived in the practice and who had been threatening to retire for many years – did retire. She was replaced by Denise in the new post of practice manager, Denise was a young, energetic, meticulous organiser.

Our longest serving employee was the faithful Avise who was head of dispensing, a great athlete even though she had a daughter at university, old enough to be on the fringe of the English athletic team. I would come into the surgery on a Monday morning, having spent the weekend huddled round the fire, to find that Avise had done a couple of half-marathons in the mud and sleet. To help her in the dispensary we had the vivacious dark-haired Sue who was spending part of her time at college training to be a qualified dispenser. After Grace's death we also had Sue's daughter Mandy helping us out for a year before she went off to become a medical student.

On the secretarial and typing side we had the calm, groomed, poised Victoria who acted as practice manager when Denise was away. There was also the hard-working Jean, the good-natured Ann who did two or three sessions in reception, and the conscientious Pat who probably had the longest association with the practice. Whenever Pat was on, there was always a cup of coffee waiting as soon as I arrived at my desk. Not least we had our treasure, Mrs Vincent, who kept us supplied with immaculate white coats, and with the help of her daughter, kept the surgery spick and span.

We had built an extra room to the surgery which enabled us to have two nurses, Deborah and Gill, who gradually increased the scope of their work so that they were now taking all the blood samples, ear syringing, dressing, treating varicose ulcers, doing some stitching themselves and running a Well Woman clinic. They had a blood pressure clinic, and their own immunisation clinic. Debbie and Gill also operated an electro-cardiogram which could be taken to patients' houses as well as being used in the surgery.

The final member of our indoor team, was our midwife, Amanda, a kind, caring, excellent midwife, successor to the stalwart Nurse Plank. Amanda was petite but made up in energy for anything she lacked in size. She was employed by the local health authority as opposed to being employed by us.

We were gradually building up into an expanding team offering fuller facilities. Where our work was decreasing was at the hospital. It was now almost completely transformed into a geriatric hospital with a few general practice beds and a casualty department. Henry Johnson could no longer do his surgical sessions there, and Jack Hart and I were no longer called on to do any anaesthetics. Ron Dickinson still took tonsils out but he had to go over to Winchcombe where a new main hospital had been built.

When I had first come to the practice we did virtually everything for our patients. I anaesthetised all my own emergencies as well as doing routine lists. All the midwifery was done at home or in the tiny nursing home in the town. We were virtually a self-contained unit. Now we worked in quite a different capacity.

Coming back from holiday, I found that at last we had been computerised. In the dispensary there was a row of what

looked like television sets, rolls of paper, telephones and other machines. All prescriptions for people who were on long term medication had to be computerised. You had just to quote a number and the computer would say if the patient had had too many pills or what pills were due. It was all quite terrifying. Even the typewriter terrified me. There was nothing more startling than to go into the office to have a word with whoever was typing, and find the typewriter tapping away on its own from its memory bank.

We did more surgeries now and fewer visits, but we seemed busier than we did when we worked much longer hours. I think this was because we tried to work office hours. When I first came to the practice the evening surgery started at six and went on until it finished. Now the evening surgery started at four and if the building hadn't been cleared by half past six all the staff were beginning to get agitated.

All consultations were made by appointment and Saturday mornings were for emergencies only. This was reasonable: patients would quite happily make an appointment to see their dentist during the week, fitting their business arrangements around it, but were horrified that the doctor would not be available to syringe their ears on a Saturday morning. We slowly educated them to the fact that we, like them, quite liked weekends off. Whatever hours they worked during the week, it was very rarely that they were called out of bed and, at the most, their total number of working hours was probably about half of ours.

Things always go round in circles. This was proved by one of the Winchcombe practices, a large practice of eight doctors whose morning appointments system was becoming overwhelmed. They stopped morning appointments in favour of a free-for-all, and kept appointments just for the afternoons and evenings, which was the system they'd used years ago.

It had been much the way with small hospitals. As soon as one enlightened government department had managed to shut them all down, another had the brilliant idea of opening them all up again as community hospitals. There was even talk, as the Tadchester hospital was reduced down to its new structure, of enlarging it to include some operating beds. But all this was in the distant future and they all required that most inaccessible material, money.

One of the biggest upsets of all however (apart from Grace's death, which really shook the structure of the practice) was that Steve Maxwell, our senior partner, was talking of retiring, or at least cutting his work to the absolute minimum as well as getting married. He had been such a good doctor, such a marvellous senior partner, counsellor, friend, philosopher, and probably the best man I had met in my life. He had been in practice in Tadchester for forty years, and it was difficult to imagine work in the practice without him.

His forthcoming wedding had the town absolutely buzzing. Few people could have been given more wedding presents that Steve. He is the only man that I know to have been given twenty-two toasters as wedding presents.

'I know why you're retiring,' I said to Steve, going into his consulting room one day to find half one wall covered with piles of gifts. 'You want to open a shop.'

Steve, who had managed every other problem in medicine

145

and life without a qualm, found his present situation almost too much to handle.

'Just think of all the letters to write,' he said surveying the hundred or so presents piled against the wall, 'and these are only some of them.'

I don't know whether it was the strain of the forthcoming wedding, but Steve certainly didn't look as well as usual. We tried to entice him out for a bachelor night but he would have none of it.

'Good heavens,' he said. 'I'm far too old for all that sort of nonsense.'

I popped into his consulting room at the end of his last surgery before the wedding. I found him sitting at his desk with a misty look in his eyes.

'You OK, Steve?' I asked.

'Fine, thanks, Bob,' he replied. 'Just thinking.'

'No last-minute regrets?'

'Good heavens, no,' he said, smiling. 'I just wish I'd done it sooner.'

Without any doubt Steve was the best-loved man in our town. Not only for his kindness and his meticulous medicine: many an attractive and well-educated spinster had hung on hoping one day perhaps, just perhaps, she might be playing the part that Nancy Doone, Steve's fiancée, would be playing from now on.

The day of the wedding dawned. There was tremendous excitement in Tadchester. It was almost like a carnival day. The whole town turned out to see them married at St Mary's Church and those who couldn't get into the church lined the streets and cheered them as if they were royalty. The sun shone magnificently. All traces of whatever strain I saw in Steve's face had gone, and on his wedding day both he and the bride looked happy and radiant.

There was no formal reception. The wedding party moved to the town hall where there were drinks and toasts before they got into Steve's car and drove away. The crowd had patiently waited outside and there were more crowds of people waving and cheering right up until the outskirts of the town.

Steve was sixty-seven when he married. It was so good to see him so happy and with the perfect bride. I hoped that many years of happiness lay ahead of him.

* * *

The wedding had an extra bonus for us in that all the children had come home for it. Paul and Gill came from Aldermaston with the news that Gill might be making us grandparents in six or seven months' time. Trevor and Jane travelled up from Brighton.

Jane had passed her degree in the history of design and could not tear herself away from Brighton. She had worked both in the theatre workshop and in the Brighton Festival and in the main Brighton theatre, sometimes as a dresser. They had offered her a part-time permanent job there which fitted in well with her ambitions.

Jane wanted to make and design clothes. She had thought originally of opening a shop, but decided she would use the markets first. We had to provide her with sewing machines and overlockers and press-studders and a host of other equipment. The name of her shop, if it had have come off, would have been *Duff* and she made this the motif on her clothes labels. It was a mouth shouting 'Duff' and I personally thought it was awful – it looked like an advertisement for false teeth – but I am sure she was a much better judge of it than I was.

Trevor and Jane had found a large top-floor flat on the Brighton-Hove boundary with a view of the sea and beach and decided to buy it. It was half the price that Trevor would have had to pay in London and it did mean that they were between them investing in bricks and mortar.

It seemed strange for Pam and I to sit there and listen to

Paul and Gill talking about their house and bathroom fittings and to hear the most undomesticated person in the world, Trevor, coupled with one of the untidiest, Jane, talking about how spick and span they were keeping their flat. It was so lovely to have them all together – and Gill who had become just as important to us as any of our own children.

Eventually the time came for them to leave us. Both couples were setting off by car.

'Well,' said Jane, 'it's about time we were going home.'

'I'm afraid that goes for us, too,' said Paul.

We watched Paul and Gill get into their brand new firm's car and Jane and Trevor get into Trevor's Fiesta van and set off for home. This was the first time in our lives that where Pam and I had lived wasn't home for all our children. It almost cut us to the quick. Pam had tears in her eyes as she saw them go.

'Fancy, hearing them say that,' she said. 'That they're going home.'

'Well,' I said, 'we've two homes that we can always go and visit, and we've got a choice of Berkshire countryside and the Thames, or Brighton and the sea coast.'

'But the awful thing is that our home isn't their home any more,' said Pam. 'They have homes of their own.'

'Yes,' I replied. 'I'm afraid things are going to be different from now on.'

ON HOLIDAY AGAIN, DOCTOR?

Contents

CHAPTER 1

Back to the Wall

I had my back to the wall.

I literally had my back to the wall. This particular wall being the outside of a Moroccan toilet in the Todra Gorge.

Behind the wall, a very distressed New Zealand girl in a long white nightdress was trying to cope with a severe attack of gastro-enteritis. Her only light source was the matches she struck in the less acute stages of her attack to give her some idea of her footing, which was two precarious mounds in the shape of feet.

If toilets were rated in an amenity range of one to ten, this one would have been given minus one.

On my side of the wall, I was facing three shouting, gesticulating Moroccans who were advancing, intent on doing me some bodily harm.

I'd never known how I would behave with my back to the wall, being threatened by hostile tribesmen. As a youth I had read in the *Hotspur* and the *Wizard* how simple it was: just hit them with a cricket bat.

To my own surprise – I'm not generally a violent man – I was longing for one of them to get near enough to lay my hands on him.

I was just about at the end of my tether and these three gesticulating gentlemen were in danger of making it snap. One of the ingredients of my incipient bravery was the fact that all three of them were much smaller than I was, although had I laid hands on them I would probably have found knives flicking out from every pocket.

They were after my women. When I say *my* women, I was part of a band of 29 travellers, mainly women, supposedly on a conducted camping and hotel tour of Morocco.

The men got closer, screaming: 'Why do you keep the women all to yourself?' My fists clenched in pleasurable anticipation of the first blow. Then I said in my best French: 'It is best if Nameless Tours never visit the Todra Gorge again.' At these magic words my potential attackers immediately changed into drivelling, apologetic men, backing off with a thousand apologies. They were only joking, they had suddenly seen that their action could have involved them in a major loss of income. At this moment my New Zealand girl poked her head round the door and said that she was well enough to return to our room. 'Our room' meant a furnished Oxo cube that would have made the Black Hole of Calcutta look like a four-star hotel.

This was another disastrous day on another disastrous tour. When we got to the Todra Gorge, our guide-driver said there would be no need for us to put up our tents that night. There weren't enough tents to go round anyway, and he'd found us a room which we could all share. He then disappeared with the most striking blonde in the party to some private accommodation, and this was the last we saw of him until the morning. Our room was about the size of a small dining room and 28 of us were expected to spend the night there.

There had been trouble in the evening. We had with us some precocious young Australian and New Zealand girls who were egging the local boys on. As most of the local women went round looking like bell tents with only a small slit for them to look out of, the sight of our scantily clad Australasians was more than they could bear. The fact that they were only being teased made it even worse.

2

There was some vague sort of Moroccan music in the evening, some talk of drugs and then the arrival of the local Chief of Police. We couldn't quite make out what it was he wanted; whether our girls had been taking drugs, I don't know. The girls were now terrified – we had 30 or 40 menacing-looking Moroccans advancing on us – and the whole party looked to me for instruction.

The fact that I was looked to for leadership in the absence of our driver was not that I am a natural leader of men: it was just that I was middle-aged.

My wife Pam feels it does me good to get away into the wild every now and then, so I'd booked for this trip across Morocco. From the brochure, it sounded very similar to the marvellous Sahara trips I'd had, but I found when I got there that the trip was for under 35s. Being 53 at the time gave me some position of seniority.

'Right, everybody,' I said in best boy scout fashion. 'Slowly and casually back towards our room.' We managed to make a steady retreat and shut the door. Some of the girls were whimpering with fright.

'There's nothing to worry about,' I said, although I felt worried sick. 'Just bed down for the night. It'll all look quite different in daylight.'

The door started to open and one of the Moroccan men outside tried to join us. I shut the door firmly on him and sat down leaning against the door, hoping at least to get a little sleep. Being, as usual, overweight, I made a good doorstop to protect the chastity of our women passengers.

All the travellers weren't under 35. Robin Treaton was in fact 47. His contribution to calming the fears of our girls was to take two of the more nubile ones naked into his sleeping bag with him. This might have sounded crowded but the room was so small that this was just about par for the course. He lay in the middle of his bag grinning from ear to ear. 'Not a bad holiday eh, Bob?' he said.

Everybody settled down and I was half-dozing in my sitting position as doorstop when my little New Zealand girl got up

3

from the far side of the room, ran across the sleeping bags and vomited straight over me. 'Quick!' she said. 'I must get to the toilet!'

We opened the door. Outside there were about 30 Moroccans sleeping with blankets or coats wrapped round them. I had to escort her, tiptoeing over the sleeping bodies to the toilet where I had my confrontation with the three violent men. We had no further trouble from the men after my magic words, but the New Zealand girl's condition did not go away. About every 20 minutes she would jump up and I had to escort her through the sleeping throng back to this filthy toilet, which I wouldn't have liked on a good day and, on this particular day, I hated. I had no assistance from any of the other 28 members of my party, some who slept soundly; some, mainly the women, who didn't sleep a wink. Apparently someone in the room asked whether I was all right, facing the mob outside. The questioner was immediately reassured by Robin from his crowded sleeping bag, who shouted, 'Don't worry, he'll be all right.'

At last dawn came. My little New Zealand girl was now almost completely dehydrated, but some of the worst aspects of her symptoms had disappeared. As the room stirred, all modesty was forgotten. Men and women who had been strangers just a few days ago were now intermingled, pulling clothes on, some of the women crying, but all of us welcoming the dawn as it arose.

I opened the door gingerly. All the sleeping Moroccans had gone and there was no sign of the three who had threatened me in the toilet.

Our driver-cum-courier appeared, full of beans, with his blonde companion. He asked if we'd had a good night and was nearly lynched on the spot, while his blonde companion was ostracised by all the other lady members of the party. We were a sorry lot.

Our next night's stop was a camping stop beside a swimming pool. We unloaded the bus, managed to get up enough tents to cover all of us, but it did mean people sharing a single tent. I had a quick dip in the pool, a cup of coffee, two sleeping capsules and slept for 24 hours. I awoke in blinding sunshine to find all the party in bikinis happily chatting away around the pool, with food cooking on some stoves, all as if nothing had happened.

My trip to Morocco was a potential disaster from the beginning. I had done some desert travelling and, knowing how cold it was at night, had taken two sleeping bags. Both were stoutly wrapped in an old tent bag with my name and, as an extra precaution, the tour party's name stencilled on it. I was the epitome of an efficient traveller.

Unfortunately they couldn't find my sleeping bag at Casablanca airport, so I spent the two weeks of the trip using the working sleeping bag of the driver, an oily old bag he used to lie on when working under the bus.

The main problem with this particular expedition was numbers. It was Easter, many of the tour party were schoolteachers on holiday, and we were 29 people in a 29-seater bus. This sounds reasonable, but normally there are only 20

5

people on each tour. There were only tents and equipment for 20 people, and at least a third of the bus was required to carry equipment, personal belongings, tents and cooking utensils. The tour was supposed to be a mixture of camping and native hotels. We cooked for ourselves as we went along. There was to be some time in a proper hotel in Marrakesh where we were promised beds, baths, showers and everything. I couldn't wait.

As well as the position that I'd assumed as deputy leader of the party, because I was a doctor there was always a morning surgery. Not only had people developed conditions while on the tour, some were wanting advice for problems they'd had for 20 or 30 years. On my first day, a very nice young girl had come up to me asking if I would mind having a look at her legs. She had quite a serious generalised condition called Erythema Nodosum for which she should have been hospitalised straight away (and in fact was immediately on her return from the trip). But once we'd started there was no way back, so we were carrying one really ill person from the very beginning. This girl was an extremely nice lass who made as little as possible of her painful legs and did her best to get something out of this disastrous holiday.

At last the move came to Marrakesh, a beautiful town with one of the biggest casbahs I've ever seen. The only thing that spoilt it was the fact you couldn't walk a yard without being bothered by touts who were offering anything from silk scarves and dresses to their grandmothers. We stayed at the Charles Foucald Hotel: it was extremely comfortable and the food was good. I even managed with one of the Dutch passengers, a very attractive young lady, to have a meal at the Mirimour Hotel, Churchill's favourite watering place in Morocco. Perhaps the holiday wasn't going to be too bad after all.

We were due to leave the hotel on a horseriding trip for three days, but disaster struck again. The number of people and the limitation of the equipment on the bus meant that plates weren't properly washed and hygiene wasn't looked after. After 24 hours in Marrakesh, half of the party were down with severe gastro-enteritis, at least as severe as the little New Zealand girl, who was now fit enough to join in all activities. Not so a dozen of

6

the other passengers who were far too ill to leave the hotel. As all in the party were much younger than I, and had been brought up on the National Health, they assumed that it was quite normal for me to stay and look after them. Robin Treaton acted as a runner for me, going to the pharmacist with prescriptions, and coming back with bags of charcoal and various medications.

One girl was in hysterics because her boyfriend had gone off on the riding trip, leaving her ill in the hotel. That was the end of at least one of the many partnerships in our group.

I'd come well prepared for any medical eventuality but hadn't thought I'd be looking after nearly 30 people. We just about managed until I went down with the gripes myself, having it as bad as most or even worse. I did find a secluded room for myself to endure my illness in private.

I had been sharing a room with Robin Treaton, but felt I was cramping his style. Unfortunately for him our double room was marked as the Doctors' Room. The first day that I was in isolation, Robin who didn't know an aspirin from an enema but was assumed by the hotel staff to have some sort of medical qualification was dragged protesting to the room to see the hysterical girl whose boyfriend had gone off on the riding trip.

The staff forced their way into her room to find that her gastro-enteritis had been so acute that the carpet was showing signs that she had not always made it to the communal toilet. To find that Robin had been forcibly propelled into her room in its dishevelled state as her medical adviser, was too much for the poor girl. She collapsed on the bed, screaming at the top of her voice. The management and Robin fled, leaving the mess for the boyfriend to clear up when he came back.

Somehow we survived our two weeks. We went to Agadir, we went up into the Atlas mountains. It was all a bit of a blur. We saw the mud fort where Lawrence of Arabia had made part of some film, but it couldn't have been Lawrence of Arabia, it must have been Peter O'Toole . . . I was becoming disorientated. Yes, I remember: it was another night when our guide-driver announced that instead of tents he had triumphantly found us another of his Black Holes of Calcutta. On this occasion there were no marauding Moroccans in the toilet. I think our young girls had learnt their lesson.

The plane home was delayed for ten hours at Casablanca airport. When I arrived at the airport, having spent a fortnight in an oily, cold sleeping bag, I was greeted by a smiling official with my two sleeping bags done up in their beautifully numbered tent bag. Then to my great surprise, just as the plane was about to leave, all the other passengers gathered in a group. A spokesman came forward to say how much they'd appreciated the great care I had taken of them during the stay, and there, as a present from all my sick passenger patients, was a Moroccan silver bowl. I almost wept.

The silver bowl is now on my mantlepiece as a reminder never to go to Morocco again, at least not with Nameless Tours at Easter.

CHAPTER 2

A Town Like Tadchester

I am not really an experienced and intrepid world traveller, but the fourth partner in a group of five and a half partners in general practice in a little Somerset town called Tadchester. Tadchester is a market town with a rising population of about 8,000. It stands on the estuary of the River Tad in one of the most beautiful parts of the Somerset coast, with the resorts of Sandford-on-Sea and Stowin nearby. Although primarily a market town, it still has some fishing, an increasing amount of light industry and a small mine that produces pigments, a residue from the time when the main industry of the town was coal-mining.

In Tadchester you're not just a Tadchester resident, you are either strictly Up-the-Hill or Down-the-Hill. The town is split by the river, with high ground on one side that leads eventually down to the coastal resort of Stowin, and flat ground on the other side which was presumably marshland in years gone by and which has been reclaimed. The river goes down to the sea, passing the shipbuilding yard of Peargate, round the corner from which is the other seaside resort of Sandford-on-Sea. This physical division by the river means that you are either an Up-the-Hill or a Down-the-Hill person.

In the past this had important social distinctions. The

9

population of Up-the-Hill tended to be the have-nots, whereas Down-the-Hill they tended to be the haves. It has levelled off over the years with the coming of light industry which was mainly Up-the-Hill. Now, although there are no social distinctions between the halves of the town, there is no lessening of the rivalry.

We were the only general practice in the town and also took care of the local hospital. Of the five full partners, each had his own area of responsibility in the hospital. Steve Maxwell, the senior partner had a special interest in medicine, Henry Johnson the second senior was the surgeon, Jack Hart the third partner was the anaesthetist. I, the fourth partner, was reckoned to be an expert in midwifery, although in the more recent years this meant just sending expectant mothers to the new midwifery hospital at Winchcombe.

Our fifth partner was Ron Dickinson, an accomplished athlete who spent a great deal of his time running, jumping, swimming, sailing, water skiing and removing the local tonsils. Our half-partner was Catherine Carlton, the delightful wife of a dentist, who was a much nicer doctor than all of us. Catherine gave the proper balance to the practice and was always available for ladies to come and talk to about things ladies prefer to discuss only with other ladies. We were a happy and well-balanced team, living in a delightful area.

One of the reasons I had moved to Tadchester in the first place, apart from the fact that I liked the partners and the partnership, was because it was in a lovely holiday area. I felt that living near the seaside would mean that at holiday time I wouldn't have to travel very far. However, I'd only been in practice for a few months before my appearance on the beach meant that an impromptu surgery would shortly assemble.

No matter how secluded the bay, eventually patients would track me down, and before very long there were few local places I could visit for relaxation or refreshment. A patient on the beach with a few drinks inside him was often much less inhibited than he was in the surgery, and much more difficult to get rid of.

It had long been my ambition to have a holiday at home where I could get stuck into the garden and do odd things around the house, but whenever I had time off at home news would flash round the grapevine that I wasn't at the surgery. People would drop in with: 'I know you're on holiday, but you're the only one that understands Grandma. I won't take a minute of your time.' Which meant taking an hour of my time.

Once while moving house I was walking along the street with a chest of drawers on my shoulder, when I was stopped and asked if I was on duty. 'No,' I replied. 'I'm off sick with a chest complaint.' And I staggered on with my mighty load. My questioner looked puzzled.

It's not always appreciated how onerous the working hours of general practitioners are. When I started in general practice I attended an average of three home confinements a fortnight. I was on every other week for emergency anaesthetics for the hospital, apart from all other practice commitments and emergencies. It was not uncommon to miss a whole night's sleep and have to work the next day. Sometimes all the partners would be together at night, operating on some vital case, and still have to appear the next day.

Once I missed two whole nights' sleep running and continued working. But on the third day of this marathon I went out on a visit, came to a crossroads – and forgot which side of the road one drove on. If doctors were airline pilots or even lorry drivers, we wouldn't be allowed to work these hours. It's one of the quirks of our society that there's no restriction on the hours worked by a man whose job, ostensibly, is to keep people alive.

Holidays are important for everyone, and doctors in particular. Doctors, alas, must get away from their home base, otherwise the holiday just becomes an extension of their work. Most doctors take six weeks' holiday a year. On the other hand they probably work, as I did, 17 to 20 weekends a year, most public holidays and every Christmas. I worked out that if I had every weekend and bank holiday off, plus just a fortnight's holiday, I would actually have more time than I did with the six precious weeks that I took away from the practice.

With the enlightened partners with whom I worked it was agreed that every seven years we should take 13 weeks off to go and do our own thing; anything from working in a mission hospital in India to lying in the sun in Italy. Thus, although it would appear that I and my family have taken lots and lots of holidays everywhere, as we obviously have done, many of them I would have swapped for a quiet undisturbed week's pottering about the house.

Many patients think that their doctors are continually on holiday. I can see a patient 30 times in one year, but if I happen to be away on the 31st occasion he visits the surgery, I'm accused of letting him down and never being there when he needs me. Whenever I announce I'm about to take some well-earned break – which usually means rushing around working twice as hard both before the holiday and for the first week I'm back – there are always raised eyebrows from my quite bewildered patients.

Speaking in chorus they say: 'What? On holiday again, Doctor?'

CHAPTER 3

In Transit

One of my close friends was Chris Parfitt, Editor of the *Tadchester Gazette*, known to everyone as C. P. I thought it would be a great idea for him and his family to join the Clifford clan on a fortnight's holiday in France.

C. P. was reluctant at first. He'd known several longstanding friendships break up during family holidays together. And he wasn't too keen on Abroad *per se*, after one or two unfortunate experiences out there.

His National Service in the Sudan had put him off strong sunshine for life. In transit in Malta he was narrowly missed by a shotgun blast, aimed by a local farmer who was peeved about previous damage done by British squaddies to his drystone walls.

On a family holiday in Spain, the hotel was crammed with overweight Germans who commandeered the swimming pool every day for mass bellyflop sessions. And he made the mistake of watching a bullfight in Barcelona. A young matador botched one of the kills and C. P. left the bullring feeling sick.

In Tangier he'd been horrified by the stumps of arms shoved under his nose by mutilated child beggars, and by the sight of a suspected petty thief being hauled screaming into the local police station for what promised to be a horrendous beating-up.

In Italy he'd been put off his cannelloni at a pavement cafe by the sight of a starving and mange-ridden cat hobbling painfully across the road.

Even in Gibraltar he didn't have the luck. One morning the hotel bar provided lashings of *tapas* – crispy bits of fried fish provided free with the drinks. They were delicious and C. P. ate his fill.

Next day, when he'd recovered from an all-night bout of food poisoning, he discovered that the fish were horse mackerel. Not only that, they'd been collected from a dry dock which had been drained to service a British aircraft carrier. The horse mackerel had been eating all the waste discharged from the ship, richly supplemented by the throwing-up of the sailors returned from a night on the town.

'So all in all, Bob, you could say I'm not one hundred per cent keen on the idea,' he said. 'Apart from anything else, you can't get a decent pint.'

C. P. had the journalist's occupational liking for a pint of beer, and treated the drinking of one with reverence. A badly kept or sloppily served pint – even worse, a pint of keg beer – was to him the equivalent of breaking wind in church.

Eventually, however, he agreed to put it to a family council. His wife Joyce and their children, Clive and Janet, were wholeheartedly in favour. Democracy prevailed by a vote of three to one.

We got down to the planning – Pam and myself, our two younger children Paul and Jane, and the Parfitts – for a fortnight in France. We'd decided to travel in a Ford Transit van and work our way down to the Dordogne: camping a few nights, staying *en pension* a few nights, and finishing up for a week in a villa I'd booked.

I'd seen the villa advertised in a medical magazine. It was expensive, but it was set in magnificent Dordogne countryside and sounded luxurious.

With all our luggage and camping gear, the van was full to

bursting. A tentative suggestion from C. P. that we might find room for a barrel of Barnsley Best Bitter to tide him over until he got used to the filthy French muck, was outvoted.

'Perhaps as well,' he said. 'Temperamental stuff, that. Doesn't travel well.'

We decided to go by hovercraft, taking the cheapest route from Dover to Calais, forgetting that we'd have to drive to Dover, and that we'd have an extra day's travelling through France before we got anywhere near the Dordogne.

The hovercraft sailed at about eleven in the morning, so it meant a chilly dawn start. I had a few twinges of regret on the journey toward Dover as we passed Southampton and Portsmouth, where we could easily have taken ferries to Cherbourg or Le Havre.

Somewhere near Guildford in Surrey, the holiday began with breakfast at a Happy Eater.

'Last bacon and eggs for a bit,' muttered C. P. 'May as well make the most of it.'

We arrived at Dover with time to spare. Knowing how bad we all were at handling money, we decided to buy all our duty-free liquor there and carry it round with us. It would mean that, even if we overspent in France, we would still have something to show for it at the end of the holiday.

In 40 minutes we had crossed the Channel. There's always a tremendous excitement about landing in France: the thrill of putting the Channel behind you, of seeing your first gendarme, of driving on the other side of the road and hoping you won't make a mess of negotiating the junctions.

I had elected to do all the driving. C. P. did not get on too well with the horseless carriage, and admitted to being the worse driver in the world. Even had he claimed to be the best, his family would soon have put the record straight.

We had a leisurely drive south for about 200 miles to our first campsite. It was leisurely mainly because the heavily laden van was reluctant to go above 50 miles an hour, and also because we stopped a couple of times for coffee, bread and pâté in the squares of delightful little villages.

The weather changed towards evening. When we reached the campsite the sky was leaden with cloud, and rain was lashing down. We'd arrived just in time: there were only a few places left on which to pitch a tent.

With the help of the boys, I put up the huge compartment tent I'd bought from my friend John Bowler, consultant physician at Winchcombe Hospital, thankful for the rehearsals we'd had on the lawn at home. C. P. and Joyce were going to sleep in a tiny two-man tent he had borrowed from a cartoonist friend of his. If the cartoonist was in search of material, he certainly got plenty from the stories when we got back.

The two-man tent had one basic drawback: it didn't have a flysheet.

So wherever C. P. or Joyce touched the canvas – and it was impossible not to in the confined space – water would start seeping in. The contortions they went through trying to avoid the drips would have earned them a diploma in advanced yoga.

Finally, they settled down in their sleeping bags. Just as Joyce was nodding off she woke up with a start and said, 'Christopher John!' – she used C. P.'s full title when she was annoyed –'Christopher John! Stop that!'

'Stop what?' murmured C. P. sleepily.

'You know very well what,' said Joyce. 'We're having none of that in this little tent!'

'I never touched you,' said C. P. Or at least he started to say it when he, too, felt a nudge from under the groundsheet.

He put his ear close to the spot and heard a muffled 'Eek-eek . . .'

Rats!

As he found out next day, he'd pitched the tent in the gathering dusk over a series of rat holes, and now the occupants were trying to get out for their night's scavenging.

'Er . . . yes, Pet. Sorry about that,' he said, sitting up in his sleeping bag and batting hard at the groundsheet as if he were trying to get comfortable. Thankfully, it worked. The rats

17

were either scared off by C. P.'s clouting or found another exit.

Joyce had had a phobia about rats ever since seeing a TV version of *1984*, and no tent in the world would have contained her had she suspected there was a family of them under the groundsheet. But suspecting nothing worse than that C. P. had been getting frisky in a confined space and inappropriate circumstances, she drifted off happily to sleep.

Next day C. P. dismantled the tent and lifted the groundsheet to reveal several well-used rat holes. The scream Joyce let out was some indication of what her reaction would have been the night before: she jumped into the van, slammed the door, and refused to come out until the tent had been re-pitched on a rat-free piece of ground and the offending holes filled in.

We were staying a couple of days at this campsite, the idea being that we would get acclimatised to France. With the cold and damp weather, we became more acclimatised to a wet weekend in Llandudno. Still, we had fun.

Paul and Clive, who were then only in their teens, went down to the local bar and sampled their first French beer, feeling very adult and devilish. It's difficult to believe that both are married now, with a child each, and that Clive is teaching in Germany.

Jane was a couple of years younger than Janet, and thought it marvellous to have this 16-year-old sophisticate as a friend. They talked and giggled far into the night, discussing pop stars and teeny-bopper heart throbs whose names I'd never even heard. Again, its hard to believe that Jane is now 23, a dress designer and theatre stage door-keeper and that Janet is a Fleet Street journalist.

We all ate in the main tent. As we started on the coffee after breakfast, peering out at the sheeting rain and trying hard not to shiver, C. P. had a brilliant idea.

'It's a bit early in the day, Bob,' he said, producing a bottle of duty-free brandy, 'but I think a drop of this in the coffee will work wonders for our chests.'

It did, too. Before very long, the weather didn't seem so bad after all.

The rain kept up. Brandy in the coffee became a regular mealtime treat and, if the truth were to be told, something to be taken as an anti-damp specific between meals.

The next leg of our journey looked, on paper, like a straight run, but it turned out to be up and down, round and about, and a real grind. We had managed to find room in the van for a case of French wine. C. P. promoted himself to wine manager and happily nursed the case in the back, sampling it now and again to make sure that it was travelling reasonably well.

Eventually we arrived at a most beautiful campsite at Argentat, dominated by a large château, and with pine forests surrounding a great lake.

The château offered some social amenities, including a *plat du jour*: sometimes steak or fish with chips. It saved our girls cooking, and the chips made C. P. feel more at home.

For the first couple of days the rain still came down, and we kept up with C. P.'s prescription for our chests. By the time the sun came out on the third morning, we'd drunk all our duty-free except for a bottle of bacardi rum.

'Amazing,' said C. P. 'But at least we won't have all that extra weight to carry around.'

The bacardi had its own medicinal uses. With the sun came swarms of gnats, all of which seemed to home in on my bald spot. Within minutes I was covered in angry bites.

'Here,' said C. P., brandishing the bacardi. 'Rub some of this on. It'll keep them away and take some of the sting out.'

'Are you sure?'

'Positive,' he said. 'Never been known to fail.'

The Frenchman in the tent opposite looked in amazement at the mad English: one sitting on a folding stool, the other dabbing him on the head with what he could have sworn was bacardi rum.

(It worked, though. Whether or not it was my trust in C. P.'s faith in the curative powers of bacardi, I don't know. But the stings eased a bit and the gnats seemed to keep away after that.)

The Frenchman opposite certainly got his money's worth. He'd heard that the English were eccentric, but this was something else. He was fascinated by the goings-on and spent most of his day watching us. He even arranged his table outside his tent so that he wouldn't miss anything at mealtimes.

C. P. decided to take the lads fishing. He wrote the *Tadchester Gazette*'s angling column, and a session at the lake by the château promised some nice copy.

'What about bait?' I asked.

'No problem,' said C. P. 'We've got some cheese, and we can rescue some of that stale bread.'

The eight of us consumed vast quantities of French bread, which is only palatable when it's fresh. Any bread left at the end of the day was consigned to the camp dustbins.

C. P. went down to the dustbins and returned with armfuls of old bread. The Frenchman watched in horror. Not only were the English mad, they were incredibly hard up, raiding the dustbins for their daily bread. He missed his mouth with the croissant he was eating, and collected a noseful of crumbs.

C. P. and the lads did quite well on the lake, returning the fish alive from their keepnets to the water, as befitted humane British anglers. The French took away everything they caught, down to the tiniest tiddler, to make into bouillabaise.

'Bloody barbarians,' muttered C. P.

The next morning, Clive and Paul were stricken with the gripes, a result of overdoing the food and drink in the local bistro the night before. After rushing to the latrines and violently throwing up, they both stretched out on the ground outside their tent, pale and sweating, and groaning loudly.

The Frenchman watched, horrified. Serve *les Anglais* right for eating all that stale bread. This time his ruminations were interrupted by his fork, which missed his mouth and jabbed him painfully in the ear.

When the lads recovered, we packed up for the next stage of our journey and moved off, leaving behind us a very disappointed Frenchman. No more mealtime cabarets from the English eccentrics.

We were all excited about the villa. 'You'll enjoy it,' I said. 'For what we're paying, it must be good. These villas are really superb: marble bathrooms, huge iron cooking ranges, old oak beams, scrubbed pine tables. The French really know how to look after these old places.'

What I had forgotten was that we were hiring this place from an Englishman, and an English doctor to boot.

We had a pleasant, meandering drive through the most beautiful countryside, with C. P. in the back overseeing the wine, and eventually reached the farm that had been given as a landmark.

The only other building in the vicinity was a broken-down barn-like building with its shutters up. We were standing outside the barn, consulting the map, when a buxom middle-aged lady approached us from the farm. In halting French, I asked her the whereabouts of the villa.

'*Ici*,' she said, pointing at the barn.

'*Ici?*' I cried. 'You mean *this*?'

'*Oui, Monsieur*,' she said, beaming proudly. And then, looking serious, she asked if there were any young children in the party.

'Nobody under the age of 14,' I said.

'Good,' she said. 'Because I have just put the rat poison down.'

My God! This ruin was our villa – and it was infested with rats!

At this point Joyce nearly fainted. Rats under the tent were bad enough. But rats in our luxury villa . . .

I turned the huge key presented to me by the farmer's wife and pushed open the creaking door. Inside, we were greeted by the spectacle of naked light bulbs hanging on cords from cracked and peeling ceilings. For eight of us there were only six chairs. The kitchen contained a few rusting and rudimentary cooking appliances and a large rickety table. The upper rooms contained beds whose mattresses appeared to be stuffed with rejects from the local brickyard. In a corner of every room was a pile of poisoned bran.

There was a visitors' book in the hallway, scribbled over with strange messages. One said, 'Be kind to our four-legged friends,' and another read, 'Man the lifeboat when it rains.' Our four-legged friends we were to meet soon enough. When it rained towards the end of the week we were wishing we did have a lifeboat: the roof had more than a few tiles missing. I realised that I must have had a few tiles missing myself, to have booked the place at all. Luxurious, it was not.

However, we soon made the best of it. We had sunshine, we had a balcony, we had grapes we could pick off the verandah. In the village beyond the farm was a little shop which sold very drinkable wine at a few francs a bottle. Before we had even unpacked, C. P. and the lads had slipped up the road and returned lugging a couple of crates between them: the shop-keeper's entire stock.

'Look at this!' chortled C. P. 'Cheap enough to wash the floor with! And there's even money back on the bottles.'

Things got off to a rousing start that night with a firework festival in the village. A squad of drum majorettes arrived, dressed in bright uniforms with cowboy boots and very skimpy skirts: a spectacle that did not go unappreciated by the lads nor, I must confess, by C. P. and myself.

Then the village band turned up to lead them. Or it would have led them if the bandleader had not popped into the bistro for a quick one. The quick one became two quick ones, then three or four slower ones. Outside, the bronzed thighs of the drum majorettes were turning blue and goose-pimply in the cool evening air.

Every so often one of the bandsmen would rush in and indicate that the bandleader's presence was respectfully but urgently requested. But with the French equivalent of 'Just one for the road, old boy,' he would order up another drink.

Finally, in came a bugler, whose entreaties, like the others', were ignored. In desperation, he put his bugle to his lips and at point-blank range blew a blast of the 'Marseillaise' into the bandleader's left ear. The maestro took the hint and staggered out, wincing and clutching his ear, to lead the parade.

They made a fine sight, with the band and the drum majorettes keeping perfect step, even if the bandleader didn't. The girls goose-pimples soon disappeared, and a good time was had by all.

It was a lively, noisy, tuneful and enjoyable evening, with a performance out of all proportion to the size of the tiny village. Clive and Paul practised their A-Level French by chatting up

some of the local girls. Any further hopes of a spot of *entente cordiale* were dashed by the presence in the shadows of several large French *mamans*. Marshal Pétain's resolve at Verdun – 'They shall not pass!' – had nothing on that of the average French matron.

'Never mind,' said Paul to Clive. 'They'd all grow up like their mothers anyway. We'd soon be fighting out of our weight.'

Back at the villa, which in the light of the naked bulbs made the House of Usher look like an Ideal Homes showplace, we enjoyed a leisurely supper. Ominous scuttling sounds from darkened corners, and from the rafters above the table, indicated that our four-legged friends were willing to clear up any leftovers.

'I want to go to the toilet,' said Joyce, 'but I'm scared stiff.'

'Leave it to me,' said Clive. He picked up a tin tray and marched into the bathroom banging it loudly. 'Nothing in there, Mum,' he said. 'You'll be perfectly safe.'

Joyce went in the bathroom and closed the door. All was quiet for a couple of minutes, and then came a piercing shriek of, 'Rats! Let me out!'

Poor Joyce had been washing her hands when from behind a piece of broken panelling had padded a huge rat, which must have mistaken the tin tray for a dinner gong. Her screams sent it scuttling back again, but it wasn't the best preparation for a good night's sleep.

Fishing in the area was good, and we bought licences at the local bicycle shop. C. P. had some trouble asking for a tin of maggots, until he discovered that the French name for them was *asticots*. He was horrified to discover that the container was little bigger than a tobacco tin and that it held only a few dozen scrawny bluebottle maggots.

'God!' he exclaimed. 'In Britain we'd get ten times that amount for half the price!'

But he wasn't in Britain, and that was the best the shop could offer. Grudgingly, he pocketed the tin and set off for the river.

He didn't do too well on that trip, reeling in just a few small roach. It seemed that even the fish weren't too keen on the locally-bred *asticots*. And what made it worse was the Great Maggot Explosion.

Keeping his eye on the float, he pulled out a tin from his pocket and filled his pipe. Still keeping an eye on the float, he struck a match, applied it to the bowl of the pipe, and inhaled deeply.

There was a series of sharp explosions and an ammoniac smell as if an old stable was burning down. C. P. broke into a massive coughing fit, dropped his rod, and staggered around with watering eyes.

'Bloody Norah!' he gasped, and pulled the tin from his pocket.

It wasn't his tobacco tin at all, but the tin of *asticots*. The explosions had been half a dozen unfortunate maggots and the ammoniac smell was the smoke from the sawdust they were packed in.

'How was it?' I asked, when his coughing had subsided, trying hard not to laugh, but soon giving up.

'I can't recommend it,' he wheezed. 'It'll never replace the old-fashioned Three Nuns.'

The eight of us explored some of the towns nearby, enjoying a cup of coffee, glass of beer or a cognac at the boulevard cafes, soaking up the atmosphere and generally watching the world go by.

C. P. even developed a taste for French beer and would squeeze in an extra swift one when it was time to go home. 'Home' was still the villa, where the rats had become bolder and would appear on top of the cooking range or the huge kitchen dresser. After the wives and children had gone to bed, C. P. and I used to sit up on rat-watching duties with a glass of wine in one hand and a heavy walking boot in the other. When a rat appeared we would let fly with a boot.

Whether it was the wine, the unwieldy missiles, or that we were just not good at boot-throwing, our aim was not up to Bisley standards. By the end of the week we'd not hit a single rat, but had severely depleted the villa's small collection of crockery.

On our last day it rained heavily. Water poured through the roof and down the walls. The lifeboat would have come in very handy. Still, we'd had fun.

'Tell me again,' I said to C. P. as we mopped the sodden floors. 'We *have* had fun, haven't we?'

After a tiring two-day haul back to the Channel coast, we stayed overnight in Calais at a very comfortable hotel. The bill for our rooms, a few litres of wine and a very liberal *petit déjeuner* came to about half what the English equivalent would cost. It was just as well, because by now we were flat broke, with not even enough cash to stock up again at the duty-free shop.

The hovercraft crossing was rough – there had been some debate as to whether the sea was too rough to risk the crossing – and several of the passengers were violently sick. A bunch of them at the back blamed their sickness on the smoke from the pipes which C. P. and I were puffing at contentedly. Our children, who overheard them discussing the practicalities of a maritime lynching party, pretended not to be with us.

'Don't know when they're well off,' said C. P. as we put out our pipes in deference to the cries and threats from behind. 'I could have been smoking those bloody maggots again.'

So that was France: sunshine, rain, food poisoning, explod-

26

ing maggots, the House of Usher and all. Our wives and children voted it the best holiday they'd ever had.

Even C. P. said he'd known worse.

CHAPTER 4

Family Matters

Most people say, when their children leave home, how much easier life is.

I've not found this to be true. After the children's schooling, there's university or polytechnic. After that there's marriage. After that there are houses and after that there are grandchildren. Instead of parental worries decreasing as our children get older, they seem to increase.

Our elder son Trevor, after taking a couple of law degrees, decided that it was an actor's life for him and became a successful actor-writer.

It was great fun to follow him around seeing his stage performances. Of his more recent shows, *Caught in the Act* was the funniest farce I've ever seen. It was at the Royal Exchange Theatre, Manchester, and starred Michael Denison and Gabrielle Drake of *Crossroads* TV fame. Hopefully it was going to go to the West End.

Trevor always seemed to be in work. He followed the performance at Manchester by having a large if not major part in a TV series called *Star Cops*. This is not going to make him an overnight star but should make him a familiar face on television. He did achieve transient fame in a Shell TV commercial, where he was jumping about behind a counter. Then he was flown to Germany for a day to do a liqueur advertisement. Because of his TV commitments, he was unable to do a day's filming in New Zealand which would have meant his spending a week there.

He had in the previous year become the New Zealand Schweppes man. This meant a week's filming as several characters which included a yokel, a butler and a barmaid – possibly the biggest barmaid in the world.

Some months after this advert had been shown in New Zealand, he heard that not only had he received the Gold Award presented by their commercial television for the best character in television adverts, but also the Silver and Bronze.

The awards are in the form of medals which he wears on his dinner jacket at formal dinners, just to confuse everybody.

Although they lived a long way away, our children were still able to present me with various medical problems and alarms.

On one of my rare trips to London, when lunching at the Lansdowne Club with the film and theatre director, Peter Cotes, I was paged on the telephone. It was my younger son Paul, ringing from a hotel at London Airport where his electronic components firm was holding an exhibition.

He said that he'd started to vomit some black stuff, and now was vomiting blood. What should he do?

I told him to get himself driven to Reading Hospital to the Casualty Department, where I knew one of the surgeons. I abandoned my lunch and caught the first train to Reading.

Happily nothing was seriously amiss, although they did have to take him to theatre and poke a tube down him to make sure.

As most of Paul's work lay in the west of England, his firm asked him to move further west. He and his wife Gill were living in a tiny cottage in Aldermaston, a lovely old Jacobean village spoilt by the traffic. His cottage was further spoilt by the fact that most of the traffic seemed to enter the front bedroom at five o'clock in the morning, and leave via the bathroom.

They put their house up for sale. Their sale, as well as the usual ups and downs and near-sales, was further complicated by the fact that our dear daughter-in-law Gill had now become pregnant. Pam's great ambition of becoming a grandmother was about to be achieved.

Paul had nearly sold his house about six times when they eventually found a positive buyer, a very young lady whose only problem was that she was having some trouble with selling her own house. Not that she hadn't found a buyer, but her particular purchaser was extremely difficult. His first demand was that the sale could only go through if the purchase was completed on the 8 August. This was the day Gill's baby was due. It was so important that Paul didn't lose his sale that he had to agree.

Paul and Gill were buying a lovely little town house in Cirencester, Gloucestershire. The owners of the house, a Mr and Mrs Morgan, had taken Paul and Gill to their hearts. They had not only given them masses of furniture, but told them not to worry about dates. They'd already bought the house they were moving to and, whatever happened to anybody else, the Cirencester house was Paul's and Gill's. This was a great weight off their minds.

Liz, Gill's mother, had come back from India: not only was Gill having a baby, but her elder sister Joanna was also expecting four weeks before Gill's baby was due.

The months seemed to fly by, and I kept in constant touch. One evening I rang the house to see how Gill was. Liz answered the phone and said, 'Oh, she's resting.'

What I didn't know was that she was resting in Basingstoke Hospital, and a few hours later Paul rang to say that we were grandparents to a dear little girl called Daisy May. Pam was over the moon.

Daisy May had arrived a fortnight early, well ahead of moving day, which was very thoughtful of her.

As well as being fortunate with the Morgans, Paul was also lucky with his solicitor, a Mr Kaxe of Gardner and Leader at Thatcham, who really put himself out on their behalf.

Just after the birth of the baby he had to break the news to Paul that the man who was buying Paul's purchaser's house, and who had insisted that they move on the 8 August, now said he couldn't move until the 28th. They had no alternative but to fit in with this request.

Mr Kaxe came into his own when the second moving date was looming. Suddenly the solicitor of the man who was buying the house from Paul's purchaser presented the young girl with 100 points to answer. She managed to answer 99 but he refused to accept anybody's word about the hundredth: he wanted it in writing.

When the girl said that she would send it round by car – and this meant a journey of 60 or 70 miles – he confessed what the real trouble was: the man wasn't ready for the move and everything would have to be postponed for a further week.

It created a problem; the exchange of contracts was only a few days before the completion date, the said 28th. This delaying tactic meant there was no possibility of their completing on that date, the day Paul actually planned to move and for which, for the second time, he had the furniture vans organised.

On the 27th, the difficult solicitor promised Mr Kaxe that he would exchange contracts on the 28th. Mr Kaxe asked if I could bridge Paul for a week. If so, his move could go ahead on the 28th, providing contracts were exchanged on that day, and the removal vans wouldn't have to be cancelled.

I scraped my coffers bare and just managed to produce the right amount.

The day of the move dawned but there was more trouble in store. First, Paul's furniture van broke down on the way to him. The next van that came wasn't big enough, so they had to send away for a trailer. They were almost completely packed, when Mr Kaxe said they might have to unpack again. He had that morning telephoned the difficult solicitor to formalise the exchange and found that the chap was not in the office – he had gone away and was in fact moving house himself.

31

Phones were buzzing all over the place. Meanwhile, there was Paul, sitting with his packed furniture outside his house.

Eventually Mr Kaxe managed to get hold of the senior partner of the chap who'd disappeared, so did the solicitor of the girl who was buying Paul's house, and the Morgans' solicitors from Cirencester joined in. Together the three solicitors threatened to approach the Law Society if something wasn't done.

The senior partner of the firm was quite unaware of what had been going on. He went down to his junior's office and found complete chaos. He managed to sort things out, and by lunchtime had exchanged contracts.

The go-ahead to Paul and Gill came through and the furniture went off. Gill, Liz and Daisy May arrived safely in Cirencester to find that the kindly Morgans had left them milk and bread as a welcome present.

So, happily, it all ended well. After I'd sweated for a week at the prospect of my life savings going down the drain, completion date did follow up as promised and my money was safely returned.

Moving to Cirencester meant that Paul and Gill were marginally nearer to us in Tadchester, but with Trevor and Jane sharing a flat in Brighton, we were rather strung out as a family.

I still talked about my offspring as our children, though Trevor now was more than 30, Paul was approaching it and even little Jane was 23.

Jane was busy trying to establish herself as a dress designer. She had this terrible logo, which looked like a pair of false teeth shouting DUFF, stuck on all the dresses and T-shirts she made.

Having been initially disappointed about some promised shop premises, she'd been going round markets to sell her dresses. Now a few friends, each with a special skill to offer, managed to obtain a tiny shop in part of Aladdin's Cave at Brighton.

One of the friends made jewellery, one bags, one hats, and two of them made dresses and shirts. I don't think any of them was making a profit, they were just about breaking even, but they'd made a start.

Jane kept the wolf from the door by being the night stage door-keeper at the Royal Theatre, Brighton. They had many pre-London runs in Brighton and it was interesting to hear how nice the vast majority of the really big stars were who took part.

Jane was often given a bunch of flowers, a box of chocolates, or some other gift for her help as stage door-keeper. She was always treated politely and generously.

We enjoyed visiting Trevor and Jane in Brighton. The only problem was that their flat was about five storeys up and I always felt I needed an oxygen mask by the time I'd reached the top.

The flat was a great boon for both Trevor and Jane. Trevor, who worked all over the place, particularly in London, was most often able to commute from Brighton. They both loved Brighton itself with its shops, cinemas, eating houses and pier. You could just see the sea from their lounge window and everything was so close at hand. With good local transport and a good train service to London, they hardly needed a car.

Life had changed for us in that instead of us looking forward to the children coming home, we now had to make the long journeys to Cirencester and Brighton to visit them in their homes.

Paul worked very hard and conscientiously at his job, which meant doing a lot of his bookwork on Sundays. Jane, with six nights at the theatre was very tied down, and when Trevor was on location he was hardly available at all. But it was a great comfort to see them all settling down, doing well, and working so hard.

We were very proud of them.

*　　*　　*

We had a bereavement in the family. Our little Cairn terrier, Suzie, who had been getting blinder and deafer, finally went to sleep one day and never woke up again.

She was 17 years old.

We had had her since she was nine months and she'd been an absolute joy. In the end we weren't sorry to see her go because she'd lost all appreciation of any real quality of life; she couldn't see properly, she couldn't hear properly, she bumped into the furniture, and she couldn't tell one member of the family from another. The only instinct she had left was for food, and she would eat anything that was put near her.

Happily, her end was peaceful and we buried her in a quiet little spot in the garden.

Suzie had a pedigree as long as your arm but her teeth were a bit crooked. Perhaps she'd been reared to breed or to show and was not good enough for either. But we fell for her as soon as we saw her.

We hadn't told the children we were buying a new dog, Pam had just said when she'd brought them home from school that there was a surprise. They opened the front door and there, on the top of the stairs, was this tiny dog. Instantly Suzie rolled over on her back, presenting a little hairy tummy to be scratched. Immediately she was one of the family.

She followed the children everywhere, and was part of every game. When there were no children about, she vigorously chased rabbits all over the garden.

Only once was she ever successful in her chase, catching a tiny baby rabbit which happily she didn't harm. We were able to disengage it from her mouth and it ran away back to its mother.

She was marvellous at Hunt the Chocolate Button; she knew all the rules of the game. She would be sent outside the room and the chocolate button would be hidden somewhere. To great excitement the door would be opened. Suzie would charge in, sniff all over the room, and never fail to find her prize.

Over the years she had some very amorous encounters, particularly with the little Pomeranian down the road, but she never actually had any puppies. She did have one or two false pregnancies which were terribly distressing to her. These didn't disappear until she had a hysterectomy.

She had become ill, drinking copious amounts of water, and we couldn't understand what was wrong.

The vet diagnosed precisely: a septic uterus. After her operation she soon changed from a sickly dog into a bright and happy one again.

We missed her sadly. Now with both dog and children gone, the house seemed to echo around us.

*　*　*

We decided to have another dog and Pam set her heart on a West Highland White terrier. There didn't seem to be too many about, but we eventually found in the local paper an advertisement for a bitch just the other side of Winchcombe. We rang and enquired about her and decided to call in on our way to visit Paul and Gill. If we liked the dog, we could pick her up on the way back.

We both knew perfectly well that we'd buy her as soon as we saw her. We arrived at a lovely old thatched cottage. Outside was an adult West Highland, tied to a stake. According to the owner (who led us to assume that the dog was the mother) she had to be kept tied up because she was so fond of water. Loose on her own she'd be straight down to the river, would be a long time away and very wet when she came back.

We were taken into the kitchen where a tiny quiet fluffy little dog, snow-white from a recent bath, was exploring the floor. She was a bit quiet, but lovely. We paid our money and agreed to pick her up in two days' time, at the end of our visit to Paul and Gill.

Before we set off on our way home from Paul's, we rang up to say what time we'd be calling. The daughter of the house said 'Hang on, I'll get mother.'

Mother came sobbing to the phone to say there'd been a terrible accident – the puppy had got out of the yard and the Land Rover had run over it.

They did have another puppy left from the litter but he was a male. Would we like to have a look at him?

We were terribly disappointed, especially Pam. We said we'd come and have a look at him but my suspicions were aroused a bit.

People who misused drugs, and were trying to get extra supplies, usually told one of three classical stories: One, that the drugs had fallen out on the drive and a car had run over them. Two, that the cabinet had fallen off the bathroom wall and the dog had eaten them. Three, the most common of all, that they'd left them in the pocket of their jeans and had put the jeans in the washing machine.

The story of the Land Rover sounded very much like one of these, but perhaps my years in medicine had give me a too-suspicious nature. We were buying a dog, for heaven's sake. I immediately put such unworthy thoughts from my mind.

When we got there we were completely charmed with the little puppy. He was much livelier than his little sister, recently deceased. Straightaway we named him Billy, and agreed to take him instead.

The lady of the house gave us a great bowl of prepared food, some sort of tripe concoction. She gave instructions to feed him only on this and to make certain that he went the next day to the vet to have his parvo injection.

We brought Billy home and he was absolutely gorgeous, running about on the grass and chasing the ball.

We took him to the vet's the next day. The vet thought he was a bit young for the injection, but in spite of this gave him the lot, parvo, hardpad and distemper.

Twenty-four hours after the injection, Billy started vomiting. We returned him to the vet, who said that this was quite normal when a puppy was settling into a new habitat.

He wasn't much better the next day so I rang up, to be told by a rather snooty receptionist, 'Stop worrying. This is how puppies always are.' I accepted that I only knew about human ailments and that perhaps she was right, but I certainly would have been worried if he'd been a human being.

Billy got worse and I spent the whole of the night with the little chap, who was obviously very poorly in my arms.

We took him to the vet again the next day, who now agreed that he was very poorly, and that he had only a 50-50 chance of survival. Billy was admitted to their little animal hospital, where he died 24 hours later.

It was amazing how upsetting was the loss of this little puppy that we'd had only five days. We were heartbroken.

Samples had to be sent off to find the cause of his death. They took some time to come back but we eventually found that he had died of parvo virus. The fact that he'd been given an injection while he had it would certainly have diminished his chances of survival. This particular virus meant that we couldn't have any dog to visit the house for six months, and if we did decide to have a new dog in six months' time, he would have to have been immunised against parvo before he came.

I got in touch with the lady we'd bought the dog from, and broke the news. She was horrified, but on closer questioning revealed that the lovely old adult dog outside wasn't his mother; that he had in fact come from Wales, from a friend down there. I was offered my money back but, being soft, only accepted half. I didn't pursue the matter, but I had my suspicions that Billy and his sister might have come from the kind of mercenary and heartless puppy farms we read about now and again. Nor did I entirely believe that the sister had been run over: she might have met the same fate as Billy.

So for six months we were dogless – not even friends could bring dogs round to see us – but we were determined not to make the same mistake again.

A patient of mine, Mrs Gater, who ran the Spire Ridge Kennels, said she would get a puppy from a breeder for us and keep it until after it had had its first injection.

That's how we obtained our Bertie. He wasn't an instant replacement for Suzie, who'd been with us for so long, but was as lovable a little dog as you could find anywhere.

He was terribly good natured. You could take a bone from his mouth, he was as soft as butter. There were only two things he really disliked. One was wheels: for some reason he would dash at anything on wheels. The other was papers or letters being delivered through the letter box. If we weren't about he'd try and pick them out of the letter box himself, and he'd rush about, up and down the stairs, until the paperboy or the postman had gone. But he loved all people and all dogs. Each day, Pam would take him for walks along the river bank, where he'd meet all sorts of friends.

We spoiled him, I'm afraid. He jumped on chairs, used to climb up the side of my armchair, sit on the back, and try and lick my nose.

When Pam was away, visiting Paul and Gill and grand-daughter, Bertie would climb up on the back of my chair and sleep precariously on the top, just touching my head to make sure I was still there.

When I walked him along the river bank, I found I had no ordinary dog – everybody knew him. I've always been a bit frightened of big dogs and when I saw some great Afghan hound or an Alsatian bounding towards us, I'd slip the lead on, only to hear the owner shout, 'Oh, that's Bertie! It's all right – they're friends!' And Bertie would go off cavorting in the long grass. He was a real pleasure and the house rang to his barks.

He was a great watchdog, standing for ages looking out of the lounge window, one paw on the sill. As Paul said, he'd bark at a falling leaf. Gill said perhaps he was born in Barkshire!

There was one aspect about him that worried me. He made me think, for the first time, that reincarnation is possible. He was a sort of cross between a prostitute and a missionary.

If he could get into the bedroom he would run in, jump up and lie on the pillow, legs astride, with an expression that said, 'Come and get me.' There was something voluptuous about it.

He was never allowed in the bedroom at night and, in fact, was a very good dog at bedtime. On command, he would go off to his basket in the kitchen and never, even from his first night, cause a fuss.

The missionary side of him appeared when he watched television. He was the only dog I'd met that was a television addict.

During Wimbledon fortnight you'd see his head go from side to side, following the ball. But if either sex or violence appeared on the screen he went absolutely mad, jumping up, scratching at the screen and trying to interfere.

Jane called him Bertie Whitehouse and said he ought to go on the Watch Dog Committee – he would have made an ideal censor. In fact his taste was quite discriminating. He loved nature programmes and would watch quite happily and then go round to the back of the television set to see where the animals had gone to.

Although, at times, Bertie did make me wonder what he'd been in a previous life one reassuring fact which made me feel that he was a dog, and only a dog, was that he had a girlfriend, an 11-year-old Jack Russell bitch called Lilly. They could sense each other as if by radar; if Bertie's tail wagged in a certain way we knew Lilly was round the corner. With tails wagging like propellers they tore up and down the river bank chasing each other and playing with enormous exuberance. They were a joy to watch. Occasionally they would stop and play something completely different. Then there was no doubt that Bertie was a dog.

CHAPTER 5

Just Deserts

One of the great joys of taking the children on holiday was their bubbling excitement when we were taking them somewhere new, particularly if we were renting a cottage or an apartment.

Among the first cottages we ever rented was Mermaid Cottage in Virgin Street, St. Ives, Cornwall. We liked it so much that eventually we went there two or three times. The children loved it because it was quite close to the harbour and beach, quite close to the town and far too close to the amusement arcade, where they would nip off and spend all their pennies given half a chance.

It had a stable door. You opened the top half of the door, stood behind it and watched the world and his wife go by. With a view from a stable door, even washing-up could be made interesting.

We often visited Wales at Easter. There was always great excitement when we arrived at a new cottage: all the rooms had to be explored, decisions to be made as to who slept where. But there'd be hardly any sleep that night because there were fresh discoveries to be made in the morning. Where were the nearest shops? Where was the nearest beach? There were a hundred and one things to find out.

We had a flat in Solva, Dyfed, overlooking a beautiful tree-lined creek which wound down to the sea.

We had a farmhouse in Haverford West with a trout stream, or a supposed trout stream, running through the four acres of ground that went with it. We never caught anything in the stream but we could always, as most fishermen do, live in hope.

We had a cottage near Milford Haven for the first holiday that Gill came on with us at the beginning of her eight-year courtship with Paul. On the way back home we stopped at a pub for lunch. After the meal, on the table in front of Paul was left a dirty plate, piled with odd bits of fish and chips and pie.

Paul's reaction was quite simple. He picked it up and handed it to Gill. Gill took the plate uncomplainingly and took it back to the bar.

I let Paul have a mouthful in the left ear for his discourtesy, but it was then I realised that one day they would probably get married.

* * *

We had several pleasant holidays in the Channel Islands. A short one in Guernsey which we loved, then a much longer one there after Trevor had fallen in Sark, broken his hip and been shipped to Guernsey. We had to attend him daily at the marvellous Princess Elizabeth Hospital.

Years earlier, Pam and I had gone with our friends Janice and Kevin Bird to Jersey. We'd been on holiday with them several times and this was probably the least successful, partly because the food at the hotel was so poor. The evening meal consisted of a miniscule portion of meat, one potato, one sprout and a couple of beans each. Afterwards we had to retire to the Chinese restaurant next door to supplement our diet.

Pam had just lost her mother. Jane, who was only a few months old and had been weaned hurriedly to give Pam a break, was left in the capable arms of her godmother, Zara, back in Tadchester.

We went round seeing the various sights, but the weather was indifferent so one evening we thought we'd go to the pictures. Pam had been silently worrying all the time about having left Jane at home. The title of the film was little comfort. In huge letters across the front of the cinema it demanded: *WHATEVER HAPPENED TO BABY JANE?* Kevin and Janice went in, but Pam couldn't face it. We went off and had a cream tea instead.

I once paid a visit to Jersey on my own. It was the beginning of my sabbatical leave: 13 whole weeks off. I was hoping to write most of a book in this break and wanted symbolically to break the pattern of work.

It was March. I couldn't get any sunshine locally, so I thought Jersey would be a change. I could work in peace and quiet, with just a chance of better weather. I booked in at one of the best hotels, which was inexpensive out of season.

What they'd forgotten to tell me was that they were completely renovating the hotel. When I arrived there, the corridors were filled with workmen. There was scaffolding all over the place and power saws going every day, augmented by the noise of riveting and banging. I had to disturb about five men every time I went in and out of my room. It rained all the time outside, and everything was shut down.

Eventually I came home early for some peace and quiet. In view of the circumstances, the tour operators refunded me some of my money.

* * *

It seemed that every time I went on holiday without Pam or the family, some sort of major disaster took place. Although I had a great number of experiences away from the family, I could hardly call them holidays.

There were two exceptions: my trans-Saharan crossings.

In *The Sunday Times* one day I saw advertised a trip across the Sahara, organised by an enterprising little travel firm. My patient partners agreed that I could disappear for five weeks in the middle of winter on condition that I provided, and paid for, a locum.

I booked to fly out from London to Paris, to Toulon, to Algiers, to the Oasis of El Golea, then a 4,000-mile trip around the Sahara by Land Rover.

In Tadchester it was exciting news for the local gossips. The fact that I was leaving my wife for so long could only mean that we were breaking up.

As the time drew nearer, Pam's face was getting longer and longer. But on the strength of the fact that I was having an expensive trip she managed to get an expensive sewing machine out of me, explaining how much money she was going to save by making all her clothes while I was away.

The day finally came and I suddenly found myself at London Airport in a bush jacket, having hardly flown before, wondering what on earth I was doing. I was travelling with five other people who were booked on the same Saharan trip: a lady gynaecologist, a Yorkshire plumber, a vicar, an army officer who was spending his leave from Aden crossing the Sahara, and an artist who had some personal problem he wanted to get out of his system.

I was very apprehensive about flying. Just the bang as the plane took its wheels up made me think it was the end. This intrepid explorer had to be reassured by the passenger next to him.

A rather suspicious looking chap with a day's growth of beard hovered near us when we changed planes in Paris. He came up and introduced himself as an American anaesthetist. We found, reminiscing about our medical student days (he had trained in England), that we'd actually fought on the same programme when the hospital had boxed against Cambridge University. Halfway through the trip I asked why he hadn't made himself known to us in London.

'Now I can tell you,' he said. 'I'm Jewish. Travelling round Arab countries did not seem the most sensible thing to do. I only made up my mind I was definitely going when I reached Paris.'

We spent our first night in Algiers in the Hotel St. George, where General Eisenhower had his wartime headquarters, then we flew on to the oasis of El Golea where the Land Rovers were based. There we met the leader of the party, an ex-Colonel from the Sudan Defence Force, a delightful chap called Tommy.

Thus began five magic weeks.

First we explored El Golea, a large administrative oasis of 15,000 inhabitants with its magnificent ruined fort Ksur, a reminder of the days when the Tuareg nomads were masters of the desert. The local hotel boasted that it had 30 lavatories; unfortunately nobody seemed to have cleaned them out for several years.

We eventually set off from El Golea, spending the first night at Fort Mirabelle, a disused French Foreign Legion fort. The bleak outlook of the mud fort, set in a barren and featureless plain, took away any thoughts of the Foreign Legion's being glamorous and gave some example of the stark brutality of the legionnaires' lives.

From Fort Mirabelle to the next oasis – In Salah – we crossed the Tademait Plateau. The plateau is similar to a bleak 500-mile aerodrome runway, as wide as it's long with a perpetual wind blowing. It's baking hot with scorching sunshine in the day, but freezing at night.

In Salah was, until the turn of the century, the base for the warlike Tuaregs and a crossroads for camel caravans and traders. It was also a slave market; it's only a few years since slaves were sold there and you can still find the odd slave pottering about. There was a constant battle with the sand which gradually seemed to be taking over the town. Leaving In Salah, we entered the Arak Gorge where there was some vegetation, game, gazelle and mountain sheep.

Travelling so far meant a good deal of sitting in a bumpy Land Rover, but setting up camp at the end of the day provided plenty of work for everyone. There was fuel to be fetched, fires to be lit, Land Rovers serviced, tents erected – all this apart from the routine cooking and washing up. The day usually finished with a drop of duty-free around the camp-fire. We stopped putting up tents after a couple of nights, sleeping out in the open under the clear desert sky, which made the stars appear so much nearer.

From the Arak Gorge the countryside became more broken and interesting. We travelled the great Hoggar route to reach Tamanrasset, a beautiful oasis 5,400 feet up, only developed during the last 70 years. It's clean, with tree-lined streets and looks fresh and in good order, with two hotels, several cafes, and even a cinema trying to establish itself.

We thought we'd try a meal out and visited the Cafe of Peace. We asked for a typical Algerian dish and were served egg and chips on enamel plates. The waiter managed to hold two plates and pick his nose at the same time. A clever trick, but we weren't impressed.

The Hoggar is composed of vast granite masses, partly covered with lava, which time has eroded into fantastic lunar shapes. After a few days in Tamanrasset, which included a trip up into Hoggar Mountain, we went to the hermitage of the French priest, Charles Foucald. Father Foucald set up the order of The Little Brothers and Sisters of Jesus, some of whom were in retreat at this spartan hermitage.

The members of this order impressed me more than any other group of people I have met. They don't preach, they don't teach, they just settle in deprived communities and live by example. They don't offer western medicine or any other special technical help.

One aristocratic French lady had been living under a tent with the Tuareg for 15 years, and one other little sister had been working in a South African factory and living amongst the poor. These two ladies had such an aura about them that I would genuinely not have been surprised to see haloes round their heads.

We then set off south for Agades in Niger, passing through some of the most beautiful scenery in the whole of the Sahara, stretches of golden sand broken from time to time by curiously shaped outcrops of rocks which looked like giant sculptures.

From Tamanrasset south there's less traffic and we navigated mainly by looking for the wheelmarks of the giant Saharan lorries that used the route. We crossed the Algeria-Niger border at a place called In Geuzzam, quite a frightening experience. It's rumoured that guerrilla fighters are trained there, and the border guards put every obstacle they could think of in our way and generally made things as difficult as possible for us.

Inside Niger was quite different, there was a sort of freedom about it. In northern Niger there's some vegetation and further south an almost East African type of scrubland. The area is frequented by nomads with their flocks of sheep, goats, cattle and camels. Game was plentiful; gazelle and ostrich would race away in the distance as we drove by.

Agades is one of the main crossroads of the Sahara, with a bustling market centre where camel caravans unload cargoes of salt and dates. It was an incredible sight at night to go into the market place where there were probably two or three thousand camels, hundreds of little fires, traders, silversmiths, blacksmiths and cooks. It was a scene straight from the Arabian Nights, spread out over half a mile.

We made a trip from Agades into the Air mountains which

revealed a completely different landscape; some of the foothills are inhabited by an almost negroid ethnic type living in beehive huts, a complete contrast to the nomad Tuaregs in their tents.

We went on to an area of tin mines; not mines as we think of them – the tin is taken from the surface. The village we visited had had some sort of missionary teachers who had taught the children to read and write, and some of the villagers could speak good French.

Having given them a taste for what lay in the outside world, the missionaries had left them in these primitive surroundings. It brought it home very much to me how important it is not to interfere with a settled way of life: the teaching and do-gooding had broken up a community and made the young people dissatisfied with their life at home. Their only alternative was to hang around the towns in the oases 500 or 600 miles away or try and get casual work at the oil wells that were beginning to spring up.

One excitement in the village was when we were called to help a man who had fallen 40 feet down into the communal well. With ropes from the Land Rover we managed to haul him out, to the cheers of the surrounding villagers. There were more cheers when I offered him five francs to do it again.

We had a real adventure crossing the Tenere desert. It's not many years since this was first negotiated by a motor vehicle. Called the Dreaded Tenere Desert, it consists of 500 miles of

flat sand between Agades in Niger and Bilma, which is the sort of Siberia of Niger. As well as being an important salt-producing area, it is also a penal settlement.

The desert is swept by sandstorms on an average of one every two or three days and no one is allowed to cross without one of the few guides who know its routes and dangers. It's a 500-mile stretch with only one waterhole marked by a single tree, 'the only tree in the Tenere Desert'. This tree is unique in that it's the only tree to feature on maps of the world.

The Tenere is magnificent; miles of flat sand like an eternal beach. There are two routes: the easy one to the north which is uninterrupted flat sand and the more difficult route to the south, which we took on my second trip when we crossed with guides through the sand sea to explore the rarely visited oasis of Fachi with its medieval fort structure.

On reaching the Bilma Oasis with its salt mines and gardens, we paused for a rest and a couple of camel rides, then headed north through broken country, back into Algeria, to an oasis called Djanet at the foot of the Tassili Plateau.

I have climbed and spent a few days on the Plateau twice, and it's similar to my visual image of Conan Doyle's Lost World. We climbed up from the lush oasis of Djanet through barren rocky strata to come out at 6,000 feet on to this fascinating and ever-changing landscape of trees and water and fantastic rock shapes carved out by the gales.

One of the main objects of the expedition was to study the profusion of prehistoric carvings in the area; frescoes first discovered in the Twenties by a Frenchman called Henri Lhote. Some of the frescoes are not cave paintings, but drawings cut in the overhanging ledges in the warren-like canyons of the plateau and spread over a large area. Concentrations of the best are found near the approaches of the plateau and include figures of elephants, giraffes, hippopotami and rhinoceroses, which disappeared from this area thousands of years ago.

Then came the journey back via Djanet with a different view of Algeria, mushrooming oil wells and the oases of Ouargla and Hassi Messaoued with some sophisticated shops. Then there was the transport centre of In Amenas which seemed to be filled with Poles, Czechs or Russians – but with not a woman in the place. It could easily have been a Wild West town except there were no cowboy hats – there was something quite frightening about it.

We had our last stop near El Golea and then came the real tragedy of our present times – the speed of travel. On both Sahara trips I went on, after our first or second day we discarded our tents and slept in sleeping bags out on the sand. I'd lived in the open for five weeks, away from what we would call civilisation, with a small group of people. After I'd slept in the desert the night before and had breakfast in El Golea, it was frightening that I was home for tea in Tadchester that afternoon.

Still, I came back with the best suntan I've ever had, and with a great love for deserts.

I did some medical work for this adventurous little travel company and was invited a couple of years later to repeat the trip, taking round some rich Americans and acting as medical officer. Even going on almost the same route a second time did nothing to dispel the magic of the journey.

We were led this time by Ken, a young bearded Scotsman, and Julie, a superb cook, both experienced desert travellers, and Jim, the engineer of the party. We weren't exactly roughing it in the desert: our first meal out after El Golea consisted of soup, game pie filling with tinned new potatoes, peas and a bottle of Algerian red wine, followed by canned fruit, condensed milk, cheese, coffee and a bottle of white wine. By the time we had reached Djanet before our climb to see the Tassili frescos, Ken and Julie had fallen in love. Jim wanted to work on the Land Rover engines so the three of them decided to stay in Djanet and let me take the party up to the plateau. As none of our Americans spoke any French, my French was the only link between our guides and donkey drivers.

On the way up we bumped into a couple of Swiss, a journalist, Bernard Joliat, and his friend, a motorcyclist named Dede. They were hopelessly ill-equipped for such a venture, their main equipment being cameras, and their footwear only gym shoes.

All my boy-scouting instincts came to the fore as I proudly led my team of eight Americans, one Englishman, two Swiss, two guides, three donkey boys and eleven donkeys. I got them all up and back safely and Bernard and his wife, who visited us in England later, have remained friends of mine ever since.

Not only had the tour of the plateau done me good. It had obviously helped Jim, who had got the motors running the way he liked them, and done wonders for Ken and Julie who became engaged and, in fact, married shortly after the trip was over.

As medical officer I was in charge, of course, of all things medical. Alas, the only patient was me. In the Bilma Oasis, the furthermost point of our trek, I developed a pain which I recognised as a kidney stone. The whole expedition was laid up for a couple of days until I had recovered.

We were staying in the Oasis guest house, which was a mud hut with two iron bed frames. As the invalid, one of the bed frames was allotted to me, and the other to an American lady doctor in the party who was designated to look after me.

She was what is known as an abdominal angiographist (no such people exist in England – we can't afford them). Her sole medical duties in the U.S. were to illustrate with various radiological techniques, the different organs of the abdomen by squirting dyes up several unmentionable places.

She was nonplussed to be confronted with a real illness and it took a great deal of persuading to get her to give me a pain-relieving injection.

Our prolonged stay did mean that our group was invited to two parties by the local dignitaries; one for the group on its own, the second in the company of two astonishing American ladies.

A boxcar plane had landed on our second day in this isolated oasis. Out had stepped two immaculately groomed American women in spotless khaki bush jackets and skirts, notebooks in hand. They were representatives of the Diners Club who were looking for eating places in Africa to recommend to their company.

Not only had Bilma no eating places: you had to take your own food with you, otherwise you might go hungry. Because of my kidney stone I missed both parties. On the third day I passed my stone and, from being contorted in pain, I was suddenly completely better. This was fortunate, in more ways than one, as I was called to a native hut to treat two semi-conscious Niger airmen.

They'd been living it up on the local jungle juice the night before, I was told. Could I get them in some sort of shape?

I did what I could and to my horror, an hour later, I saw them being driven off back to the plane with our American Diners Club ladies – this was the aircrew that was going to fly them out.

They somehow got the plane off the ground and we watched it fly away into the distance. What could one wish them but *bon voyage* – and happy eating?

In later years uranium deposits were found in this area of Niger and – who knows? – you may well now be able to get a good meal in Bilma by passing a plastic card.

I was fortunate to see the Sahara at its best. Alas, I

understand that things have changed now. There's a tarmacadam road from Algiers to Tamanrasset and even in the beautiful, isolated Tenere Desert there are oil stations and oil rigs.

Touring companies are no longer able to do their own thing. If you do cross the Sahara you have to go in Algerian trucks with Algerian drivers, Algerian cooks and Algerian food. But, who can blame them? It's their country, after all.

CHAPTER 6

Two Loves

They say that it's possible to be in love with two women at the same time and I have to confess that, for most of my adult life and even during some of my schooldays, I have had two continuous and contemporaneous love affairs.

One has been with the River Thames and British Inland Waterways. The other has been with France.

As a family we have made various sporadic raids on Spain, Italy, Portugal, and I had a disastrous weekend in Austria, but to date we have found no good reason why we should go beyond France for our Continental holidays.

I first got to know the Thames during the war. When I was at school we would cycle up from south London to Folly Bridge in Oxford and hire one of Salter Brothers' camping rowing boats. The boats had three pairs of oars and metal hoops all the way down over which a canvas cover could be placed, just like *Three Men In a Boat*. The seats pulled out and mattresses pulled down. On two occasions during Easter holidays, we rowed the Thames, mooring on the bank at night and cooking our meals over wood fires. We had to be in bed by dark as there was a blackout, and we occasionally varied our spartan cooked diet by going into the local British restaurants in Wallingford and Goring.

Although I've grown too old for it now, this is the real way to travel on a river, with a pair of oars or a punt where you are down at water level and your progress is slow enough to take in everything that's going on. In later years, as regular visitors to the Thames in cabin cruisers, we've met boats similar to those of my schoolboy days with men in striped blazers and straw boaters, following the course of Jerome K. Jerome's intrepid trio. How I envy them.

Our first cruise was from Folly Bridge with Janice and Kevin Bird, when our children were too tiny to go boating. It was in the early Fifties and our boat was like an older sister of *The African Queen*, broken down more often than it was on the move.

Then one Easter, with Trevor about eleven, Paul nine and Jane a baby left in Zara's care, we went with a widow friend, Margaret Doe, and her daughter Sally, from Thames Ditton to Wallingford. We'd hired a 42ft Maid Line boat, in which Johnny Morris later made a film on the Thames.

We hadn't many of the modern amenities in those days. I remember Pam and I going to bed wearing every article of clothing we'd brought with us – two pairs of trousers, three sweaters, towels wrapped round our heads – and waking up in the morning to find icicles hanging like stalactites from the ceiling of our cabin.

Five or six years later, during a glorious summer, we took my mother and Jane, now old enough to come with us.

We had a scorching fortnight, travelling from Maidenhead up to Eynesham and back. It was so hot we often had to keep the boat moving just to get some breeze and stay cool.

On this particular trip Paul was just into fishing, and had brought along every possible bit of tackle available, all the right gear. Jane wanted to fish, too, so my mother put a bent pin on a piece of string and tied it to a bamboo rod. Jane pulled them out twice as fast as her expert fisherman brother.

Having a fortnight, we could take our journey at leisure. We visited Cookham, Marlow, Henley, Goring and Streatley. Trevor and I played golf at Hurley and I took Paul to see his first professional football match – Oxford *v*. Birmingham – and from then on Paul became a devoted Oxford United follower. He was faithful to Oxford until his move to Cirencester, when parenthood and distance stopped him. He'd become very involved with the team; in later years he used to write, for the Oxford United programme, match accounts and humorous stories which Gill illustrated.

There is no doubt that we got the most from the river on our trips with Lynne and Joe Church. They had given up jobs as teachers to live the good life in Devon. They grew their own vegetables, fished, prawned, lobstered and set up a hospital for injured birds of prey, such as sea hawks and kestrels.

Baby owls were brought to them as tiny little balls of fluff. Two that were so small that they could never learn to adjust to the wild life, and had to be kept on as pets.

Joe is the only man I've known who's had a love affair with an owl. It used to display for him and, even when it heard his car coming in the distance, used to get terribly excited. Alas, it was a male, so one had to conclude that it must have been gay.

Joe fought an almost losing battle to save the River Torridge in Devon which changed from an abundant salmon river to an almost dead river through the combination of effluent from various commercial enterprises, silage seeping from farms and, worst of all, almost untreated sewage pouring into the estuary.

He told me of one occasion when the authorities were trying to prove that the sewage effluent went out to sea by emptying boxes of oranges into the sewage wastefall and tracing their progress.

To their great surprise, half of the oranges landed upriver near Weir Gifford. He was bitter that millions of pounds were being spent on cleaning the Thames, resulting in salmon being caught up as far as Godstow Lock, whereas his own river at home was going progressively into decay.

When Lynne and Joe were aboard, they were always pointing out birds we didn't know, or lampreys and other unusual fish.

Walking along the towpath at Pangbourne one day, we found a live pike in the middle of the path. How on earth it got there I don't know. We thought it must have been charging after a small fish and got carried away, but there it was: not a fisherman in sight and a live four-pound pike lying at our feet. We managed to get it back safely into the river.

When we travelled on the Thames with Joe and Lynne we weren't trying to get from one point to another, we just ambled. But to most boat hirers the main achievement seemed to be distance – Oxford and back or Lechdale and back. Every boat had its throttle out to the full and they'd travel in packs from lock to lock. We cruised along, gently, perhaps having a pub lunch during the day. Pub lunches on the Thames are so inexpensive, it was almost cheaper eating out than on board.

At night we'd moor, out into the wild as far as possible from any other boat. Lynne's little border terrier, Jenny, and our Bertie would race off together. The dogs explored a thousand different smells along the bankside, rolling and tumbling in energetic doggy games.

Joe and Lynne were tremendous company.

I awoke one night to find the boat heeling over to port. My immediate thought was that the river level had fallen and our bank mooring ropes were holding one side up, whilst the other side had gone down with the falling water.

I yelled to Joe in the front cabin, 'We're heeling over! I'm going out on to the bank to check the mooring lines.'

A sleepy, 'I shouldn't worry, Skip,' was the only reply I got from Joe.

But I did worry. I got out of the boat in my pyjamas, got on to the bank flashed my torch. To my amazement, all the mooring lines were slack and the boat was riding on an even keel.

I climbed back on board and snuggled down into my sleeping bag. I just couldn't understand it.

At breakfast next morning Joe and Lynne had some obvious shared secret. They kept giggling and Lynne kept on saying 'Go on. Tell him, Joe.'

Eventually Joe, hardly containing his laughter said, 'It's like this Skip . . .' (For Joe to call me Skip was incongruous, as he had a full beard on his face that was the spitting image of the sailor on the old Players cigarette packets.) 'You know Lynne bought a new dress in Abingdon yesterday? Apparently I didn't take much notice of it.

'Well, she only buys a dress about once every hundred years and was very upset about my lack of interest. She was so upset that I climbed over and joined her in her bunk to comfort her. It gave the boat a bit of a list. That's when you jumped out to check the moorings. We were laughing so much, seeing you on the bank in your pyjamas, that we decided to put off any more comforting until we get back to Devon.'

He roared with laughter, knocking his teacup over Lynne. Lynne jumped up as the hot water splashed over her, sending all the breakfast things crashing to the floor.

'You're a clumsy oaf, Joe Church!' she said, mopping herself with a tea towel.

'You're going to have to comfort her again, Joe,' I said. 'But, as Captain of this ship, I order in future that all comforting be confined to the river bank. The Skipper must get his sleep even if the crew don't.'

Still, the mystery was solved. The keeling-over did not join the *Marie Celeste* as one of the great unsolved riddles of our time.

With a friend, Pam Knowles, Pam and I once went up the

Oxford Canal in a fibreglass boat as far as Rugby. The canal had some beautiful spots, but so much of it could be improved: silted-up stretches, overgrown and crumbling banks, faulty locks. With three million unemployed in Britain, you would think there could be some way of directing energies towards improving facilities such as this.

This particular holiday was distinguished by the fact that it rained without stopping. The toilet arrangements on the boat were very inadequate and I spent a lot of my time crouched behind hedges under an umbrella answering nature's calls. We were more than pleased to get home. The holiday coincided with Wimbledon Fortnight and I think the tennis fans had an even worse time than we did.

We had canal holidays, too, going up the Severn, along the Stratford and Worcester Canal to Kinver. The beautiful and unique Brecon Abergavenny Canal runs along the Usk Valley where time seems to have stood still. Villages along the canal seem to be back in the Twenties, both in looks and prices. I remember getting marvellous meat pasties for 10p each, and four of us dining with a bottle of wine for about £6 – this was only about ten years ago.

Our ambition was that one day, perhaps when we'd retired, we would live on the Thames and have a boat moored at the bottom of the garden. We would also have liked to have retired to France. Whenever we went on holiday, too – as the children kept reminding us – we always wanted to buy a cottage where we had stayed. I'm glad we never did because it would have tied us to one spot. It's much easier to go and hire somewhere with a new area to explore, not having responsibilities of owning and maintaining a property.

The more we went on the Thames, the more we liked it. We used to manage a trip most years. Although at one time it seemed that the river would become choked with boats, in later years they actually started to reduce in number. Boating is not a cheap holiday and the English weather is unpredictable. The Thames is not always predictable, either, as we found to our cost when it flooded and we were stuck at Sonning Lock for a few days.

It's much cheaper to get a package holiday and it's easier on the mums: food is prepared, and mums get a rest from the cooking and washing up. But it's not nearly so much fun for the rest of us.

* * *

Our first camping trip to the Continent was with Kevin and Janice Bird to Spain. Then came the first one with the children when, in a Volkswagen Dormobile, we also took Pam's father, Jerry down to the South of France. You could say Jerry was a late starter: he began his camping/caravanning life at the age of 75.

From then on, as a family, we criss-crossed France, sometimes going to Italy – usually making for the Mediterranean – but camping all over the Dordogne, Brittany, the Jura Mountains, and most often in the real heart of France itself; in small unknown places with municipal campsites by a river. Often we were the only English family on the site, and became part of the camping community – our children mixing with children from Sweden, Holland, Denmark, Belgium, Germany, France and Spain. Somehow, as children do, they all managed to communicate, in no way hindered by speaking different languages.

It was a great sadness to me when the children grew up and started to go on their own holidays: Trevor to see actor friends in New York; Jane to Poros in the Greek islands, to be followed home by a stream of letters and telephone calls from a Greek barman with the first letter headed, 'Well, what do you think of we Greece boys?' Paul and Gill toured with friends in the Dordogne and Cognac country.

Pam and I did a fly-drive from Lyons, exploring the Drôme area of France, staying in the delightful town of Crest, then crossing the Rhône Valley up through the Ardèche to the spa of Vals les Bains.

At Vals les Bains, we were shown around the spa, where the patients were having mud baths and being hosed down. I think spa treatment is a much under-used branch of medicine. Many of the therapies, analysed, don't offer much clinical help, but there's no doubt that most of the procedures made people come out feeling better. That, I've always felt, is the basic purpose of the practice of medicine.

We then travelled south and down to Arles. As it was out of season, we had the amphitheatre and coliseum to ourselves. We crossed to the busy, crowded Avignon, a lovely university town where the students seemed to spend their time sitting around having coffee. Next we headed north, up to Orange, again to have the place to ourselves and enjoy a leisurely procession through the triumphal arch.

The last night we spent in Vienne, where I'd played rugby in 1947 and where we were thrashed 47–3 by the local side. I tried in the hotel to find out if anybody remembered us but nobody did – it was a long time ago – although they still had a good rugby team in the town itself.

*　　*　　*

With the arrival of Daisy May, our first granddaughter, the whole holiday cycle with children began again.

Paul and Gill loved France. Paul, given an opportunity, would go and live there. As he travelled on business in his car he would play language cassettes to improve his French, just in case his firm decided to open a branch out there.

We wanted to find somewhere convenient in France so that we could perhaps rent an appartment and the children and grandchildren could come over and see us. We might even have the chance of keeping grandchildren to ourselves for a spell.

We decided that it would have to be in Normandy or Brittany, so we went off on two short holidays of exploration. We had six days of being driven round by our neighbours, Stan and Pauline Williams, in their Range Rover. It was the first time I'd ever been on the Continent and not been the driver, though I think navigating was almost as difficult. The great advantage of a Range Rover is that you are that much higher and see so much more of the countryside. We crossed from

Portsmouth to Cherbourg in September in very uncertain weather, landing up near the Pegasus Bridge for our first night.

We saw what looked like quite a smart motel and, on enquiring about the cost of a room, I thought the receptionist said *soixante-cinq* i.e. 65 francs. I marvelled at the price, because this was such splendid accommodation.

'Are you sure there isn't a *cent* – a hundred – mixed in there somewhere?' Stan asked. Later we discovered that he was absolutely right – there was a hundred mixed in. The rooms were 650 francs – £70 – a night.

It was complete luxury: we'd never stayed in such opulence. There were peach-coloured dressing gowns hung behind the bathroom door, bowls of fruit on the table, and we had the most enormous and expensive dinner. We had hoped to start with mussels, which were on the menu, but they were off that night. Instead we got raw sardines in milk with apples. Then masses of ham in cider with cauliflower cheese. Already we were just about filled to our eyebrows. We passed on the next dish which was going to be toasted cheese and opted for a patisserie, hoping for a little bit of local apple tart.

When they brought the flambé trolley our patisserie proved to be a baked apple on pastry, crêpes cooked at the table, placed on the apple then covered with massive amounts of cream and calvados. Then the whole thing was set alight.

I spent the whole night sitting upright in bed with horrific indigestion.

The hotel was obviously aimed at the American market – people came over to visit the many graveyards near the old battle areas there – but it was good value for money.

This most expensive restaurant, which we thought would be pretty empty, eventually finished full. It was rather disappointing for me, with such splendour, wonderful dishes, immaculate waiters and waitresses, that only Stan and I were in a collar and tie. The rest of these international diners were in jumpers and open necked shirts. It somehow took the edge off things.

We saw Deauville, which disappointed us. But we loved Torville, another seaside resort, that had originally been made popular by *les Anglais*. Then we motored without stopping through Lisieux down to our next planned stop at Bagnoles-de-l'Orne, a beautiful little spa town with a lake and, nearby, a huge spa centre with 30 hotels grouped round it.

We stayed at a very nice hotel just by the lake. Walking into the town we had a first-class meal for £6 or £7, a fraction of what we'd paid the night before.

We had two days there and, unexpectedly, we'd brought the sunshine with us. Having two nights in Bagnoles-de-l'Orne, we were able to picnic and travel round, visiting Domfront and Mortain, then on to Dinard where I'd booked us into the Grand. We'd started this as an expensive holiday, I thought – let's finish it with a flourish.

The Grand is a beautiful old hotel overlooking the bay at Dinard with St. Malo the other side of the bay. There was always something happening: busy little fishing boats going out, the ferries leaving St. Malo, literally hundreds of sailing boats and motor launches, all in wonderful sunshine. We took the ferry across to St. Malo and walked round its outer walls.

They had all been knocked down during the war, but were now re-built exactly as they used to be 300 or 400 years ago. The narrow streets opened up into cafe areas, enabling us to sit in the sunshine, drinking cups of coffee and watching people walk by.

The Grand at Dinard is a lovely old hotel, created by our Victorian forefathers: great big old-fashioned rooms, views over the bay, lovely dining rooms, lounges, a very smart restaurant with reasonably priced food for the type of hotel. But again, there was hardly anyone in a collar and tie.

There was a course or convention for economics students going on. The students, dining in these surroundings in jeans and open shirts somehow didn't fit. Perhaps it showed how old-fashioned I was.

We called in at Dinan on the way back, had coffee down by the River Rance, then home by ferry. Just to show how small the world is, on the ferry we bumped into seven people we knew well. I said to Pam, 'You can't take your mistress anywhere nowadays.'

Once home, we were eager to get back to France to explore further. We thought that probably Dinard was the best area to get an apartment: by car it's only three and a half hours from Cherbourg. There's a night boat to St. Malo from Portsmouth and then either a ferry across to Dinard, or a short journey round by car to meet the boat.

We set off for a four-day trip with a doctor friend and his wife from Berkshire, Jim and Tighe Reeves. We spent a night in Portsmouth, crossing to Cherbourg and then driving down along the coast to spend our first night at the beautiful fishing port of Honfleur. We would have loved to have stayed longer in Honfleur. It's a picture postcard sort of place but, like most French coastal towns, busy with fishing boats coming in and out and a dredger working in the harbour.

We had one night there. Next day we went for coffee and shopping in Lisieux. Then we went for a picnic to a spot we'd found in the wood near Bagnoles when we'd been with Stan and Pauline, finishing our day in Dinard.

This was October and most of the hotels were shut. We didn't make for the Majestic or the Grand, but looked for something less pricey and found a marvellous hotel right on the shoreline. The Hotel de la Vallée was a third of the price of the Grand, had excellent food and accommodation, with the waves virtually lapping at the door and fishing boats landing their catch outside.

We'd been lucky with our weather in September; we were even luckier with our weather in October. It was hotter still.

The passenger ferry was closed down by now, so we had to go to St. Malo to the hypermarket by car for the girls to shop and the men to buy our wine. Small world again – Jim bumped into one of his patients in the hypermarket.

We found a splendid apartment at Residence Hoteliere Les Pins in Dinard which we booked for a month for the last half of May and the beginning of June for the next year. It would hold six, so we hoped to have the children and friends over for short bursts with us, as well as ourselves going off further into Brittany. We forget that France is such a big country, with so much to explore.

I don't forget that England is beautiful. In fact, I don't think there is a more beautiful country. If only we could be guaranteed sunshine, I'd probably not travel at all.

CHAPTER 7

I Nearly Went to . . .

I still went occasionally to London to broadcast for a BBC magazine programme. After one such programme there was a party for somebody leaving. We all became quite merry and one of the young and very presentable presenters, Mary, was looking for somebody to go with her to Moscow the following October.

The producer of the programme couldn't; apparently he was *persona non grata* behind the Iron Curtain. I don't know whether it was one drink too many, but suddenly on the train home I realised that I'd promised to escort a young, nubile and very attractive BBC presenter for a few days in Moscow.

Mary was a great girl with a good sense of humour so I sat down and wrote her a very careful letter saying that to travel hopefully is better than to arrive. Anticipation is all. Taken to its logical conclusion, it is even better to not set off at all, merely nearly to go somewhere. The relevant part of the letter, which I reckon is very sound advice, read:

Every year we hear that more and more people go on holiday. Five million to Spain, seven million to Blackpool or wherever. Going away has its hazards: one is exposed to all sorts of new diseases, muggings, hijacking, food poisoning, as well as spending considerable amounts of money.

One of the very much neglected arts, in a society which neglects most of its art, is the art of nearly going somewhere. A planned resurgence of this art could help restore both mental and economic stability to this country and it is an effective counter-inflationary method.

Nearly going somewhere is not as simple as it might look. I am at present nearly going to Moscow next October with a lady I met at a party. If you are nearly going to go somewhere it's not enough merely to carry the thought in your mind. You have to make the same planned approach as if you're organising some bona fide holiday, be it in England or on the Continent.

Carelessness can cause havoc. For example: it's no use preparing nearly to go somewhere with an out-of-date passport: the situation could arise when you might actually have to go somewhere and need a valid passport. Not only would you not be able to appreciate nearly going to the place in future, but you might get the sack as well. So it's best to have two passports: one for show and one for blow. The ideal second passport for the practitioner of the art is a surrendered one with the corner clipped off which everybody knows is no use at all.

It's no use going to a travel agency for up-to-date brochures. You must search the back of your desk for last year's brochures where obsolete dates and prices are quoted, but which include all the anticipatory blurb to whet your appetite about the place you're nearly going to.

The best time to arrange to nearly go away is when you have some prior commitment. If you want nearly to go to Paris, for example, try and fix a date which you know will coincide with your admission to hospital for the removal of your gall bladder.

The main benefits of nearly going somewhere are the saving of money and the preserving of friendship. It's on holiday that you most often quarrel with your friends and on holiday that you spend more money than usual.

Nowadays there is the additional benefit that if you never leave your back garden, the chances of being held hostage by an Arab hijacker are very small indeed.

An added bonus is if you can persuade someone to pair with you in the pursuit of this art. If, for example, you are able to say, 'Jimmy Saville and I nearly went to Majorca last year', not only will you be accepted at any party, but all your colleagues will be in awe of you.

Nearly going somewhere has been a tradition in my family and it's been a matter of family honour when planning nearly to go somewhere to go about it industriously. It brings many fringe benefits; now I have an aunt who says she was nearly on the *Titanic*; my grandfather says he was nearly in the San Francisco earthquake and, more recently, my eldest nephew was nearly in the Mediterranean when a ship was hijacked. Most of our family folklore is based on situations when members of the family were nearly present, and it is only by diligent bookkeeping that they've been able to show how very near they were to being there.

Finally, for the person who decides he is nearly going somewhere, 100 per cent physical fitness is essential. Regular exercise, clean living, abstinence from smoking and consumption of alcohol and regular medical check-ups will ensure this. Unless you're actually fit enough nearly to go somewhere, there's no point in nearly going somewhere at all.

I posted my letter to Mary on a Monday, expecting a fairly amusing reply. However, I had a phone call on Wednesday from John, producer of the magazine programme. 'We want you to take part in a live broadcast on Sunday,' he said.

'I can't get up to London,' I replied, quite excited about the thought of the broadcast.

'You don't have to worry about that,' said John. 'I've fixed for you to be linked in from an unmanned station.' He named a place near Winchcombe that I'd never heard of, not realising that the BBC had these places.

'What's the programme about?' I asked.

'You're going to be hoisted by your own petard,' said John. 'Doctor Robert Clifford will read his piece on "The Art of Nearly Going Somewhere". You've got to be careful when you write to us.'

The following Sunday I made my way up to a strange place, some sort of listening post for people who monitor foreign broadcasts. Everybody walked around as if they still had their headphones on. I reported at the desk and was met by a huge man who seemed upset that his Sunday was being disturbed. He marched me off into a bungalow next door. The lounge of this bungalow was an actual little broadcasting studio equipped with a few switchboards.

I sat down to wait, wearing a pair of headphones and listening to a programme. My escort sat down to read the Sunday paper. Suddenly over the headphones came a voice: 'Are you there, Doctor Clifford? This is John here. You'll be on in five minutes.'

It was all very disorientating. I could hear the programme rattling along, and then came John's voice: 'Hello, Doctor

Clifford, down in the West Country. How are things there?' I replied with some non-committal phrase. 'Good – and now we'd all like to hear about this new art you've devised of nearly going somewhere.'

I then read the letter I'd written for Mary. There was a sort of 'Thank you' in my headphones, then dead silence in the room as the programme was cut off. It was very strange: I didn't know whether I'd been broadcasting or not.

'Was that all right,' I asked my escort.

'I suppose so,' he said, not having listened to a word of it. He rattled his keys, impatient to be off, and I came away with a very weird feeling. I'd been talking into space and I couldn't believe that thousands, perhaps even millions, had been listening to me talking to myself in this bungalow. Anyway, back home I'd see what Pam thought.

'What did you think of the broadcast, then?'

'What broadcast?' she said. 'I thought you'd just gone for a rehearsal.'

I rang my secretary, whom I'd instructed to listen.

'What did you think of my broadcast?'

'I don't know,' she said. 'It was all in French.' She'd obviously got the wrong programme.

I now was really disorientated. I'd been sitting in the bungalow thinking I was giving a broadcast. Had *anybody* heard it? I walked out to the garden to collect my thoughts and there was Stan Williams trimming his roses along the fence.

'Are you nearly going to do some gardening, Bob?' he asked.

All was well, it *had* been broadcast. I don't know how many people listened to the programme, but I might have started a new art. I could quite easily be the head of some new culture. Or I might nearly . . .

CHAPTER 8

Achilles Heel

There's no doubt that marriage is a lottery, and in my marriage I won a top prize. Pam is all the things a wife should be: loving, patient, caring, supportive, tolerant. People say we've achieved the perfect balance: she gives and I take.

She's the nicest lady I've ever met. Putting up with me has proved that.

I was always bombarding her with visitors, sometimes at very short notice. My second son, Paul, has inherited this trait. This was most obvious when he had his rock group and was hoping to emulate the Beatles.

A few minutes before a meal he'd arrive with three friends, saying, 'Is it all right if they stay and eat with us?' Paul had even less insight into the preparation of meals than I did.

Pam was almost unflappable. She had though, like everybody else, her Achilles heel, just one small area of vulnerability which, when affected, would cause all the calm to disappear.

She liked to have her furniture in exactly the same rooms and kept in exactly the same position as she put it. If I moved an armchair from one side of the room to another it would bring her almost to a state of frenzy.

The only other thing that would upset her was a story I continually told against her.

I would say, 'If I walked in with a beautiful young woman and said, "Oh, Pam, I met this nice young woman from the *Folies Bergère* and I asked her back for the night," Pam's reaction would be, "Oh dear. I wish you'd let me know sooner and I would have put clean sheets on the bed." Whereas if I moved my favourite armchair from one side of the room to the other, one would have thought World War Three had broken out.'

She didn't like me telling this story, nor did she like me moving furniture.

Over a period of time, Pam seemed to get quieter and less interested in what I did. There was a flurry of the old spirit when I said, 'Les Hoyle asked would we like an old desk?' She then gave a spirited monologue about not wanting old desks.

It was a most beautiful old rolltop inlaid mahogany desk, which had secret drawers and a writing pad full of quills. It was a very valuable piece of furniture, so I accepted it and took it upstairs, hiding it in my study.

Pam didn't mind, providing she couldn't see it. I used it as a work desk for some time, but suddenly realised that it was more than probably the most valuable piece of furniture in the house. Rather than be left in my darkened study, it would look much better in our lounge, although admittedly it would take up a fair amount of room.

Pam was now much more into this disinterested state and I wondered whether she was getting depressed. I thought that suddenly she looked older.

Plucking up all my courage I broached the subject of my desk. 'Look, darling,' I said, 'the most valuable piece of furniture we have in the house is my desk in the study. I think we should have it in the lounge. It's very ornamental and it would be better looked after downstairs.'

'If that's what you want,' Pam said, 'fine,' and went on reading a book.

Without wasting a moment in case she changed her mind, I

shot upstairs with Paul. The two of us managed to get the desk down and assembled in the front lounge, where it looked really good.

Pam appeared not even to notice it was there and seemed to get progressively slower and continued losing interest in things generally.

I had a good look at her one evening and it seemed as if she'd aged even in the last month. Suddenly something clicked at the back of my mind – Myxoedema. This means you're short of thyroid. It's an insidious condition, very slow in onset, a bit like a gramophone slowly winding down. People who are short of thyroid often lose the outer third of their eyebrows. Pam hadn't, but very often this is a diagnostic factor. You also get some skin changes and hair changes, and can become constipated. I found she'd put on weight and there were one or two other little physical signs.

We did some blood tests, and Pam's thyroid proved to be very much underactive. An underactive thyroid is one of the easiest conditions to treat. All it means is taking some thyroid tablets to make up for the thyroid hormone you're not producing, and over a few months you start firing on all cylinders again.

Your hair becomes soft, your skin becomes smoother, you have twice as much energy, you feel better, you lose weight and, as they say, you become more regular.

The day after the first thyroid tablet, Pam suddenly felt quite light-headed and much more alive. After about a couple of months she was back to her old self again, full of energy. It was a joy to have her back as she'd always been.

A few months later we were sitting in the lounge when Pam suddenly looked up and asked, 'What's that desk doing there?'

'It's been there for the last four months,' I said. 'You didn't mind me bringing it down.'

'Good God,' she said. 'I must have been ill. Anyway, now it's here, I expect it can stay: it does look quite nice.'

Just to test she had fully recovered, I switched all the armchairs into different positions in the lounge after Pam had gone to bed. I shot off to work early, and came back at lunchtime to find her furious. 'What do you mean?' she said. 'Changing everything round when I'm not there? Just because you got away with the desk, don't think you're going to get away with everything.'

I was completely reassured. 'It's all right, darling,' I said. 'I was just seeing whether you were on the right dose of thyroid tablets.'

'You monkey,' she said. 'I had a feeling it was something like that – but don't you dare try it again or I'll stop your egg sandwiches.'

Egg sandwiches are part of the family folklore. When I got married I was a nine-stone wonder, but after five years I'd gone from nine to about 14 stone. I attributed this to the egg sandwiches that Pam made so beautifully. Unless I stopped Pam's tablets, there was no chance of my sneaking any desks or any other furniture in without Pam's full approval – not in the face of a threat like that.

*　　*　　*

It wasn't only Pam who was found to have an illness. I had recovered well from a coronary bypass operation of three years ago, but five months after the operation I contracted a virus infection.

I kept it at bay with lots of fluid and plenty of aspirin. I managed to keep on working, knowing that if I stopped at this stage I might never start again.

It left me, I think due to the aspirin, with more indigestion than I usually have. I've always been a bit prone to indigestion and was suspicious that I had a condition called hiatus hernia. This is a very common condition and it's thought that 60 or 70 per cent of the population suffer from it.

It means that the valve at the top of the stomach is weak to varying degrees. Acid, which can happily live in the stomach, splashes the lower end of the gullet and burns it. With a hiatus hernia, you're likely to have some problems when you're bending forward or lying down.

Stomach complaints are usually investigated by two procedures. The first is a barium meal, in which you swallow some white stuff, which is photographed as it goes down. The other is a gastroscopy, in which a tube with a light on the end is pushed down your gullet to examine your stomach and duodenum.

Gastroscopes are marvellous instruments nowadays, narrow and flexible. Everybody I knew who had had one said a gastroscopy was nothing, but I – who had always had a bit of trouble swallowing even pills – developed almost a phobia at the very thought of it.

One of the unpleasant symptoms of hiatus hernia is that sometimes, at night, acid will come up into your mouth, turn down towards your lungs and make you cough – very unpleasant and quite frightening. One of the factors that make all this more likely is weight and I'd started to creep up from the 12½ stone that I was after the coronary bypass to 14 stone.

The barium X-ray showed just what I thought it would – a hiatus hernia with a bit of what is known as a reflux œsophagus, i.e. acid coming up and splashing the gullet. I put myself on a slimming regime, but failed to lose any weight. I'm not a big meal-eater, but I do like the odd sandwich, piece of cake, biscuit and, if nobody's looking, bar of chocolate.

John Bowler, consultant physician at Winchcombe Hospital, encouraged me to have a gastroscopy. 'You haven't completed your investigation,' he said. 'Until this is done, anything could be happening.'

Even though I'd been through a very major operation without much trouble, this particular procedure I was attempting to avoid at all costs.

I tried everything I knew to be a physician curing himself, but my stomach got worse rather than better. Eventually I gave in to John Bowler's pushing and agreed to go and see a gastroenterologist in Winchcombe, Eric Crew. He was a

delightful man to whom I'd sent many patients. He gave me a good looking-over, examined my barium meal reports, showed me that for some reason my stomach was standing on its side instead of lying down, which he said was probably due to fat, and talked about high-fibre diets.

Just when I thought I'd got away with it, he said, 'But of course, we must do a gastroscopy to make sure there's nothing else going on.' He arranged for one to be done two days later.

I spent the next 48 hours making my will and putting my affairs in order, which was absolutely stupid. I'd sent dozens of patients for this procedure and none of them had complained. They said they didn't even know it'd been done – particularly when Eric was doing it – but I was convinced I'd be the first GP to die from a gastroscopy.

At the hospital they gave me a jab in my rear quarters as a pre-medication. Then Eric sprayed a local anaesthetic in the back of my throat and said, 'Now I'm going to give you a little injection to put you into Happy Land.' He injected something into my arm and I felt pleasantly drowsy. Just before this injection I'd had to grip something like a serviette ring in my mouth in case I clenched my teeth. In this pleasant drowsy state I could vaguely feel something happening in my throat. The next thing I knew was Eric saying. 'I've finished now. You can get up, have a cup of tea in half an hour, and then go home.

'All's well. You've just got a bit of hiatus hernia with some reflux and inflammation at the lower end of the gullet. Follow the diet and I'll see you in six months.'

It was all over – and I'd hardly felt a thing.

What children we men are! Just the fact that there was nothing nasty going on almost cured me on the spot. I stuck to Eric's regime, started knocking off weight, ate plenty of bran took some tablets he'd prescribed and from the great lump of fat I'd become, a svelte figure began to emerge. Even better – my indigestion started to disappear.

CHAPTER 9

Fishing Dangerously

Now and again I would get three days off in a row. It was not enough time to get away any distance, but enough for three consecutive days' fishing on the River Tad.

Three days' fishing I found ideal. There was time enough for the weather to change after a bad start; time for a sudden shower to freshen up the water in a hot spell; for sulking fish to come back on the feed; for another run of sea trout; for a new hatch of flies on the water; time to explore new swims when familiar ones proved unproductive; to observe and predict the changes in flow and water level.

By the end of three days I'd usually had enough fishing for the time being, without my interest starting to flag. And there was a lot to talk about afterwards in the Tadchester Arms with John Denton.

John was the water bailiff on the Tad, an expatriate Mancunian for whom the job was more than just a living: he ate, drank and slept fish and fishing; knew every hole and eddy along the river.

He was enormously patient with the junior anglers, quietly coaching them in the proper way to fish, and teaching them the respect they should show to their catch and the wildlife of the waterside.

He was not quite so patient with adult anglers he caught cheating, poaching, ill-treating their catch, or littering or damaging the banks. He would give them the benefit of the doubt and let them off the first time with a warning. But if he caught them a second time, then they seldom tried it a third. John was a big lad.

During my three-day sessions, he would join me on the bank for a couple of hours, morning and evening, making sure that I knocked off in the mornings at twelve noon for a break. Twelve noon was the time when the fish stopped biting or, to put it another way, when John knocked off for his lunchtime pint in the Tadchester Arms. The fish miraculously came back on feed at closing time.

I was glad to have John with me on the first day of a session in early March. We were fishing the Tad from a field in which grazed a herd of about twenty bullocks. They were some distance from us and behaving as bullocks usually do: quietly munching the grass and generally mooning about. But something was worrying John. Every so often he would glance over his shoulder at the herd, whose grazing pattern was bringing them slowly closer.

'What's the matter, John?' I asked. 'Bullocks are harmless, surely?'

'Normally, yes. But you mustn't trust 'em too far. I'm keeping my eye on that big bugger there: the one that's making a nuisance of himself.'

One of the bullocks was nudging and butting his neighbours; sometimes playfully, but sometimes as if he meant it. The recipients of the butting simply snorted in protest and moved away, at which the big bullock would turn on another victim.

The disturbance was speeding up the animals' natural movements towards the river and the herd was about 30 yards from us when John muttered, 'Hey up, our Bob! Look at that.'

I looked over my shoulder to see the big bullock attempting to mount one of its comrades, who kicked up his heels and lumbered off.

'That thing hasn't had a proper job done on him,' said John. 'As a bull he might not be up to much, but a straightforward bullock he isn't.'

The creature swung round, presenting its hindquarters to us. There, between its legs, swung a modestly sized, lopsided but unmistakable scrotum. The castration pincers may have accounted for half its potential, but they'd obviously left the other half intact.

Some further inexpert and unsuccessful attempts at mounting its fellows left the bullock in a temper. After galloping around the herd a couple of times, it moved down towards the river. Ten yards from us it stopped, squinted shortsightedly, lowered its head and sniffed, then snorted and pawed the ground.

'Do just as I say, Bob,' said John in a hoarse whisper. 'Get up slowly and walk backwards towards that gate in the hedge. Leave the tackle where it is and keep your eyes on me laddo there.'

Both of us stood up slowly and started walking backwards.

John quietly unzipped his anorak.

'Take yours off as well, Bob,' he hissed. 'Behind your back. And no sudden movements.'

'OK, John,' I hissed back. (Hissing seems to be catching.) 'But what for?'

'I'll give you the word when to run. If the bugger gets too close, throw your anorak over your shoulder. He'll stop to toss it around for a bit.'

The bullock walked, snorting, to our baskets on the bank and tipped both over with sideways scoops of its horns. Then it lifted its head, fixed us with bloodshot eyes, and broke into a lumbering trot.

'Right, Bob!' yelled John. 'RUN!'

We turned and ran. Both of us breaking records for a hundred-yard sprint over tussocky pasture. Behind us we heard the pounding of hooves, speeding up and gaining rapidly.

I was just about to throw my anorak, reluctantly, over my

shoulder when I reached the gate. How I'd got so quickly to a
point so far away I'll never know. There were two almost
simultaneous thuds as John and I vaulted the gate and landed
heavily on the other side.

The bullock skidded to a stop, rattled the bars of the gate
angrily with butts and scoops of its horns, then lost interest and
lumbered back to annoy the herd again.

'Thank God we kept the Country Code,' puffed John. 'If we'd left that gate open we'd be looking like something from the last reel of *Blood and Sand* by now. I see you didn't use your anorak, by the way. Didn't fancy a bit of the old corrida, then?'

'To tell the truth,' I said, 'it's a present from Pam. First time I've worn it. Even as a fishing story it would sound a bit far-fetched – my new anorak ripped to bits in a bullfight. Why didn't you use yours?'

'It's got all the tools of my trade in the pockets: credentials as bailiff, books and permits, copies of the byelaws and Water Authority regulations. If they got scattered to the four winds I'd be lost. What's a bailiff without his rule books? Besides, as a story it's like yours – who the hell would believe it?'

We picked ourselves up, dusted ourselves off, and were debating whether it was safe to go back and retrieve our tackle, when a crusty old farmer appeared, waving a knobbly walking stick.

'Hoi!' he bellowed. 'You annoying my cattle?'

When the old farmer got close enough, he recognised John, who explained about the bullock. To save possible future damage to anglers and the rest of the herd – but with the rest of the herd mainly in mind – the farmer promised an early appointment for the brute with a hamburger parlour.

The farmer was not exactly keen on anglers. The previous year he'd had a couple of bored and drunken anglers waving jackets at his bullocks in bullfighting passes, shouting '*Toro!*' and '*Arriba!*', and threatening to deliver the *coup de grâce* with rod rests.

'Running all the meat off my stock,' he muttered. 'Drunken buggers. I fixed 'em, though.'

'What with?' I asked. Naively.

'Two barrels of a twelve-bore in the arse of their pants,' he chuckled. 'Never did come back for their tackle. Made a fair bit out o' that, I did.'

. . .'Well, that was enough excitement for one morning, John,' I said, taking the top off a pint in the Tadchester Arms. 'I thought fishing was supposed to be relaxing. An aid to peace of mind, longevity and all that.'

'So it is, in between being in peril of your life,' said John. 'Did you know that in 1982 angling killed more people in Britain than any other single sport or leisure activity?'

'Get away.'

'True. Eleven anglers went to the Great Match Peg in the Sky. Ten by drowning. Official Census Office figures, those are. But it's not that bad, really. Angling's bigger than all the other participant sports put together. Eleven out of three million anglers isn't a lot. Much safer than crossing the road. Or getting stung by a bee.'

'I'm glad to hear it, John. But, come to think of it, the first time I met you professionally was when you came to the surgery with a damn great treble hook in your backside. The second time was when a pike minced your finger.' John winced at the memory of the treble hook, put into him by a cack-handed novice angler, and again at the memory of the pike's teeth. 'And you've put a fair few patients my way since, from accidents on the river.'

'Right,' he said. 'And I've sent a fair few more straight up to Casualty at Winchcombe Hospital. You've not seen the half of 'em, Bob. But mainly, thank God, they're small accidents. Nothing serious. Most of 'em are stupid, like that hook I copped for. And like the old boys who flake out with a heart attack as soon as they hook a big fish. But some of them are downright weird.'

'Weird?'

'Weird. Who would believe that a cow could fall on anybody, for a start?'

'Go on, John. I'll buy it. How could a cow fall on anybody?'

'From the top of the bank. The cow grazed right to the edge, slipped and fell right on a bloke fishing at the bottom. Good job it landed on its feet, or he'd have been dead. But its legs were straddled wide and it couldn't get up. All you could see of this bloke was his wellies, sticking out from underneath. He couldn't even shout for help, not with his head under a damn great udder. Luckily there were a few of us around who heard the crash.

'It took six of us to get the cow on its feet. And then it had the cheek to lift its tail and flop all over the bloke's face. I've heard of a pat on the back, but this was ridiculous. I told him it was good for the complexion, but he didn't seem too thrilled.'

John was in his stride now, and for the next hour I listened to a steady stream of bizarre events that normally happen only in *Carry On* films.

One angler, bending over his tackle box, was butted into the Tad by a sexed-up ram. In the tupping season, even the supposedly harmless sheep can't be trusted.

Another angler had to be sent for specialised treatment in London after being bitten by a tiny and innocent-looking lamb.

He contracted a rare and dangerous condition called *orf*. Orf must have been endemic around Tadchester: it was the second case I'd heard of in my time there.

Swans are notorious for their viciousness towards anglers. Anglers are notorious for their viciousness towards swans, so perhaps they cancel each other out. John, whose duties as bailiff were towards both anglers and swans, swore he kept an open mind.

'But *geese*,' he said. 'Geese are something else. You get swans one, two, three or four at a time. Geese you get in gaggles, and if you get a gaggle around your groundbait, you might just as well pack up and go home. Look at that poor girl last summer.'

'What poor girl last summer?'

'Not one of your patients, Bob. Winchcombe job, this was. She was with her boyfriend walking along the river bank, feeding the ducks and generally messing about. Wearing a short skirt. She bent down to pick up a crust she'd dropped, and didn't notice the geese behind her . . .'

He paused for a swig of his pint.

'Go on, John. The suspense is killing me.'

'Bloody near killed her as well. She bent over, presenting a perfect target, and she was goosed by the gander. Before she could draw breath, about half a dozen geese got into the act. I ran her and her boyfriend in my Land Rover over to Winchcombe where they diagnosed multiple abrasions and galloping hysteria. She didn't half carry on. I bet she's worn brass knickers ever since.'

You have to forgive John. Now and again he lowers the tone.

It's a fact, however, that farm animals attracted by groundbait or sandwiches can get very short tempered when the angler tries to dissuade them. One angler on the Tad was bitten by a goat. The resultant swelling put his casting arm out of action for a fortnight. Another was bitten by a pig, from which he contracted a nasty dose of swine fever. Several were savaged because they put a hand into a bucket of groundbait

85

and failed to notice the rat having a free meal inside. (Anybody who thinks a rat is not a farm animal should spend a week on the average farm.)

Nightfishers often get a nasty fright when a wandering cow blunders into their tent. Others have their tent collapse around them when the cow decides that it makes a handy scratching post.

Bullocks – even successfully treated bullocks, unlike the half-equipped freak which chased us – can sometimes turn frisky, if not nasty, and do a fair bit of goring, butting, squashing and trampling.

Horses are often the culprits. One bunch of young anglers had to take to the water when a horse ate their lunches – even down to the pork pies – crunched their beer cans with its teeth, swigged the contents, and then attacked them with flailing hooves. The teenage lads, up to their waists in water, felt thoroughly ashamed of themselves when a tiny girl ran down to the river with a bridle, scolded the horse soundly and led it quietly away.

Exposure and hypothermia are common, either because anglers fail to dress properly, or sit for too long in windy stretches of the water. Another cause is the duckings, to which even the most agile and sober angler is occasionally prone.

'But most of the duckings happen in the afternoon,' said John, 'when the lads have overdone things a bit in the Tadchester Arms. The trouble then is that often they don't feel the cold. They'll carry on fishing soaking wet.

'The worst case of hypothermia I've heard of, though, happened nowhere near the water. Poor old Sid Williams, it was, early last December. The "ding-dong-merrilys" had already begun at the Tadchester Anglers' clubhouse. Sid got well tanked up there one night and two of his mates had to take him home.

'With friends like that you don't need enemies. The cowards just propped him against the door at midnight, rang the bell and ran away.'

'I bet he got into trouble with his wife,' I said.

'Not straightaway. His wife didn't hear the bell. Poor old Sid spent a freezing cold night, slumped spark-out on the doorstep, until he was found by the milkman. Blue, he was. Three days in hospital before they'd let him go. *Then* he got into trouble with his wife. Ruined his Christmas . . .'

Another frequent cause of accidents, apparently, is the angler relieving himself on the bank, as he has to in the absence of public conveniences, deep in the cover of the undergrowth. Nettle rash is common enough, but far worse are stings and bites from small insects.

'One bloke was bitten by a gnat,' said John, trundling on remorselessly. 'You wouldn't believe this, but by the time he got home, his willy was the size of a small marrow. A horrible purple colour, too. He didn't want to tell his wife what was wrong, but she insisted. Fat lot of help she was.'

'Why?'

'When he showed her his willy she fainted clean away.'

'Thanks, John. I'm trying to drink this pint, if you don't mind.'

'Oh, you've heard nothing yet. I could hear the screams of one poor lad a quarter of a mile away.'

'What had he done?'

'Just gone for a jimmy riddle in the undergrowth. What he didn't see was an electrified cattle fence. Wasn't a high voltage, thank God, but it certainly brought the tears to his eyes.'

'I bet it did. How was he afterwards?'

'You could say,' said John, snorting into his glass, 'that he was feeling a little dicky.'

Served me right for asking.

CHAPTER 10

A Collection of Characters

Mrs Layton died peacefully at the age of 91.

She survived the last eleven years on sheer courage and determination. She lived in a neat little bungalow with her bachelor son Dick who, as well as holding a responsible job on the council, did a bit of farming on the four-acre plot upon which their bungalow was sited. There was a half-acre apple orchard and a three-acre field in which Dick used to plant a yearly cereal crop.

This smallholding rated quite a number of agricultural implements and scattered about the place were old tractors, harrows, ploughs. I don't know what profit it brought Dick but it certainly gave him an interest and definitely a lot of hard work.

Mrs Layton was a lovely, quietly spoken, busy little lady who kept a spotless house and took tremendous care of Dick.

Dick was a very nice hardworking affable man who thought the world of his mother. As far as she was concerned, nothing was too much trouble; if there was anything she wanted, whatever it was, somehow Dick would produce it.

Mrs Layton hadn't been too well for a good number of years, but round about her 80th birthday her health began to deteriorate rather rapidly.

She had very severe arthritis, some heart trouble and skin trouble. We kept her going with various medications, she saw several specialists and still managed her home.

Dick's tea was always ready on time and Dick always took her breakfast in before he went off in the mornings.

Another very important member – and she could certainly call herself a member – of the household, was the auxiliary nurse. Lynne called in at least once a week, initially to help Mrs Layton with her bath, tend to her wants, perhaps do her hair and a whole variety of jobs, such as shopping, beyond the call of duty.

Nursing auxiliaries are very much unsung members of the National Health Service. They make such a difference, in very practical ways, to so many patients' lives. Lynne in particular had her own brand of cheerfulness and caring, not only with Mrs Layton, but with all the other people she visited. We depended on her as we did our district nurses and health visitors.

Although I routinely visited Mrs Layton, Lynne would always come and tell me if she thought she needed an extra visit. She really was a treasure.

Unfortunately, in spite of all the medication we gave her, Mrs Layton's health got progressively worse. Her main troubles were her hips. Her left hip, when I had it X-rayed, was fused solid, but her general condition was such that I couldn't risk sending her up for an operation. However, I was called to her in an emergency one day to find her lying in agony on the floor. She'd fallen and fractured her hip and had to go into hospital.

Her general health was so poor that I didn't think for a minute she could cope with an operation, but after she had been in hospital for a couple of weeks, with talk about traction, she was sent to theatre and given a total hip replacement.

She took longer than is usual to get over it, but in a month she was home, walking about better than she had been for a year or two.

Although each year she lost ground a little and had several other medical emergencies – some awful skin trouble and a couple of visits to hospital – she still maintained her home. There was, of course, always a reason for her to maintain her home: she had Dick to look after.

This was not an Oedipus-complex type of situation: they were both forthright, caring people, and Dick sought every practical aid that would help Mother.

Eventually it got so that she couldn't dress herself. Lynne had to get her up in the morning and put her to bed at night. But I'd still find her in the kitchen, peeling the potatoes, walking around with a frame, hardly ever complaining. 'We do our best, Doctor,' she'd say. And so it went on. The date of the hip operation to the time of her death was about nine years, and without Dick and Lynne to support her she certainly wouldn't have survived that time. Without Dick to look after, she wouldn't have wanted to survive that time.

Her end, when it came, was peaceful. She literally just couldn't put one foot in front of the other, couldn't be left at home. We got her into a little nursing home and she died there after a fortnight.

She was a wonderful, courageous lady and I can see her serious little face as I sit and write this. Dick would have an awful time managing without her, but he was a very active and able man, occupied with all sorts of things, so eventually he would come to terms with it. Lynne, who had got to know her so well over so many years, was heartbroken to see her go. If I'd been asked twelve years before Mrs Layton died how long I thought she might live, I would have given her about a year. But she had a reason for staying alive and was loved and cared for. I think these things are probably the strongest medicines there are for the treatment of any patient.

* * *

Alma Tranton was one of my favourites. She lived alone in a very nice house about three miles from the surgery. She had a tiny dog who used to yap around whenever I came near, and would never come near enough to let me stroke him.

Alma kept pretty well. She'd led a very adventurous life, a great figure in the Girl Guides, and as a young woman had done all sorts of things. She'd been camping and exploring, and had sailed to Australia with a group of Guides in a boat. A real character.

She came from an army family and was born after her father's death in action, as he had been born after *his* father's death in action. In the First World War she'd lost 34 close relatives—cousins, brothers, sisters and uncles.

She had her father's diary, his day-to-day account of his experiences in one of the Afghan campaigns towards the end of the 19th century. I was fascinated by them and tried to get them published for her, but they were all about what happened to him and he failed to mention exactly what was going on in the war, so many publishers were not interested.

His descriptions were marvellous. He was either in the advance guard or the rear guard of the column as they marched to Kabul. When they made camp he'd go off fishing, or hunting for birds with his gun, and a great deal of his writing was devoted to his hobbies.

The officers had regular weekly mail from England. They obviously ate and drank well, with a glass of port every evening. War seemed much more clear-cut in those days. They were fighting heathens who were thought of more as a sort of sub-species rather than fellow human beings.

For much of the way, the column went by train. There's an account of an incident when the train couldn't get up the hill, so they all got out and pushed. Then, outside Kabul, they all stopped for the day and had a gymkhana. Alma Tranton's father won the 100-yard dash. Once they'd packed up the things from the gymkhana they picked up their rifles and set off to war again.

. . . I came back from a weekend off duty to find that Miss Tranton had been sent into hospital by Jack Hart. When I called to see her I found that she had a fractured femur.

'How did you do this, Alma?' I asked.

'Oh,' she said, 'I was playing football with the dog and fell over.'

This was typically Alma. She took it all in her stride, had a new hip put in, came back and resumed the running of a household.

She had a good home help and an invaluable friend, a teacher called Anne, whom she'd known since she ran a Guide troop. Alma in her mid eighties and Anne, about retiring age, used to go off together on holidays, caravanning all over England. Then as Alma got a little more frail, they gave up the caravan. At 85, Alma stopped driving herself and had to rely on Anne. Eventually Anne retired from teaching and spent more and more time with Alma. She didn't come and live with her all the time but they used to take it in turns: sometimes Alma staying with Anne at Guildford, sometimes Anne staying with Alma at Tadchester.

Although she became progressively limited in her movements, Alma was full of life. She was still going strong at 88 and, although I'd strictly forbidden her to play any more football with the dog, she kept on going; partly because she was the sort of person who would have always kept on going. It was because of her army background, and because she had a friend who cared for her and would come and look after her, repaying some of the kindness that Alma had shown her when she was younger.

*   *   *

Alfred Scott had cancer of the lung. It meant his going into hospital to have one of his lungs removed. However, the condition was caught early enough; he could manage perfectly well on one lung and he made a good recovery.

Naturally, he worried whether he might get a reccurence but, as he ticked off the years, he became more and more reassured. During this time his wife Elizabeth, although holding down a full-time job, had taken care of him.

He'd become fit enough to go back to work after a couple of years and his X-rays, the clinic, and I myself – at last, after six years – managed to reassure him that the disease that had ailed him was now in the past.

In this sixth year his wife Elizabeth had a heart attack and a stroke. She was severely incapacitated, dangerously ill, and came out of hospital with little use of one leg, and no use of one arm. She also had what is known as nominal aphasia, which meant that she could understand everything that was said to her but was unable to reply. She'd get all the words wrong. She'd say something like, 'It's in the basket,' and keep on repeating it. She was patiently nursed by her husband, who gave up work to look after her.

With physiotherapy she improved to such an extent that she could walk around the room, get in and out of her wheelchair and her speech slowly and steadily improved. In fact Elizabeth Scott slowly and continually improved over five years.

Jack used to take her out in the car. He would take her

wheelchair down a ramp from the house. She could hoist herself into the car, she could walk with a stick about 50 yards, and she made more and more sense with her speech.

They never grumbled, were always a great pleasure to go and see, and they were always delighted to see me. Elizabeth often needed a bit of reassurance, sometimes no more than my taking her pulse, and then she'd feel happy again.

She had one bad period – she wasn't sleeping very well and was getting depressed – so I ordered some tablets for her. They were a mixture of sleeping tablets and tablets to help her with depression; my prescription was for two at night.

The next time I saw her she was very very much better, thanked me for the tablets and asked for some more.

On my next visit she looked a bit pained and Jack explained to me that the new bottle only said two at night.

'That's what I ordered in the beginning,' I said.

Elizabeth had been taking two of these tablets three times a day. I would never ever order that many for anybody. I managed to get hold of my original prescription and discovered that it was, in fact, a dispensing mistake. But, strangely, this large dose of drugs completely transformed Elizabeth. Whether it reduced the considerable irritation from her stroke I don't know, but this dose of drugs which would have kept me asleep all the time, kept her awake, feeling much better, much more alert and solved most of her problems.

Twelve years after Jack's operation and six years after Elizabeth's stroke, they were still going strong, still enjoying life, still going on trips and outings. Keeping going because they needed each other. They couldn't manage without each other, a brave, resourceful couple who were leading as full a life as most people in spite of Elizabeth's limitations.

*　　*　　*

Another of my favourites was Alfred Black. Mr Black in his late seventies developed maturity-onset diabetes; that is to say, he'd got a bit of sugar in his water and had to take tablets for it.

His wife, who was a couple of years older than him and who used sometimes to get a bit confused, also developed diabetes a few years later.

Hers was more difficult to control. She started having trouble with her feet, and eventually had to have some of her toes amputated.

But she got over that and we got both of their blood sugar levels under control. I used to see Alfred at all the flower shows and agricultural shows. He used to write up the prizewinners for the local papers.

Again they were both a pleasure to meet. Unfortunately, Mrs Black got progressively confused and didn't know who her husband was sometimes, but they jogged along. I would sometimes pick up Mr Black from the bus stop when he was using his bus tokens to get to Winchcombe to get shopping he couldn't get in Tadchester.

The Blacks celebrated their Diamond Wedding anniversary and gave me one of the largest pieces of cake I've ever had to

eat, just in the middle of one of my many attempts to get slimmer.

They lived happily on for another three years and then Mrs Black's health deteriorated. She had to go into hospital and she died.

Mr Black was much helped by a niece until he got back on his feet again. He missed his wife a great deal, but she'd been a tremendous physical effort to look after the last few years. He used to come along to the surgery to see me, and always had a joke and a laugh. Only rarely after his wife died did he ask me to go and see him, and then only when he had something like bronchitis, which kept him in bed.

I had another great big piece of cake on his 90th birthday. I still give him lifts when I see him waiting for the bus into Winchcombe. He always has a twinkle in his eye, I always pull his leg, and he goes happily marching on.

* * *

I often think how lucky we are as general practitioners to be able to enter people's homes, to have an inner view of their lives, to appreciate that duty, love, friendship and just being plain nice are the secret formulae for staying alive.

Mrs Layton and Dick, Alma and Anne, Jack and Elizabeth Scott, Alfred and Mrs Black were just some representatives of the very best of people it was my privilege to look after.

I certainly got as much from visiting them as they got from me. They'd all lived great life spans, defeating impossible situations, showing tremendous courage and I was proud not only to call them my patients, but to call them my friends. There was little doubt in my mind either, that I needed them rather more than they needed me.

CHAPTER 11

Stirling Quality

Miss Stirling was the matron of a hospital for mentally handicapped people which, like so many similar buildings had previously been a Poor Law Home. On the main road between Stowin and Winchcombe, it was looked after mainly by a psychiatrist from Winchcombe, but Jack Hart was the attendant GP, calling regularly to deal with the day-to-day medical problems of the residents. I was his second-in-command, going when I was on duty or if he was away on holiday.

A number of the patients in this hospital were very happy people. Mentally handicapped, they'd spent all their lives in institutional care. They were large, happy children who lived to great ages with insufficient insight to appreciate problems, and who looked forward to their holidays, treats and surprises. In some ways they were lucky.

There was also a ward for very handicapped children who'd spent their lives in crash helmets and boxing gloves to prevent them coming to harm. Unable to communicate, incontinent, having to be fed, they were pathetic sights. The nurses were very attached to them, however, and voluntary visitors used to come and make special efforts to communicate with them.

Overall, Wayside Hospital was one of the best, most efficient, happiest, spick and span medical institutions I've been to.

It was spick and span because the matron, Miss Stirling, was one of those people who had the drive to get everybody enthusiastic about their work. Rather than wait for painters to come from the local area or group hospital, for example, the nurses painted the walls of their own wards. They organised fêtes, jumble sales and sponsored walks to provide special treats and amenities for all the patients. The unions grumbled that people were being done out of jobs but, with the state of the National Health Service, things just didn't get done without voluntary effort. The standard of care and cleanliness and facilities of this hospital were absolutely superb, and all due to the driving force of the matron.

Miss Stirling was so good that she got promoted. Promotion meant leaving her beloved Wayside Hospital and being in charge – as a sort of supervisor with no authority – of three hospitals: Wayside, St. Luke's and Field Farm. It also meant that one of the most useful women I've ever met in the National Health Service was now made completely impotent – simply because she'd done so well.

Because of some national economy cuts it was decided to close down Field Farm and its 20 beds. Miss Stirling and one of the psychiatrists from Winchcombe asked if they could buy it from the National Health Service and run it privately. This would take a great load off the National Health Service, as the house – once an old country house – was in a deplorable condition.

The authorities eventually agreed to allow them to purchase the property but charged them the full market price. Once they'd bought it, they made them build elaborate fire escapes and fit every other safety precaution that one could dream of, all at great cost.

Miss Stirling invited the best of her staff from Wayside Hospital to join her in this private venture. It couldn't be a charity; she didn't want it as a charity.

Between them, about half a dozen people set to in this great house, painted and decorated it throughout, and put up interior dividing walls. When they moved in it was almost derelict with leaking lavatories, broken furniture and filthy kitchens. They refurnished it and changed the decaying country mansion into a house with the fittings and amenities of a first class hotel.

I was approached by Miss Stirling to be on an ethical monitoring committee. It wasn't necessary, according to the book, but she thought it would be nice to have a little committee to keep an objective eye on the establishment, and to be an alternative body for the residents to come to if they had any particular worries.

One of the staff Miss Stirling had brought over from Wayside Hospital was the cook, who was from now on classified as a trainer.

In fact there were no members of staff; they were all trainers. There were no patients; they were residents. There was no central dining room but three dining rooms with six or seven residents in each.

The man who wired up the building gave up his job and stayed on as a trainer. It was one of his responsibilities to supervise the residents who worked in the gardens. Field Farm hoped to grow most of its own vegetables and be as self-supporting as possible.

All the residents took part in the preparing of meals, the cleaning of the house, making the beds. It was home, and they all had to play some part in the running of it.

Although it was supposedly a private residential home, i.e. it wasn't under the National Health Service, all the residents were people whose only source of income was the Department of Health and Social Security, and they allowed Miss Stirling £133.00 per head per week.

Miss Stirling and the psychiatrist had had to mortgage their homes, produce every bit of money they had, and raise bank loans just to purchase the building. It was to be non-profit making.

Despite the dilapidated state the building was in before Miss Stirling took it over, the cost per resident per week allowed under the National Health Service had then been £330.00, almost three times what Miss Stirling was receiving now. But she managed.

She managed because she had the ability to get the best out of people and had assembled a group of dedicated workers. This, as far as I was concerned, was another face of private enterprise.

There must be a lesson to be learnt. We hear of how under-financed our National Health Service is, but Miss Stirling showed how the right person can run a more efficient unit at a third of the cost. You can bet that Field Farm, like any other National Health Service hospital I know, was crying out for money to have various things done before Miss Stirling took it over.

She was quite adamant that they were not a charity, they were part of the community. She made sure that the residents didn't go about in groups; although they were mentally handicapped, they used to go out in ones or twos, not always with an escort. They might go to a pub or cinema and they occasionally did go out *en masse* to something like a pantomime. They all had £5 a week pocket money and a post office savings book and were encouraged to fend for themselves. Field Farm wanted to give to the community at large, as well as accept from it, and the residents and staff went down and painted the local village hall.

The residents did sometimes cause problems. One of the men every week spent his £5 on cigarettes, which he smoked incessantly until they were finished. They tried every way they could think of to make him stop. Finally Miss Stirling suggested he might try hypnotism, and explained patiently that it would mean a man waving a finger in front of his face. The smoker thought about it for 48 hours, then announced his decision. 'No,' he said. 'Watching that finger might damage my eyes.'

The whole project was a tremendous effort by a few dedicated people and makes me wonder about the welfare state. Has it emasculated us? Although it was started with the best intentions of providing security for everybody, to some extent we've encouraged some people not to try and fend for themselves.

They've been brought up to believe that the state is responsible and takes care of everything, even aged relatives.

One rather bad example of this is given by two patients who arrived in the practice, to live in a council house. They paid no rent, they were given £400 to furnish the kitchen, £400 to furnish the lounge, most of which they spent on drink, and there was no supervision. They had two lodgers which they weren't supposed to have, and their days were spent begging and pinching from their neighbours. They would never try and find employment – they even managed to con £10 out of me when they first arrived. Thinking they were in trouble I asked the health visitor to go round and see if she could help them. She found that their income was in fact higher than her own salary.

Miss Stirling and Fair Farm provide a ray of hope in this disintegrating society we live in. It takes me back to the collective thoughts of three wise old men I knew many years back who said that it's not better systems we need, just better individuals – as we have with Miss Stirling and her group.

CHAPTER 12

Blessed are the Meek

Stephen Maxwell was the senior partner when I first arrived in the practice at Tadchester. I served my apprenticeship with him and I've always said he was a saint in disguise, one of the finest men I've ever met.

He worked desperately hard, coming in every Sunday and taking fewer holidays than we did. In his spring holiday fortnight, he put his potatoes in. In the autumn holiday fortnight, he dug his potatoes up.

When he'd come as a young man to the practice, there'd been the senior partner, a Doctor Watson, his very dominant wife who ran the practice, and their mentally-ill daughter.

Just before I arrived this whole ménage had moved out to the country where Steve virtually supported them. There's some complicated story that Steve promised Doctor Watson, and I never knew in what circumstances, that he would look after his wife and daughter, and that he would never marry while Doctor Watson was alive.

Steve stuck to his word and he actually married, at the age of 67, an ex-teacher called Nancy Doone, a member of one of the old Tadchester families.

He worked only part-time after his marriage for a couple of

months and then gave up work altogether. This was not just the demands of his marriage but the fact, he'd kept from us, that he was unwell. Though he hadn't looked well before his marriage, none of us knew that he'd been seeing a specialist and had various kidney and blood pressure troubles.

It seemed such a shame that he'd had to wait until he was 67 before he got married, but he was blissfully happy with his new wife. They had a nice house with a large greenhouse Up-the-Hill. Though I missed not seeing him in the surgery every day, it was great to be able to pop in and have a cup of tea with them, wander round his garden and admire his greenhouse. He kept us supplied with tomatoes, cucumbers and lettuce the whole summer.

*　　*　　*

We had to find a replacement partner for Steve, as his workload was so great. Rather than advertise in the *British Medical Journal* and have a hundred applicants, we passed the word around that we were looking for somebody and soon had five candidates recommended to us. The great problem was that each one of the five would have done us.

We finally settled on one very nice young man called David Lichen who, after doing his house jobs and vocational training, had spent two years in the Falkland Islands as a GP. There, amongst other things, he had successfully imported and planted 1,000 trees. He'd also taken to the islands a Japanese car with a special four-wheel drive that would drive over practically everything. He could claim that he was one of the few people – perhaps the only one – to have run over a fish while driving through a river. He had a picture of himself holding some large fish with tyremarks right across its middle.

He was a lovely young fellow, worked very hard and was a good physician; very much loved by the patients, which was not surprising, as nothing was too much trouble for him.

The only criticism we had of him was that he wouldn't clear off on his half day – he always had unfinished work to do. It was almost as if he had brought the spirit of Steve Maxwell with him.

It was so nice in the practice having two young people as good as Catherine Carlton, our half-partner, and David. Although we found it hard to believe, all the rest of us were getting a bit long in the tooth. These young partners were not only nice, but were extremely well informed, able gently to educate us in new techniques and advances in medicine.

* * *

All seemed to be going well with Steve and Nancy's marriage until one day we had an emergency call from a hospital in Yeovil. Steve and Nancy were on their way back from holiday when Steve had been taken ill with chest pains. He'd had a coronary thrombosis but the word from the hospital was that there was nothing too much to worry about.

I drove out to Yeovil on my half day and was reassured to see Steve sitting up brightly in bed, smiling as usual, and Nancy with him. All appeared to be well, thank God.

Steve was due to be discharged back home at the weekend. I was so pleased I'd gone to see him and was reassured that he looked so well.

Three days later Steve had a second coronary and died straightaway.

It took me a long, long time before I could really take it in. He was without doubt the nicest and kindest man and best doctor that I've ever met, and suddenly he was gone. He'd been married just twelve months. It all seemed so unfair.

His poor wife Nancy was devastated. Steve was her life. None of us had any idea how long they'd loved each other, but having at last been able to marry him, to lose him so soon was more than she could bear.

It was no coincidence that three or four months after Steve's death it was found that Nancy had cancer. Henry operated on her, but he came back from the operation with a gloomy face. 'I'm afraid,' he said, 'I've only been able to remove part of the tumour. The outlook's very poor.'

The news was broken to Nancy that the operation had only been partially successful. Instead of upsetting her, it seemed to make her more cheerful. She always seemed full of beans, either when we went to see her, or when she came to see us after her discharge from hospital.

Nancy was really just longing to die and be back with her Steve. She deteriorated very rapidly and was buried in the same grave as Steve within one year of his death. She died without any regrets about leaving life. She was just rejoining this beloved man, without whom life had no meaning.

The whole town mourned their passing. Steve had been in practice in Tadchester for more than 40 years and Nancy had spent all her life in the town.

All my partners were good men, good doctors and, what was more, good friends, but Steve was a man apart. I shall never forget him. You couldn't really describe him as being meek but he could be described as being blessed. The biblical phrase, 'Blessed are the meek for they shall inherit the earth,' was about the most fitting epitaph you could give to this finest of men.

CHAPTER 13

C. P. and the Horseless Carriage

My friend Chris Parfitt did not have the luck with cars. If any car was stranded, broken down by the side of the road around Tadchester, the local bookies would have laid reasonable odds that it belonged to C. P.

Basically it was lack of interest in the horseless carriage: C. P. reckoned life to be too full of more interesting objects and pursuits than motors and motoring. He could never have fallen in love with a car and spent the weekend polishing it, as did many of the Tadchester motoring enthusiasts. In fact he only had a car at all on condition that his wife Joyce looked after the cleaning of it.

He was not mechanically-minded. What went on under the bonnet was a complete mystery to him, and local garage proprietors made a steady living out of putting right for him what the average schoolboy could have fixed in a couple of minutes. Once he called out a mechanic because his car would not start from home. It took the mechanic all of ten seconds to diagnose a chronic lack of petrol, without which even the most finely-tuned engine has difficulty in turning over.

He could never tell one make of car from another. When asked what his new car was, he'd reply, 'A maroon one.' And mean it.

After he passed his driving test, his instructor congratulated him and asked, 'And how do you find driving in the Hillman Minx?'

'I don't know,' said C. P. 'I've never driven one.'

'Look at those letters on the wing of the car you've been learning in for the past twelve months,' said the instructor. 'What do they say?'

C. P. spelled them out. 'M-I-N-X,' he said. 'Well, would you credit it?'

After his first abortive call to the Automobile Association, he kept a card under the dashboard recording such details as Registration Number, Make of Car, Year of Manufacture . . . all the essential information which for the life of him he could never remember.

He was God's gift to the second-hand car salesman. He worked on a basis of trust. He told the salesman how much he could afford, and asked in return for a serviceable car: nothing high-powered, sophisticated or flashy, just something which would go from point A to point B without any trouble.

The salesman would sell him a car which would go from point A to point B, but omit to mention that it was in no fit state to get to point C. If George Washington himself had sold a car to C. P., he would have been tempted to slip in the odd white lie. Never give a sucker an even break, they say. Where cars were concerned, C. P. was the world's Number One Sucker.

His local garage changed hands. Instead of a proprietor who would sell him a car guaranteed not to fall apart for a week or two, he dealt with a proprietor who sold him a car which should have been pressed into a cube long ago.

'Look at this,' said C. P. when he called round at my house on his first trip in the new car. 'Not bad, eh?'

Certainly it didn't look bad. The bodywork was gleaming from the garage's pre-sale buffing-up.

I offered my congratulations on his shrewd eye for a bargain, and off he drove. There was a resounding metallic crash as the car moved away, and a complete exhaust system fell at my feet.

That particular car disgraced itself a few weeks later when

C. P. and his family drove up to Manchester for a niece's wedding, to be followed by a week's fishing on the River Lune at Lancaster. C. P. had heard from John Denton, the water bailiff, of a sure bait for salmon and sea trout: half a dozen lobworms threaded up the line like a snake. To make sure he had plenty of bait, he had packed several cans of prize lobworms from his compost heap, almost snake-sized themselves and lovingly cradled in moss.

As the car chugged up the M6 just south of Crewe, there was a horrible grinding sound from the engine. C. P. slewed on to the hard shoulder, where the car shuddered and stopped dead.

He opened the bonnet to be met by a cloud of oily black smoke. After administering the full range of his car repair techniques, which consisted of several minutes' colourful cursing and kicking hell out of the offside front wheel, he trudged off to an emergency phone and called the AA.

The patrolman diagnosed a seized-up engine, suggested that the AA Relay service be called to take the car back to its garage of origin, and that the family continue their journey by taxi.

The taximan arrived to find a weeping Joyce – upset by the possibility of missing the wedding – being comforted by her daughter Janet. Son Clive was climbing into the cab with the Relay truck driver, with instructions from his father to strangle the car salesman when the wreck was delivered back to Tadchester. C. P. himself, meanwhile, was the calm in the centre of the storm: sitting amidst a pile of luggage on the hard shoulder, gently sorting through his worms to make sure that the journey so far hadn't upset them.

'First things first,' he said. 'You can't get worms of this quality just anywhere.'

They made the wedding in Manchester just in time, then travelled up by train to Lancaster. Clive, who was a 20-year-old undergraduate was big enough and articulate enough to put the frighteners on the most villainous used-car salesman, had the engine fixed in double-quick time back in

Tadchester and drove up to join the rest of the family on the Lune.

The journey back – or half of it – was impressive. C. P. had a passion for auction sales and had a habit of bidding for the least desirable object. Joyce often had to restrain him from buying moth-eaten stuffed bears or mooses' heads that had seen better days.

At an auction in Lancaster, Joyce made the mistake of nipping out to the toilet. She returned in time to see the auctioneer knocking down a pair of buffalo horns. (Texas longhorns, really, but used as an object of veneration in the Royal Antedeluvian Order of Buffalo lodges throughout the British Isles.) This pair was enormous – six foot four from tip to tip, possibly the biggest pair known to man.

'My God,' she said to C. P. 'What idiot's bid for those things?'

'Sold,' said the auctioneer, 'to the gentleman in the glasses over there.'

Joyce looked around for the idiot in the glasses, then noticed the auctioneer's gavel pointing straight at C. P.

'What the –?'

'Ssh,' said C. P. 'I'll explain later. Always wanted a pair of those. A bargain, too. Only fifteen quid.'

The auctioneer moved on to the next lot, muttering under his breath, 'There's always *one* . . .'

C. P. soon solved the problem of transporting the horns back to Tadchester by strapping them on the roof rack of the car. He strapped them on crossways, as worn by their original owner, figuring that if he laid them on longways he'd run the risk of spearing somebody. Besides which they looked better that way.

The longhorned car made a spectacular progression on the way back to Tadchester, drawing what C. P. took to be admiring glances from other motorists. But just as the car was approaching the M5, it was overtaken and flagged down by a police patrol vehicle.

On the hard shoulder, C. P. wound down the window and smiled ingratiatingly at the large policeman.

'May I have your name, sir?' asked the patrolman.

'Certainly, officer. Parfitt. Chris Parfitt.'

'I see. I thought for a moment I'd got Buffalo Bill. Shoot it yourself, did you, sir?'

The penny dropped through the officer's heavy sarcasm, and Chris explained about the buffalo horns.

'Certainly a bargain,' said the patrolman. 'And very tasteful, I'm sure. But tied on like that they constitute a dangerous load. We don't want to have any motorcyclists stuck on the horns of a dilemma, do we sir? Now get them strapped on the other way!'

With some puffing and struggling from C. P., and some muscular and more expert help from Clive, the horns were finally arranged pointing back and front. Joyce tied a white handkerchief round the tip of each, just to make sure they would be seen.

'That's much better, sir,' said the officer. 'Safe journey. And the best of luck at the rodeo . . .'

'Smart-arse,' said C. P., *sotto voce*.

The next year's holiday saw the final demise of the old car. Or at least, the old engine. Again, the trouble started at an auction in Lancaster, where C. P. bought a huge art nouveau sideboard. It was a magnificent piece of furniture, or would be when it was cleaned and polished up, and again it was a bargain. But getting it home made the problem of the buffalo horns fade into nothing.

The cost of having it sent by road or rail would have been about ten times what C. P. had paid for the thing. So he decided to risk the roof rack. All the luggage was crammed into the boot and squashed in odd corners of the car's interior. The massive sideboard was lashed down firmly, and the family set off.

'Why do we always have to look like Ma and Pa Kettle?' asked Joyce.

There was no answer to that.

C. P. took the first driving shift and made sure he kept down to a reasonable speed. But halfway home, he and Clive swapped seats and C. P. settled down for a snooze. Clive was going back to university in a couple of days and he was eager to get home and pack . . .

When C. P. woke up, he was aware of a heavy labouring noise from the engine. He glanced across at the speedometer.

'Seventy? For God's sake, Clive! Not with that thing on top!'

'It's OK, Dad,' said Clive. 'It's a big engine. It'll take it.'

'Not for long, it won't!' yelled C. P. 'Pull in at the next service station and let's check that the sideboard's still strapped on all right.'

Clive pulled in at the next service station and C. P. got out. He was moving round the car, checking the lashings, when his foot slipped. Looking down, he saw a large patch of smoking oil spreading from under the car. He threw up the bonnet and checked the oil dipstick, one of the few things he knew the location of. There was about enough oil to lubricate a small watch.

It was a long and slow journey home. When the engine had cooled down, C. P. bought a large can of oil and used it to refill the engine. Then he bought another can for the journey, stopping every few miles to fill the car up again, and buying several more cans before they finally made it to Tadchester.

'A very nice piece of furniture,' I said to C. P. admiring the sideboard with its art nouveau decorations, both in carved relief and in different coloured veneers, which weeks of Joyce's elbow grease had revealed. 'Would you mind me asking how much you paid for it?'

'Not at all,' said C. P. 'Twelve quid, that was.'

'You got a real bargain there.'

'I certainly did. Twelve quid. Oh . . . and £600 for a new engine. Still, it could be worse.'

'Worse?'

'A lot worse. I could do it for a living . . .'

CHAPTER 14

Winter Break

We were having a cold and miserable winter; there just seemed no end to it. In Tadchester we were either ploughing through snowdrifts or being lashed by freezing rain.

On impulse, Pam and I booked a holiday only two weeks before the departure date to somewhere we knew we couldn't be guaranteed sunshine, but where the weather should be better than we were having at home.

We'd chosen the town of Faro in the Algarve in Portugal, known mainly for its airport. Everybody going to the Algarve has to land there and pick up their coach or hire car to one of the many resorts: Portugal's resorts are increasing almost at the rate of the Spanish resorts in the Sixties.

Nobody seems to stay in Faro. Everybody we questioned, even people who had time-share villas in the Algarve and landed at Faro two or three times a year, had never visited the town.

What we didn't want was a recurrence of what happened on a holiday after my coronary bypass operation three years previously.

We had landed in a concrete jungle in the south of Las Palmas in the Canary Islands, where there was no indigenous population, just endless rows of hotels and apartments, and supermarkets that all sold the same stuff.

There was only one hotel in Faro in the brochures and this was the Hotel Eva, with 150 bedrooms, overlooking the harbour. We booked a room with a sea view and a bathroom. I reasoned, if the worst came to the worst, I could sit in the bath looking out over the harbour. Although we were on bed and breakfast terms, these also included afternoon tea – what Englishman could resist that?

We read up as much as we could about Faro and it did seem an interesting little town. The first book ever printed in Portugal was printed in Faro in about the 15th century. As a budding author, I took this as a happy omen; perhaps it would give me just the atmosphere to do a bit of writing. Apparently the town was spoilt in the 16th century by the beastly English, who knocked the place down on Queen Elizabeth's orders. Subsequently a couple of earthquakes in the 18th century had done the place no good at all. Following these, a very energetic bishop had made everybody do the Portuguese equivalent of 'pull their fingers out' and got a thriving port going again, with marble works and salt works. Today even – not the bishop's doing – there are light industry and plastics. There were also promises of shopping precincts, plenty of restaurants, shopping arcades: it all sounded very nice. What sounded nicest of all was that it would probably be filled with Portuguese, who are our oldest allies and some of the nicest people on earth. (We'd had two holidays in Madeira which we loved, and I think there's nobody better than the Portuguese for looking after you: they are courteous, kind, smiling lovable people.)

Setting off in midwinter had its complications – the partners didn't look too pleased, the workload was heavy. But we were only going for a week and some of the others had been off skiing. At home, we had Bertie to think of and worries about frozen pipes and other such nasties which were epidemic at that time.

The day was saved by our Norman, who offered to come and live in the house and look after Bertie, whom he'd known since a puppy.

Our Norman first came into our lives when I was put off work with chest pains, just before my coronary bypass. I was unable to do much physical work at the time and we needed some help in the garden. Word got round that Norman might be able to spare us a day and he called to interview us. A brisk, cheery, smiling man who said: 'I'm very happy to come and help you. My name's Norman, you're Pam, you're Bob, and the first time I hear myself called "the bloody gardener", I'm off.'

Norman was a phenomenon. Although he was past retiring age, I would match him against any 25-year-old for the sheer physical graft he could put in one day's work.

When we first met him he was working two days a week, for virtually nothing, to help out at a home for mentally handicapped children. He then had ourselves and two other customers, who only rewarded him a little more.

None of his earnings was essential, he could have lived without them, but what he couldn't do without was his travelling.

Every year for one month he used to take his car and go camping in France. He'd done this for ten years since losing his wife. He knew more about France than any other man I'd met. But France was only the main holiday.

Over the three years we'd known him he'd also had holidays in Tunisia, Sorrento, Rouen, Athens, Morocco, splitting up his time between Marakkesh and Agadir, then a separate holiday in Tangier and another one in Lisbon. Before we met him he'd been to Australia, and Germany – East and West. You name it, Norman had been there.

A six-year spell of army service during the war had given him his taste for travelling. He had arrived in France just as most of the other troops were leaving at Dunkirk. Norman's French campaign was short: he drove 60 miles from Cherbourg, 60 miles back and returned to England. Then, after the invasion of North Africa, he was stationed for three years in Algiers.

Gardening had always been a great hobby of Norman's and he'd many a time won Best Gardener competitions as a young man. He had been a printer by trade and having been 30 years in the business, then worked for an industrial firm. At retirement age, he didn't retire: he just moved in another direction and worked five or six days a week from eight in the morning till four in the afternoon.

During his working life, it wasn't enough for Norman just to have a full-time job during the day. At night he had his own dance band which played for organisations like Round Table and Rotary, as well as for civic functions. He still retained his love for music and just occasionally we could coax him to play us something on the piano.

Norman came to us every Wednesday and became part of the family. He was a meticulous, well organised man. He arrived not at 7.59 in the morning, nor at 8.01. On the dot of eight o'clock, up the drive would come Norman's car. At three minutes past eight either the lawnmowers would be whirring or you'd see Norman with a barrow already filled with soil pushing it up to some corner of the garden.

I'm very sloppy about most gardening jobs, but Norman soon put me right. When, after my operation I was fit enough to do some gardening myself, he would fairly jump on me if I was putting up a fence or something and didn't do it properly.

Out would come Norman's ruler: if a job had to be done it had to be done properly and precisely. He was a craftsman, a man who kept up all the old standards, and he completely transformed our garden.

He would occasionally stay for a meal, or sometimes we would take him out for a meal. He was good company, great fun to be with, and much appreciated good food and wine. He had become, since living on his own, a most skilled and discriminating cook.

His house was an absolute joy, beautifully furnished and decorated. We were very lucky to be associated with him and had the greatest respect for him and for his judgement. A quite remarkable man.

It was a great comfort, leaving the house in the winter, to know that Norman would be there. Bertie loved him and every Wednesday he'd go absolutely mad with joy as soon as he heard Norman's car approaching.

We settled Norman in. I left some wine on my wine rack and said if it wasn't drunk by the time we came back, it wouldn't be Norman giving *us* the sack – he would be dismissed on the spot.

Norman lived quite close, so Bertie could go back and forth with him to home and we could set off without worrying about anything. Eventually, set off we did.

Fortunately we caught an early train to London, setting off the day before our flight was due and spending a night in a hotel near Heathrow, to be sure we'd be there for take-off. It was as well we did: the train journey to London, instead of taking the usual four to five hours, with changes, took nine. The countryside was covered in snow, and there were delays caused by frozen points and huge shifting snowdrifts.

*   *   *

Our flight from Heathrow to Faro passed quickly, not just because we had a meal served in the middle of it, but because I unintentionally eavesdropped on a conversation in the row behind me.

A Portuguese gentleman in a fashionably washed denim suit, with dark glasses and high black boots – he looked like the local Mafia representative – was chatting up an English lady, who didn't seem to be averse to his approaches. I learned all about their families, their cars, their hopes, their ambitions, their invitations, their telephone numbers; even the time they were going to meet in Lisbon. 'Another drink to our friendship, Belinda,' said the Portuguese gentleman as the umpteenth round arrived.

When we eventually arrived at Faro, however, and it came to luggage-carrying time, he scuttled off to look after his own stuff and Belinda was left to cope with her own. She was very good looking, but she appeared a very sensible lady too, not likely to be swayed by a few drinks and a bit of smooth talk. Somehow I didn't think they'd make it as a pair.

The Hotel Eva looked exactly like it did in the brochure, which was a very pleasant surprise. We had a nice double room and a balcony overlooking the harbour which was filled with small boats.

What I hadn't realised was how much the Algarve had been waiting for us to arrive. A girl in traditional dress had thrust a flower into Pam's hand as we left the airport. There was a card attached to it saying that this entitled us to 3,500 escudos, about £2, if we'd go and have a look at the Four Seasons Country Club. In our room was a letter and a picture from Henry Cooper, God bless him, who was offering me a complimentary golf lesson, a complimentary round of golf and a cheque for £10 for the Variety Club Sunshine Coach appeal fund, if only I would have a look at the luxury apartments and golf course at Penina.

And this was just the beginning. There was a letter from a lady called Trish, who apparently had a desk somewhere in the hotel. If we would go and spend a day at the exciting new holiday resort of Portobello, we'd have a free lunch, a bottle of wine and could win one of several marvellous prizes of free holidays, free meals or money. Stamped across it was the legend: 'Married couples only. One gift per family or group. If married, must be accompanied by spouse.' Obviously, they were having no hanky panky.

Acting on my principle that there's no such thing as a free meal, I slipped all the invitations quietly into the wastepaper basket.

We awoke on our first morning to glorious sunshine. We had breakfast served in our room and sat eating it on the balcony. Overhead was a clear blue sky; down below was a picturesque harbour full of bobbing boats. Back home, Britain lay shivering under a blanket of freezing snow. Was all this real?

Faro is a lovely little town, and it *is* a town, not a hideous concrete resort. And I believe it has more fire engines per head of population than any other town I've been to.

Just a few yards down from the official fire station which had a whole line of fire engines, most of them vintage enough to claim a place in the London-to-Brighton race, was another fire station with bold letters over the top, proclaiming: '*Bombeiros*

Voluntarios'. This was the volunteer fire brigade, equipped with a further dozen appliances, none of which looked as if its engine could be coaxed into life.

There was no doubt that firefighting was a big thing in Faro and that afternoon, a Sunday, we had a splendid display from the Bombeiros Voluntarios. There was some sort of swearing-in ceremony then a whole band of volunteer firemen – drums, bugles and red berets – set off to parade around town.

It was the first band I'd seen that had a real drum major. In England, drum majors are men who are basically non-commissioned officers who walk in front of bands, dressed up to the nines and swinging a great stick.

The Bombeiros Voluntarios' drum major was the man with the biggest drum in the band, who led the band and banged away louder than any. That for me is a real drum major – the man with the major drum.

If it should ever be my lot to live in Faro there is no doubt that I shall certainly join the Bombeiros Voluntarios. Perhaps one day I'd make it to drum major.

Our hotel was extremely comfortable and I found that it had all the polite hospitality that I associate with the Portuguese. Nothing was too much trouble, everything was relaxed. The dining room was a bit of a disappointment, though the staff were courteous and what the food lacked in quality, it made up for in quantity.

Happily, on the ground floor there was what was called a snack bar which was actually a first-class, very inexpensive restaurant where you could get any sort of meal from nine in the morning until eleven at night. It was spotless, the food was excellent and a good meal could be had for £4 or £5, with snacks for much less.

There was a free guided walk around town led by the room manager of the hotel, a lovely plump man with a great sense of humour.

We saw three fascinating museums. The Maritime Museum was beautifully laid out, with splendid models of early sailing ships. The Archaeological Museum in an old convent had some beautiful Roman mosaics which had been dug up in the town. The Ethnographic Museum showed the traditional ways of life in the Algarve, with photographs, paintings and everyday objects. Both the Ethnographic and the Maritime Museums had models of the complicated net structures used for catching tuna fish.

Pam and I are not great people for churches and historic places, but the museums and churches of Faro were special – tremendous care had been taken in setting everything up – so they were both interesting and entertaining.

The town itself was big enough to wander round. There were lots of little side streets, and we were so lucky, at least for the first day-and-a-half when the sun shone. There was a large pedestrian shopping precinct, first-class shops, innumerable shoe shops, plenty of restaurants and snack bars. I had my shoes cleaned for £1 – and noticed that the locals were charged 50p.

I wanted to get a mental picture of the whole of the Algarve, so we took a coach trip from Faro to Sagres. The day we set off on our coach tour was one of the wettest, windiest days I've ever experienced. We visited Albufeira. The last time I'd been there, 17 years ago, it was a nice little resort with a few hotels. Now it was a concrete jungle, similar to the ones I'd seen in Las Palmas. It looked frightful, but I expect if you are 20 and all you want is sun, sea, bars and music in the summer it's just the place to go. It certainly looked pretty grim on this wet and windy day.

Portimão, a fishing port we passed through, didn't seem to have changed much in the 17 years; fishing vessels were still coming up and unloading their sardines on the quay. Then lunch at Lagos, the principal maritime base of Prince Henry the Navigator, one of Portugal's great heroes, celebrated by a large statue on the waterfront. We forgot that the Portuguese sailors going off to explore new continents had much less knowledge of what they were going into than our astronauts going out into space today.

We passed on through Sagres, visiting Prince Henry's Fort,

finally arriving at Cape St. Vincent which people used to think was the end of the world. I can easily see how this happened: if it wasn't the end of the world, it should have been. It was the wettest windiest place I've ever known, with a gale blowing of frightening velocity.

I'd heard the expression, 'Lean against the wind', but this was ridiculous. Two of our lady passengers were blown completely off their feet, and you could only stand up if you were actually holding on to something. I had brought an umbrella which lasted two minutes in this torrential gale of rain and wind. For all that, it was a magnificent sight with the waves smashing themselves against the rocks.

On the way back the roads were blocked twice by fallen trees.

When I asked our guide if the weather was often like this, she said, 'No. The last time was 1946.'

That day happened to be the 600th anniversary of Britain and Portugal becoming allies. Prince Charles and Princess Diana, I saw later on television, were in Lisbon, and having just about as rough a time as we were.

But it was all fun, it was all adventure. We had made friends with a Canadian couple from Vancouver, Connie and Lloyd Measner, whose life story was a book itself.

Lloyd had been working on a prairie farm between the wars during the great depression when the great cereal plains became a dust bowl. He and Connie had met in the Yukon, working in the old goldfields. I tried to encourage him to write his memoirs – he had a fascinating story to tell – and I hope by now it's well under way.

What we liked about the hotel, apart from the care and consideration of the staff, was that there was always something going on. Every night there was music of some sort, and one night we had an excellent exhibition of Portuguese dancing, far better than anything I'd seen in Madeira. This was the real thing.

We were dragged out on the floor to join in the last two dances and, once on the floor, had to take part in a dance competition for residents, in which I am proud to say we came third. I left the floor with a bottle of wine, a gramophone record which I am sure is about time-share apartments, and a badly wrenched sternum, which had already suffered enough by being sawn in two during my coronary bypass operation. The wrenched sternum was my own fault: thinking I was a young man again, I picked up Pam in the rock 'n 'roll session and started to throw her about as I did 30 years ago.

There's always something happening in a town as opposed to a resort – a town has always to go on living. Faro is a lovely little town. You could catch a bus to the beach about eight kilometres away, and with Connie and Lloyd we caught the local train to the fishing port of Olhão. This is a real port, a real working town with a bonus of excellent shops and huge markets of both vegetables and fish.

We watched the sardine boats unloading and this was real graft – the fish were literally coming in by the ton. In addition, the small power boats were coming off the mud flats with huge net bags, probably weighing a hundred weight each, containing what looked very much like cockles. You really felt you were in the heart of Portugal.

The harbour at Olhão was surrounded by factories, and there was every chance that my Sunday night sardines on toast came from there.

I loved the laid-back attitude of the Portuguese. There were no bridges over the railway, you just wandered across the track. But at least the trains came exactly on time. On the way back we found we'd got into a first-class compartment by mistake. This meant we each had to pay an extra 30 pence. I only wish British Rail would copy their timetable and their fares.

Our week went only too quickly. There wasn't time enough to explore the town fully and there were many places locally that we would have liked to have visited, particularly the mountains. The day we set off to go back, of course, after the storms, it was blistering sunshine. But never mind: we'd had a great time and I was sure that Faro and the Hotel Eva would be seeing us again.

CHAPTER 15

Practice Makes Perfect

In spite of only a very small increase in the number of patients and a large increase in the size of our staff, life at the surgery became steadily busier and busier. Most of this was because we now offered a much more comprehensive service.

Our two practice nurses, Gill and Debbie, ran an open blood pressure clinic where you could always pop in and have your blood pressure taken. They also did all the dressings, ran a sort of weight-watchers clinic, did allergy testing and desensitisation. They did E.C.G.s for us and were gradually taking over quite a lot of the stitching up of cuts.

When I went to do a cervical smear I didn't have to wait while the woman got undressed behind the curtain in my room, I would be buzzed through by either Debbie or Gill to their treatment room and the patient would be already prepared for me. It was no longer just a case of a cervical smear, either: it was a well-woman clinic where a whole range of checks would be done.

It meant that we were practising a much better and higher standard of medicine, and patients were getting a much more comprehensive service.

I did, though, sometimes wonder whether we were getting

too mechanically minded. The dispensary seemed to grow another computer each day.

We had a special answering machine when we were on duty, in line with the computers, all of which frightened me to death. This answering machine would tell patients which doctor to ring after surgery hours.

It was quite simple before this new machine came. You just turned a switch, recorded a message, turned the switch back and there was the message. Now we had to turn about a dozen knobs, there was a great box with little red arrows, green bleeps, red bleeps. It was as though they'd put traffic lights on Birmingham's Spaghetti Junction.

You knew that it was set when a red light finally came on with an ear-splitting whistle. I really chuckled to myself one day when all our equipment failed; something to do with voltage levels. When the Electricity Board allowed voltage levels to fall below a certain level none of our equipment worked. Fortunately it only happened once, but it did show how vulnerable we were.

I was always being badgered to put my patients on the computer for their repeat prescriptions rather than see the patient myself and write the prescription on the spot. It was explained to me how much quicker and how much easier it was, but I'd never thought that ease and quickness were the main objectives of general practice. I'd always thought of us more as professional comforters who kept one eye open for people being ill, rather than just careful pill dispensers.

However, the other partners loved these new mechanical toys.

The pattern of surgery life changed as well. When I first started in practice, evening surgery began at six and went on until it finished, about half past eight or nine, but we didn't do so many of them. Now evening surgery started at four and finished at six. If the building wasn't cleared by 6.30, there was mass hysteria amongst our splendid staff.

In trying to work office hours, I think that we created many more pressures than when we took things more leisurely. Now, apart from the occasional home confinement, midwifery had disappeared into hospitals and our surgeries finished at six, but somehow we seemed to be busier and under greater stress. I think much of this was caused by trying to work to rigid time schedules.

You almost had one eye on the clock, thinking, 'Well I've got to finish this job or this visit, to be back at the surgery at such-and-such a time.' This tight schedule meant that a lot of our routine visiting, and I still did a lot (although this had again become unfashionable), had to be done after the evening surgery.

Some patients who'd been on medication for years, once they were told they were going on the computer for their medication, immediately gave up what they'd been taking. They didn't want to be treated by a machine. So although the computers were beneficial from the doctors' point of view, they were not everybody's cup of tea.

Everything is getting more efficient and more streamlined and I think this is one of the reasons why so many patients are turning from conventional medicine to alternative medicine.

I've always thought of medicine as an art. I don't think too many art students would be helped by computers.

I think the most important part of general practice is the communication between the patient and the doctor and the introduction of super efficient machinery does tend to come between them.

But I found myself in the same position as King Canute – I couldn't make the tide go back.

The surgery that I enjoyed the most was a little branch surgery in a village where there was no transport. I had to let myself in through a little side room off the church hall. There was a fire in the waiting room for the patients.

It was meant to service just the people in this small community. I would see them, make out the prescriptions, take the prescriptions back to the main surgery and have them made up. Later in the day I'd drop them down at Jones' Brothers, the paper shop in the village, and patients would collect them from there.

This surgery was like little Alice – it grew and it grew and it grew, until often it was my biggest surgery of the week. I would sometimes arrive there on a Tuesday morning to find people who couldn't fit in the waiting room standing outside the door.

It was very difficult to do a proper examination there and if it was anything really personal the patient had to come up to the main surgery at a later date.

As patients came in to see me I'd hear laughter and conversation from the main waiting room in the hall. It was like a village club. Something to be looked forward to each week. Meet all your friends, swap local gossip.

Eventually I had more patients coming from miles outside the village than I had villagers. This wasn't because I had any particular magic or was more popular than my partners, it was the fact that nobody had to make an appointment – everybody knew there was a surgery going on there and they knew all they had to do was to turn up.

I seemed to form a special relationship with the people that lived in this village.

I thought I might have to cancel my last surgery in the village before I retired from practice. I had to attend a coroner's inquest with a colleague in the morning. But I couldn't miss it. So I decided that instead of having it at eleven o'clock I'd have it at two o'clock. I put a message up on the church hall door 'Surgery changed to two o'clock'.

When I arrived at the church hall at two, there didn't seem to be many people about, certainly no cars outside. I let myself into my little consulting room and sat down. There was a knock on the door and in came Joyce Wallace, one of the stalwarts of the community.

It was a community that looked after itself, and Joyce was always to be found if somebody wasn't well or needed a meal or somebody needed running to hospital. The village ran its own aid service, getting people to and from hospital, either for medical treatment or for visiting friends and relatives.

'Oh, Doctor Bob,' said Joyce. 'Could you come in the waiting room a second?'

What was this? A casualty?

Joyce opened the door and there was the waiting room of the church hall absolutely packed with just about every villager, all on their feet clapping. I was completely taken aback.

'We all felt that we couldn't let you go away without showing our appreciation,' said Joyce. And there in the hall was a lovely garden seat and a great wrought iron flower bowl packed with geraniums and ferns – a beautiful sight, flowers of all colours tumbling over the side like a waterfall. I could have wept. I was going to miss this surgery the most of all.

There's a moral in it somewhere. They say that big is beautiful, but I've often found that small isn't so bad either.

* * *

Coupled with all these changes in the practice was a dearth of the old characters. Many of the old characters, of course, by definition, grew older and passed on, so that people like the cobbler, the blacksmith, the village grocer, the carpenter and the odd job man, disappeared. The old characters one could sit and yarn with and have a cup of tea with didn't seem to be there anymore. There were some exceptions, like our Norman, and Reg and Pam Dawkins. Reg led a successful and cheerful life from a wheelchair, and he and his wife produced the most potent home-made wine I ever drank. But even on the farms, where everything was becoming so scientific, people hardly had time to sit down for a drink and a chat.

However, like everything else, the whole circle was turning.

Young people were beginning to set up craft communities, hand-made furniture was available, and special jumpers from local wool. There were two or three new potteries. Individuals were wanting to do their own thing in their own way. People were determined not to become one of the mass but to express themselves freely, even though economically this might not be the most efficient way.

So I could foresee in the future a new generation of characters. It was strange to find, after more than 30 years in general practice, that the rugged individualists and interesting people were not now the 75-year-olds, but the 35-year-olds.

There were Alan and Edgar who could make the most beautiful hand-painted plates. Pam and I have the only one they made to celebrate the bringing up of the *Mary Rose*, a beautiful plate with the ship in the middle and a replica of Tudor design round the outside. In years to come, the plate will be a real treasure in its own right. Edgar's wife, Doreen, sculptured, painted, kept chickens, geese, and a donkey that kept all her neighbours awake with its braying.

Albert Coldheart, a patient and meticulous man, made the most beautiful models. I've had several from him including a pipe of peace and a French haycart. One Christmas, knowing of my interest in rivers and waterways, he made the most beautiful barge, accurate in every detail – lifting hatches, a walkway across, colourful, with the trading name of Robert Clifford and Company on it.

When I retired, Alan Caiger-Smith made me the most beautiful plate of a pheasant, wearing a stethoscope and

hanging up its boots. (One of my writing pseudonyms was Dr Pheasant.)

Another young patient, Jerry Walker, made the most beautiful 30-foot steam launch. He'd made every little bit of it himself, over six years. It was beautiful, mahogany with a cabin with glass engraved windows. Even the glass engraving he'd done himself, having gone to night school to learn how to do it. There were wicker-work seats to sit on; again he'd made them after lessons in the art at evening class.

One afternoon Jerry took Pam and me for a long trip on the boat down to the mouth of the estuary and back up, through Tadchester bridge, as far as the river was navigable. It was marvellous, pottering along, with the steam engine making hardly any noise at all. I could see how people loved steam.

All these characters and craftsmen were in their mid-thirties. And I think they, and people like them, might hold the answer to many of society's problems.

Machines are taking over from men in all the manufacturing industries and men are going back to the old cottage craft industries.

I can foresee a time when these things will equate, when the unpleasant difficult tasks will be done by machines and our furniture, crockery, pottery, fabrics, clothes will be, more and more, made by cottage-type industries.

With more time our leisure industries should grow, facilities should improve. What we have to do is learn how to use our leisure.

One of the wisest men that I've ever met put forward a proposition that nobody ever completely took up. His idea was that there should be no unemployment, that everybody who had not got a job should be put on the labour reserve and, to draw money for what had previously been called the dole, they would have to earn it. They would either have to learn a language, learn bricklaying, carpentry, to play a musical instrument or take part in the renovation of some of the amenities on, say, the canals and rivers. A scheme like this would increase men's skills, take away boredom and, above all, mean that men that have been pushed out by machines would be able to maintain their dignity and learn new skills. Already some steps are being taken in this direction but, with today's massive unemployment, obviously more are needed.

I remember the old Head of the London School of Economics in a television broadcast saying that society has to make up its mind whether to pay men to work or pay them not to work.

It does seem over the last few years that people have been paid, and not very well, for not working. How much better for everybody if this could be switched to the other alternative.

CHAPTER 16

Big Brother is Watching

A change took place in general practice, the most profound change that had occurred during the whole of my medical working life: probably even more profound than the actual nationalisation of medicine.

Government-inspired, it was the limitation of prescribing by doctors.

A list of drugs was issued, and general practitioners were limited to prescribing only the drugs on the list. In addition, and this addition was probably a sensible one, only the prescribing of generic names for drugs would be accepted. For example, if you prescribed Panadol tablets (a proprietary name instead of Paracetamol which is the same but much cheaper) your prescription was disallowed and you, as the doctor, had to foot the bill.

Although we had a reasonable choice, this meant we were no longer able to prescribe precisely.

After 30 years of medicine I had to change the whole of my prescribing habits. For example, instead of there perhaps being 20 different indigestion tablets, I was now limited to about two, and this pattern went through most of the drugs that we prescribed. There was, thankfully, no limitation on life-saving drugs.

The medical profession seemed to take it without too much fuss, but I don't think any of us appreciated how our freedom was being curtailed.

Gradually I adjusted to it. We were a dispensing practice and our dispensers were very good. They pointed it out if we strayed from the list or forgot to prescribe the generic formula of a preparation rather than its trade name. All seemed to go along smoothly. Too smoothly, perhaps: we had lost a precious freedom.

One January morning, I received a long letter which read as follows:

Dear Doctor Clifford,
Selective List Prescribing and Dispensing
It has been noted that during July 1986 you prescribed and dispensed items on Form FP.10 which are no longer permissible under the Regulations. Copies of the prescriptions were sent to you by the Prescription Pricing Authority and you were informed that payment for the items had been disallowed. The relevant paragraphs of your Terms of Service read as follows:

'36A – (1) In the course of treating a patient to whom he is providing treatment under these terms of service, a doctor shall not order on a prescription form a drug or other substance specified in Schedule 3A to these regulations but may otherwise prescribe such a drug or other substance for that patient in the course of that treatment.

(2) In the course of treating such a patient a doctor shall not order on a prescription form a drug specified in an entry in column 1 of Schedule 3B to the regulations unless –
   a) that patient is a person mentioned in column 2 of that entry.
   b) that drug is prescribed for that patient only for the treatment of the condition specified in column 3 of that entry; and
   c) the doctor endorses the face of that form with the reference "S3B".

but may otherwise prescribe such a drug for that patient in the course of that treatment.

38 – In the case of a doctor who is authorised or required by the Committee to supply drugs and appliances under regulation 30 to a patient, in the course of treating that patient under these terms of service that doctor –

> a) subject to paragraph 36A, shall record an order for supply under sub-paragraph (b), on a prescription form completed in accordance with paragraph 36(2), of any drugs and chemical reagents or appliances which are needed for the treatment of that patient, but, subject to regulation 30(10), shall not be required to issue that form to that patient.
>
> b) subject to regulation 30(10), shall supply for that patient under pharmaceutical services, where necessary in a suitable container, those drugs and chemical reagents or appliances but –
>
> i) shall not supply under those services for that patient any Scheduled drug, except that, where he has ordered a drug by a non-proprietary name, he may supply a drug which has the same specification notwithstanding that it is a Scheduled drug.
>
> ii) shall supply for that patient a drug specified in Schedule 38 to the regulations only where the conditions in paragraph 36A(2) are satisfied.
>
> c) may supply for that patient in respect of that treatment otherwise than under pharmaceutical services, any Scheduled drug, and may demand or accept a fee or other remuneration in respect of that supply.'

You will recall that on 11th June 1986 a letter was sent to you drawing attention to the change in the Regulations and pointing out that, having allowed a reasonable period for adjustment, the committee would in future have to consider taking formal action in those cases where breaches of the regulations occurred.

The subject was considered by a Special Reference Sub-Committee of the F.P.C. which has decided that, if infringement of the Regulations continues following receipt of this letter, they will have no option but to refer the matter to the Medical Service Committee. I must emphasise that this would undoubtedly result in a formal hearing before the Service Committee at which you could be found in breach of your Terms of Service. The Committee is anxious to avoid such an outcome if at all possible and therefore you are most strongly advised to exercise all possible care in the prescriptions which you sign and dispense.

It is hoped that you will accept this letter as the minimum action which can be taken at present and understand that the Committee is obliged to implement the statutory regulations.

Yours sincerely,

For Administrator

I just couldn't believe my eyes when I saw this letter.

I wrote a stinging reply back to the F.P.C. The F.P.C. is the Family Practitioner Committee, the country being split up into areas covered by various Family Practitioner Committees. The F.P.C. pay us, pay us for our drugs, and are usually extremely nice, helpful people.

My reply to this horrendous document started:

'When I received the enclosed letter, my first thoughts were that George Orwell was still alive and writing under a pseudonym for the Family Practitioner Committee. Please could you send me evidence of the heinous crime that I committed in July last year. (It was January when I received this letter.)'

I continued:

'We are now just one step away from my receiving a letter stating, "It has been reported that for three mornings running you were ten minutes late for your surgery, irrespective of the fact that you might have been up all night. Unless you can

provide some good reason for your lateness you will be up before the Medical Services Committee and have your bottom smacked."'

I then went on:

'We seem to have actually reached that stage. The caretaker of our surgery, a lovely old chap named Jack Richards, was reported by a nameless, faceless person for leaving work early. The fact that he arrived at work early and did a great number more hours than was required of him, and was an excellent workman, did not prevent him being suspended for about a month while the matter was being investigated. This brilliant piece of administration meant that we had to manage without a caretaker for a month.'

I concluded my letter by saying that general practitioners are a highly skilled, dedicated group of men who have tremendous workloads which include many unsocial hours, nights and weekend work, none of it compensated for by comparative time off. To be bothered on these lines borders on impertinence.

I then sent copies of our correspondence all over the place – local and national newspapers, my MP – and waited for evidence of the crimes I'd allegedly committed the previous July.

Each month I was writing on average about 1,300 prescriptions, so I should expect to make a few mistakes.

The Family Practitioner Committee produced only one prescription for an antihistamine which is not allowed – that was my only sin. But it wasn't even my sin; I hadn't signed or written

140

the prescription. It was one of our junior partners but it happened to have my number on it.

I hit the roof. I rang John Bowler, my consultant physician friend, and asked whether there were any similar problems occurring in hospital practice.

'Oh, yes,' said John, cheerfully. 'We've just been told that in future they're going to stop calling patients patients, and call them customers. Presumably we're going to have an in-customer department and an out-customer department. At the least it should help bring the unemployment figures down.'

I asked my F.P.C. for the rise in the number of people that they'd employed over the last ten years, but they didn't reply.

I had a telephone call from the man who'd sent the letter. I explained that if I had written a disallowed prescription, which I hadn't, we would have paid for it anyway. This would have meant that it wouldn't have cost the National Health Service any money, so in actual fact the N.H.S. would have benefited from it. He replied, 'Oh, no. It's not just a question of that. We could have you before a committee and fine you as well.'

I could hardly believe it. My flurry of correspondence did mean that I received a letter from one up the scale, the Deputy Administrator for the area, who said that he wanted to emphasise the action taken was decided not by non-medical people employed by the F.P.C., but by the Special Reference Panel which is composed of a lay Chairman of the F.P.C. and two medical members, one of whom is also Secretary of the local Medical Committee.

So we have now reached a stage in general practice where we cannot prescribe what we like. If we stray from the government list we have to pay for the medicine that we've prescribed; in addition to that we can be fined for actually so doing. George Orwell *was* right.

I couldn't believe that this situation existed, other than perhaps in the armed forces. I was surprised that my colleagues in the British Medical Association and the College of General Practitioners had not made more of a fight of it. I thought it was an appalling state of affairs which sadly was destroying the

relationship between general practitioners and the F.P.C. which had always been good, and would surely drive doctors towards private medicine.

I think this is all so sad. In spite of its faults, the benefits of the National Health Service far outweigh its deficits. But letters like the one I received and rules like this one would surely destroy it. If nobody else was going to fight, I was determined to, at least until they carried me away kicking and screaming.

CHAPTER 17

Lucky Dip

Pam and I were never great takers of photographs; we always relied on people taking photographs of us. But over the years we'd somehow collected a mass of transparencies and photos of various holidays. They weren't properly filed or in order or even labelled.

Occasionally we'd have an evening when we'd bring a huge box of assorted slides down and pop them in the projector. It was like taking a lucky dip. The unexpected and sometimes long-forgotten pictures would bring memories flooding back of holidays with the children.

A lovely photo of the three children sitting on the bonnet of an old Ford Zephyr when their ages must have ranged from three to 13, with Pam and I loading luggage on the roof: a well-composed photo which had been taken by a professional. At the time I was writing for *Mother* magazine and all the contributors had to write about their holidays.

This holiday was a camping one in Brittany. We were met at the ferry by a photographer from the magazine who photographed us on the quay, all over the ship, just about everywhere you could think of. All the other passengers thought we were visiting celebrities.

Camping in Brittany was memorable. I'd left the *carnet* – camping permit – at Carnac. Having set up our tents at Penvins in a storm, I had to journey back to pick up the *carnet* otherwise we'd be thrown off the campsite.

Trevor came into his own while I was away, holding the tent down while the storm did its best to uproot it. Father eventually got back to add his weight to the bottom of the tent, and we finally managed to tether the brute securely.

There were transparencies of a holiday with our widowed friend, Margaret Doe, and her daughter Sally. We'd rented a flat for three weeks in Loano, a seaside resort near the French border in Italy. Seven of us were packed in a Ford Zephyr with food for a month – mainly tinned ham – and camping equipment piled high on the roof rack. The car was so heavily-laden I daren't stop suddenly.

We got caught up in traffic on the motorway outside Versailles. Everybody was going at 70, even in the slowest lane,

and lorries were steaming past us at about 100 miles an hour. It was a nightmare. I eventually got off the motorway, and was going down a secondary road, when somebody shot out of a side road. I slammed on the brakes and the whole of the roof rack shot forward about four feet.

I managed to fix the roof rack, using the whole of my mechanical equipment – a pair of pliers, a spanner and a screwdriver – and we made our objective for our first day: Chalon-sur-Saône, about 350 miles from Le Havre.

In those days when we crossed the Channel we used to take the night boat to Le Havre with the mistaken idea that arriving in France at seven o'clock in the morning would leave us fresh for the drive south.

The boats were always crammed. Every cabin (which we couldn't afford anyway), and every reclining seat had been booked months ago. We had to find a bit of floor space to lie down or try and sleep in the car.

What it really meant was that we arrived in France in the small hours, having missed a night's sleep with a 350-mile car journey ahead of us.

From Le Havre we had pressed on and on without a stop, happy to be introducing Margaret and Sally to France for the first time and telling wonderful tales of French bread and cheese and pâté. When we'd just about reached exhaustion we started looking for some refreshment, but we seemed to have come to a part of the country that did not in any way cater for motorists.

Eventually we found a little cafe sign. A very strange woman answered the door, and we asked for bread and cheese.

'Toasted?' she said.

This didn't sound very French, but we agreed.

Five minutes later she brought out pieces of typical sliced English soggy bread, toasted and covered with packet cheese – not quite what we'd had in mind. After my public relations job on the delights of simple French food, the toasted cheese à l'Anglais must have been a big disappointment for Margaret and Sally.

We made a good campsite at Chalon-sur-Saône and had quite a nice drive the next day to a campsite by a lake near the Swiss border. From the camping book, it appeared to be a really good site, but it was in fact awful. The lake was covered in scum, there was hardly room to stand up between the tents, and the toilets ran even the Moroccan toilets a close second. You were a brave man if you didn't wear wellingtons when you set off for your daily ablutions.

We then had the most beautiful drive through the Jura Mountains and over the Mount Cenus Pass into Italy, a hair-raising experience in our heavily-laden car.

We found a lovely little Italian hilltop campsite on green grass, with good toilets, a water supply, and a glorious view over hilly countryside.

Driving in Italy seemed different, and I never got quite used to it. Outside Turin we got on to the autoroute and, although I quite enjoy driving on the right-hand side of the road, I forgot that the left-hand side was the fast lane. Having got in the fast lane I had the nightmare of trying to creep across to the slow one with every horn in Italy blaring at me.

We also took a wrong turning off the autoroute; instead of bypassing Turin we managed to go right through the centre in the rush hour. Although parts of the town were beautiful, we went through some pretty mangy, sordid areas. I just hoped the car wouldn't break down. I thought it was never going to end, but we eventually got through it and caught sight of the Mediterranean.

We tracked down our flat in Loano and I felt very much 'mission accomplished'. I settled down with a glass of wine and a large cigar – it was in the days when I was a smoker – and let the rest of the team do the unpacking.

It's a holiday Pam won't forget. She went off one afternoon to have her hair done, and came back looking very glamorous.

She sat on the beach a little off from us, reading. A nondescript Italian gentleman of middle age sidled up to her.

We all watched from about 20 yards away. Pam read on unconcernedly as he gently edged towards her. He got almost to within touching distance, then started to pick up handfuls of sand and trickle it over her feet.

This was too much for the kids. Jane shouted, 'What's that man doing to my mummy?' The startled Italian turned round, saw the watching gallery and shot off down the beach. Pam preened herself that she'd had an admirer, even though he was a fairly tatty one.

It was also a holiday Paul won't forget. We all did everything together but we felt one night that the adults should go out for a meal. We counted Sally as an adult – she was 17 and just about to take 'A' Levels. As there was an Italian family in the apartment below us, we thought that Trevor, at 13, Paul, ten, and Jane, three could be safely left.

However, at one point in the evening, Paul thought he heard ghosts. Trevor was unable to reassure him, so Paul set off into the night, wandering through the town trying to find us.

He had great difficulty, but eventually found the restaurant we were in. He stood looking at us through the window, felt that he would be disturbing us if he came in, then found his way back through the dark streets, getting lost about three times before he arrived back at the flat.

He stayed awake, fully dressed, until we came back and burst into tears when we came in – worried that we would be cross with him for having gone out.

Next day he appeared to be fully recovered and was rushing up and down the beach with a football. But we can never properly see into our children's minds and never quite know what torments they are going through.

The holiday had a grand climax. We'd got a little bit tired of our flat before the end and left it early to go to a campsite we knew at Agay, in France.

This is a beautiful campsite, set among pine trees down by the sea's edge, with a marvellous restaurant, bar, good showers and toilets, as well as a good shop. It is halfway between St.

Raphael and Cannes and not too far from our friends, Jane and Peter Churchill, who lived at Grasse.

Peter had played a very senior part in the Resistance in that area during the war.

We rang to find out if there was a chance of them coming to see us, and discovered that mutual friends had already rung them to say that we were in the vicinity. They'd got hold of a farmhouse across the road for us, said Peter, and we must go and stay there.

The next day we went to this most beautiful farmhouse whose doors opened with great big iron keys at least two feet long. The farmhouse had lovely verandahs, gardens with fruit of every imaginable type, comfortable beds, bathrooms and showers: a veritable seventh heaven.

Peter and Jane used to keep an eye on it for friends while they were away and had the use of it for their friends when necessary. It was so lovely we decided to stay an extra day and make it a hard journey on the way back.

We invited Peter and Jane for a traditional English meal, and went to the supermarket for a piece of beef. Our idea was that we should give them roast beef, Yorkshire pudding and potatoes. But the French oven in the farmhouse had a mind of its own and refused to cook it properly. The meal was a disaster.

Sadly, Peter died a few years later, but Jane recently said that they'd often had a laugh over the English roast beef that we'd tried to prepare for them.

It meant a very early start on our last day to reach Moulins and the municipal campsite in the middle of a stadium. We camped there, and made another early start the next morning, to reach Le Havre comfortably for an evening ferry. It was a hot and sticky journey. Trevor, Sally and myself were on the front seat; Margaret, Pam, Paul and Jane were on the back, mixed up with masses of shoes, thermos flasks and all sorts of bits and pieces. At one stage it was so hot that Trevor and Sally stuck together.

* * *

I think there was something about preparing meals for Peter and Jane that brought out the gremlins. Jane's brother lived in Tadchester and they often came to visit him. One night I was cook for a special dinner in their honour.

I bought the very best steak, chopped it and fried it, then started to casserole it with tomatoes, onions and various other things.

Pam's contribution to the cooking was masterful. 'You'll need some paprika,' she said. 'I'll put it in for you.'

Peter and Jane were arriving in half an hour. The food smelled gorgeous and was cooking beautifully. I took a sip of gravy from my ladle as I gently stirred it. The taste was magnificent.

Then there was an after taste – so hot and strong it nearly blew the back of my head off.

I couldn't understand it. I thought I'd try it on the children. They each in turn said 'That's marvellous, Dad,' and then clutched their heads as if hit by an explosion before they'd completed their sentence.

Pam was weeping.

'I'd swear,' she said, 'I only put a teaspoonful of paprika in it.'

I took the meat out and washed it under the tap. Luckily there was some aromatic liquid I'd taken out of the casserole before the disaster, so I re-cooked the meat in that, as best I could, before our guests arrived.

Although I'd taken a bit of the bite out of it, I had to fill Peter and Jane with large quantities of gin before I offered my spoilt meal. It went down very well in fact. Peter, who said he'd been having indigestion for years, was temporarily relieved of this complaint by my magic medication.

So, in the end, the meal was enjoyed and the evening went off successfully. But it always did when Peter was around. 'There's a party wherever he goes,' said Jane.

Peter told me once that he'd been in solitary confinement in a

German prisoner-of-war camp for a year. He swore that if and when he got out, he would live to the full every day that remained to him – which he did.

A few days after our paprika episode I was writing to some friends in America. Among other things, I was telling them about the dish that I'd spent a day labouring over. I shouted out to Pam. 'How do you spell paprika?' She came down with two identical cardboard drums in her hand, one with *Paprika* written on it – and the other with *Cayenne Pepper*. That was the answer – she'd put Cayenne pepper in my beautiful beef Stroganoff instead of paprika. No wonder it would blow the back of your head off.

*   *   *

We still have our treasure chest of some hundreds of unsorted slides and photos and on the odd quiet evening we dip into it, bringing back memories of holidays with the children, with each memory bringing back other memories.

Soon the whole cycle will be repeating itself. Daisy May and Paul and Gill are coming to France with us next year. We'll be taking plenty of pictures . . . and leaving Paul, Gill and Daisy May with the memories.

CHAPTER 18

On the Move

I was approaching my 60th birthday! Where had all those years gone?

Pam and I had decided that I would retire from general practice when I reached 60. This was the earliest I could get a pension, although it would be a reduced pension and there would be a pulling in of financial reins unless my writing unexpectedly took off.

As well as having reached the age that I could retire, I felt there were certain indications that were pointing in that direction.

I'd been in practice for 33 years and I kidded myself that the part of my brain which held patients' names had got full up.

I was always forgetting people's names. I could remember where they lived, where they'd been on holiday, their house, their car, the name of their dog but, so often their names escaped me.

When I was doing a surgery there was always a pile of notes in front of me in the order that the patients came in. If the patients had come in in the wrong order, there had been times when I had picked up the wrong card and had a long conversation about somebody else's condition.

I wore glasses for reading and close work, but had good long vision. Pam and I had taken to reading in bed before we went to sleep, and after reading I'd put my glasses down on the bedside table.

I had an urgent call one night – somebody desperately short of breath. I got dressed as quickly as I could and drove out four miles to Farmer Leach's farm, where I was told he was having breathing difficulties.

The Leaches had a large family in residence. There was Grandma Leach of 85, Leach himself who was about my age, four sons and three daughters, scattered round the house and in farm cottages, and about eleven grandchildren, all of them working on the farm.

I arrived, examined him, and realised he needed an intravenous injection and a pretty quick one at that – he had an acute bronchial spasm.

I put my hand in my pocket for my glasses. There was nothing there. They were still on my bedside table at home.

There was no way I could drive four miles back and pick up my glasses. Mr Leach needed an injection straight away. I had to ask, in despair, 'Has anybody in the house got a pair of glasses?'

Grandma Leach had – and Grandma's glasses improved my vision enough to get a needle into a vein.

The injection relieved Farmer Leach's breathing and all was well.

I made a vow to keep a spare pair of glasses in my case from then on. And I realised that my eyesight – let alone my memory – was no longer what it was.

At coffee time the next morning in the surgery, I regaled my partners with my experience of the previous night. They offered all sorts of helpful advice, such as tying my glasses to my head.

At evening surgery, there on my desk was a muddy sort of jam jar containing what looked like great black slugs.

Ron Dickinson came in; apparently he'd gone to great lengths to get these specimens for me. 'Not the same leech as you saw last night, Bob,' he said. 'But you don't need glasses for these to get blood – just stick them on anywhere and they'll get it for you.'

There happened to be a rolled up *British Medical Journal* on

the corner of my desk. I picked it up and threw it at him, catching him squarely on the head as he shot out of the door.

'You'll be old yourself one day!' I shouted after him. 'Come back and pick up these wobbly black puddings or I'll let them loose in your car!'

Knowing that in a few months' time I would no longer be doing night and weekend work, every night and weekend seemed to be that much harder. I was convinced that getting up at three in the morning on night calls was not doing me a lot of good. Night calls were usually for desperate situations – children fighting for breath, heart attacks, all sorts of traumatic things. Whenever I went out, my own heart seemed to be in my mouth before I started. I felt that perhaps I'd worked at this pace for long enough.

Also, although we loved Tadchester and all its surroundings, our children had gone away. Trevor and Jane were in Brighton; Paul and Gill in Cirencester. Because of the distances we saw very much less of them.

I read a book once where the author said that you should start planning your retirement when you're 40, i.e. put roots down somewhere and start getting to know the people in a particular area.

We had so often seen people retiring to Tadchester with dreams of a little cottage in the West of England, only to arrive there to find they knew no one, and were faced with the fact that in advancing years it's more difficult to strike up new relationships. They spent the last years of their lives lonely, depending on occasional visits from relatives and children and never really settling in the new community. They would have been much better off retiring in their work surroundings.

Although we hadn't started planning at the age of 40, we had always loved the Thames Valley, particularly the town of Wallingford. Over the years, with boating holidays, we had made friends there. Every time we moored at Wallingford we tramped around having a look at houses. Several times we very nearly put money down on cottages, but things had fallen through at the last minute.

With retirement only about six months off, we had to go into the business more thoroughly, and Pam used to make house-hunting trips to Wallingford. Having nearly bought one house, waiting for a completion date with still a few enquiries to be cleared, we thought we'd better keep our options open and while we were up there see what else was on the market.

Suddenly we found the house of our dreams, a house much smaller than the one we'd had in Tadchester, but big enough for Pam and me. It was within walking distance of the town centre and above all, had a lawn that went down to the river, with a mooring stage for a boat at the bottom.

We bought it on the spot.

For the next few months Pam was commuting up and down from Tadchester to Wallingford. Fortunately the house was in such immaculate condition that we had no decorating to do. Pam had half-moved in there about four months before I actually retired.

While she was away I stayed with a marvellous lady who used to put up the locums and junior partners, Mrs Doris Lounger. David Lichen, our new partner, had been staying with her while he was looking for a new house and I noticed that he had grown steadily stouter as the weeks went by.

I can't think of anybody less appropriately named than Mrs Lounger, a widow who had been a doctor's receptionist. Now, as well as putting up various locums, partners and people like myself, she had a morning job cleaning cars for a garage. Her work was immaculate: a car cleaned by Mrs Lounger would put about £500 on its price.

She utterly spoiled me and any of my colleagues who stayed with her. She was up and about at six every morning, cleaned my car windows and went down to the shop for a paper. So by the time I got up at about eight o'clock, breakfast was ready, my paper was there and my car was cleaned.

Her evening meals were of cordon bleu standard. And we had a common weakness – egg and chips was our favourite dish. On high days and holidays she would say with a twinkle in her eye, 'Guess what's for supper tonight?' Yes, it would be egg and chips and we would blissfully dip our chips in the yolk.

Years ago, Doris had been the head cook in a large house. It was back in the days of Upstairs and Downstairs, and she still maintained the standards of the landed gentry. She was a wonderful little woman and marvellous company.

She had a very old cat called Tommy, whose ginger hairs seemed to stick to every piece of clothing I wore. They could only be cleared by wrapping a band of Sellotape sticky side up round my fingers and dabbing it on to pick off the hairs. A small price to pay for such wonderful hospitality.

Mrs Lounger's daughter had gone to New Zealand some years before. As she had other children, she was unable to spend longer than six months at a time on her visits there. So she saved for her New Zealand trips and in the meantime kept an immaculate house and garden, ran around in a small car, cleaned cars and cared for us all splendidly.

The last few months before retirement were very emotional. I'd been in Tadchester for such a great number of years that inevitably I'd become part of people's lives. Now I was deserting them. There was party after party, magnificent presents including a pine table, benches and chairs – it seemed like about ten Christmases all rolled into one. We had a formal practice dinner where we all wore dinner jackets and made speeches and wondered why we had never done this before. I was presented with a pair of silver candlesticks and a beautiful watercolour painting.

Not only was I going to miss my partners, who were really like family, but all the wonderful assortment of characters who'd let me into and shared part of their lives with me.

Tadchester was a wonderful little town and a wonderful little community. I was going to miss it terribly. But I was missing my children more and, with Wallingford being fairly near to London, we knew we wouldn't be short of visitors.

Before I left Tadchester we'd already got our eye on river holidays and had purchased an old hire boat from a neighbouring boatyard. The boat had the luxury of a flush toilet, shower, hot and cold water, a fridge and a gas oven.

No more ablutions under an umbrella in the corner of a field in the pouring rain.

I was in that catch-22 situation, I couldn't bear to leave Tadchester and I couldn't wait to get to Wallingford.

We cleared up the house in Tadchester, which was bought by a pleasant young couple with two small children, and had our last round of goodbyes to friends and patients.

The farewell to the practice staff was held on a Friday lunchtime in the Surgery. I was actually to finish work on the following Sunday, when I would be going round with the new young partner who was to replace me. Pam and I had decided to drive through the Sunday night to arrive at our new house, to begin our new life at the start of a new day.

I had thought the staff goodbye party was muted, perhaps because we were all so upset about parting. But apart from that, it seemed that they hadn't taken quite as much trouble as they usually did when one of their own colleagues left. Anyway it was all very nice, with lots of kisses, lots of photographs taken. We went easy on the drink as we all had to work in the afternoon.

Saturday on duty was an anticlimax; not many calls, an appendicitis I had to send to hospital at 1 a.m. I hoped it would be my last night call ever.

There were only two calls on Sunday morning, so I sat with Pam reading the papers, waiting for the new young partner to arrive. We were staying at Mrs Lounger's and my replacement was expected at lunchtime. There was something strange about the morning. Mrs Lounger seemed to have lost the usual bustle associated with one of her Sunday lunches. Pam seemed ill at ease. Then, just as the new young partner arrived, there came an emergency call: would I go immediately to a visitor with chest pain who was staying in the house next door to Anne Matthews, one of our receptionists? The new partner offered to go but I felt I ought to see the job through. I shot off in my car with my heart in my mouth as usual, wondering what crisis I would have to deal with.

I tore up the muddy lane that led to Anne Matthews' lovely half-timbered country house. Standing in the middle of the road was David Lichen, directing me into Anne Matthews' drive, 'God,' I thought. 'They have sent for him as well.'

I turned into Anne's drive, noticing about 40 cars parked in the field behind the house. When I turned the corner, there were about 50 people, all with filled glasses raised to me. I could see all the Surgery staff and their husbands, my partners, health visitors, district nurses, old locums – everybody I had worked with at Tadchester over the years. This was my real goodbye party and it was almost too much. Mrs Lounger and Pam arrived about five minutes later. They, the devils, had been in on the secret all the time.

We had a marvellous party on a lovely summer's day in the magnificent setting of the Matthews' old country house on a hilltop, with a panoramic view of the whole of Tadchester. I shall never forget it. I was given a longitudinal map of the Thames that I had always wanted, an inscribed barometer for my boat from the Surgery girls, and a pair of binoculars.

They had really spoilt me, and made my last view of Tadchester such a beautiful one.

The party went on until the evening. Then it was back to Mrs Lounger's for reviving coffee, talk until the early hours and final goodbyes. We set off, aiming to arrive in Wallingford as near dawn as possible.

Our hearts were very heavy, but our spirits were high. Dawn rose as we reached Pangbourne and for the last few miles we were able to see stretches of the Thames.

Just before we entered Wallingford we turned down into a small cul-de-sac of half a dozen houses, all with lawns stretching down to the river. We went into our new house and climbed up into the bedroom which had a balcony overlooking the river.

The sun was now shining, it was a lovely day. A neighbour had cut the grass down to the river's edge and there bouncing on its moorings was our new boat *Sea Grey*. It all looked so beautiful.

I turned to Pam. She smiled. 'I know what you're going to say.'

'Yes,' I said. 'Life is going to be different from now on.'

YOU'RE STILL A DOCTOR, DOCTOR!

This book is dedicated to the memory of
CLIFF PARKER,
journalist, editor, author, contributor to many of my
books and steadfast friend for twenty-one years, a great
human being, much loved by all, sadly missed.

Contents

CHAPTER 1

Home Port

It was a beautiful sunny day on the Thames. We were moored to the bank behind a queue of four boats just above Abingdon Lock. On our right a hire boat flying a German flag was making unsuccessful passes at a post on the opposite side of the river. The post carried a big red notice saying 'DANGER – WEIR'. Perhaps weir means something less hazardous in German.

I was idly gazing along the row of boats in front and saw a tall, bespectacled man step off a boat and disappear over the side. I assumed there must be some new steps down there. Then some inner instinct nagged and I thought I'd better hop off and see what had happened. I walked along the towpath and looked down into the river. There, face downwards with one of his feet on the boat, his head lying over a wooden rail, half in the water, was a man of about seventy.

He was motionless. If he was left where he was he was obviously going to drown – if he wasn't already dead.

I shouted to the lock keeper, who had just started opening the lock gates. He came running, and between us we managed to lift the man up and drag him up the bank.

As we laid him down, he opened his eyes, spat out a mouthful of water and said, 'I don't know what happened to me ... I must have tripped or come over dizzy or something.'

He had a nasty-looking lump under his right eye and I suggested we got an ambulance and sent him to hospital. Although his injury was nothing obviously serious, I thought he might have broken a cheek bone.

Most important, he was alive, which he might well not have been if I had delayed my walk of inspection any longer.

I went back to my boat after seeing the patient safely off in an ambulance. We went through the lock and moored some way on the left-hand bank, downstream of the bridge.

Abingdon is a delightful town, prettier from the river than from the road, with a small theatre in the middle of a group of old buildings, which includes a twelfth-century

2

priory. There are always good moorings on either side of the river, with marvellous facilities on the town bank, including a toilet block that even boasts hot water.

Later that night the Abingdon lock keeper, an old friend of mine, wandered down and came aboard for a nightcap with two of the Dobermann pinschers he bred.

These dogs always frighten me to death, but they were the love of his life and he assured me they wouldn't hurt a fly. Although I could agree that flies might be safe, I wasn't too sure about fat, bald-headed doctors.

'Thanks again, Doc,' he said. 'I don't know what we'd do without you. But how come you always arrive in the nick of time? Better than the Seventh Cavalry, you are.'

By some weird coincidence, whenever I passed through the lock some medical emergency cropped up.

'Look here, Jack,' I said. 'I'm retired now. I don't know whether I'm up to all these medical emergencies.'

'Go on,' said Jack. 'You're still a doctor, Doctor.'

He was right. Although I'd retired to Wallingford six months previously after thirty-three years as a West Country GP, there was no way I could leave medicine completely behind me.

I was on various committees; ex-patients still rang me for advice; at any social functions, as soon as it was known I was a doctor of medicine, symptoms were whipped out more often than handkerchiefs. I was still on a monitoring group of a residential home for the mentally handicapped, I still read the abridged version of the *British Medical Journal* so I wouldn't fall too far behind on medical facts. My favourite page was the obituaries – I used to work out the weekly average of death to try and gauge approximately how many years of retirement I could enjoy.

I resisted all attempts to do locums, life assurance examinations for the DHSS, and other forms of remuneration for doctors who had given up general medical work.

With much heart-searching my wife, Pam, and I left our beloved Tadchester in Somerset where I had been in

3

practice for thirty years and moved to Wallingford in Oxfordshire. There we were fortunate enough to have a house whose garden ran down to the edge of the River Thames, and an old hire boat, the *Sea Grey*, which we had bought to fulfil my ambitions of dividing my time between messing about in boats and writing.

Wallingford, we found, was a delightful place. We'd chosen it after having explored many riverside towns.

You could write a book about the town, in fact, several such books have been written and there are records going back to the ninth century.

It had been a fortified Saxon town in King Alfred's time; William the Conqueror had crossed the river here on his way to London, and his second-in-command had built Wallingford Castle, which survived until Cromwell knocked it down. For many years it was one of the most important castles in the land.

Stephen and Matilda used to fight over it in the twelfth century and on the death of Stephen, Henry (who was King Henry II) became King of England and for a time ruled England from Wallingford Castle.

But that was all in the past.

The present-day attractions are numerous. It is a market town with a Friday market in the square. It has a lovely old town hall and a couple of theatres, one of which spends half its time being a cinema. It also has one of the leading rowing clubs in the country.

There is a wide range of shops, including the headquarters of Habitat and a lovely old family store, five or six absolutely first-class eating places, good river facilities and easy access to London.

Wallingford had so much to offer that there didn't seem to be any reason to go beyond the town boundaries. We bought our clothes in Wallingford, our furniture in Wallingford, we dined in Wallingford, we had our entertainment in Wallingford – theatre and first-class films. It was a real community with a tremendous number of people putting in a great deal of work to provide facilities for their fellow citizens.

The old Regal Cinema had all sorts of functions – badminton, roller skating, and from time to time a flea market. At the Kinecroft Theatre we saw a wonderful rendition of the opera *La Traviata*. The bigger theatre, the Corn Exchange, run by the Sinodun Players, was a delightful playhouse seating about four hundred.

The people who ran the ticket office, the bar staff, the house managers, the lighting experts, were all local people who did it all for nothing.

It was a truly remarkable little town and we counted ourselves lucky to find a house with a river frontage and our own mooring.

CHAPTER 2

Maiden Voyage

It was a great pleasure to be able to walk down to the bottom of the garden to see *Sea Grey* lying at her mooring, a piece of driftwood round one of the front mooring ropes and her fenders bumping against the concrete steps whenever a boat passed.

She looked gleaming white and new. She'd been painted up by the Maid Boat Yard before I'd bought her and, in fact, she was a stately lady of eighteen years and had done her stint as a hire boat.

I had taken her down the river to my friend Andrew Corless at the Sheridan Boat Yard and he'd given her an overhaul and put a pulpit on the foredeck. Not that I'd suddenly gone religious – the pulpit is the front rail of the boat that helps stop you falling off when manoeuvring. He'd also fixed a new back handrail and fixed up navigation lights and a searchlight.

I had been extravagant in adding these lights, and chose the very best quality. They were paid for by a legacy from a wonderful ex-doctor patient, Jackie Dean, who suffered from innumerable complaints and, nursed by her sister, had lived ten years longer than anyone had expected. I

wanted to do something special with her gift and the boat
navigation lights seemed fitting and proper.

I arranged for my successor in the Tadchester practice,
Dr Lichen, to come up from Tadchester and bring up
Mary, the sister who had looked after Jackie for so long.

We set off for an evening trip down the river, with
supper on board, then came back in the dark with our
navigation and searchlights on, travelling peacefully up
the river.

I said, 'This is Jackie's present to me, Mary. She's showing
us the way home.'

It was a wonderful evening and it felt as if Jackie was
with us.

The sky had a peculiar colour that night, and was lit by a
great red moon. Mary said this was only the second time in
her life that she'd seen such a moon – the day after she saw

7

her first red moon the last Great War had broken out. Happily, there were no new world wars associated with this particular moon.

Cruising along the river in the dark, gliding along slowly so as not to disturb other moored boats, had a special quality of its own. It was almost as if we were travelling in a different world.

On other night trips like this friends would sit on the bow as we headed into the darkness. It was a unique experience with the river wildlife about us. There was something very moving about it.

We were lucky that we lived on part of the Thames that enjoyed the longest stretch between two locks. It was seven miles from Benson Lock, just upriver from Wallingford, down to Cleeve Lock, one of the smallest locks on the Thames.

We could either go upriver, moor below Benson and go into the town, or travel downstream almost to Cleeve Lock, where the Beetle and Wedge Hotel served bar food and had a first-class dining room, and, on the opposite bank, Ye Olde Leather Bottle pub also served excellent food and beer.

We were always made welcome and given a cup of tea at the Sheridan Boat Yard just above the Leather Bottle. We'd known Andrew and his wife Jackie from previous trips over about ten years after they had opened their chandlery and boat yard.

Andrew was much travelled, a bit like Paul Theroux's *Railway Bazaar* but not yet in print. He'd been on the trans-Siberian railway across Japan, down through South America, and across India, but his days of roaming were decreasing as he began producing sons at the rate of knots. To date he'd produced three.

I was lucky to have the Maid Boat Yard, with their big hire fleet, so near to me. They would always cheerfully help me out if I was in trouble and I could take on diesel and water there. Andrew, on whom I looked as my first engineer, took care of overhauls, maintenance, as well as break-downs, new equipment, etc.

Sea Grey was 27 feet long and an Elysian class boat. She was about 9 feet in beam, which meant that she couldn't go up any of the canals as the maximum width of boats for these is 6 feet 8 ins. She had a centre cockpit and wheel-house, and two things we'd always longed for, a flush toilet (which went into a tank which had to be pumped out) and a shower.

Once the engines had been running for about ten minutes we had hot water in both front and back cabins and in the shower room. The only slight disadvantage to the water set-up was that the pump on any one tap would turn on any other taps which had been left open, including the shower.

When our daughter Jane and some friends were using the boat, one of the boys in her party was very surprised to find it started to rain warm water whilst he was sitting on the toilet in the shower room.

We were to have our maiden voyage with our friends from Devon, Joe and Lyn Church.

What a difference to other boats we'd been on together.

We could push anything we wanted down from the house by wheelbarrow – no more carrying of supplies and equipment for miles.

Our diesel fuel tank held 35 gallons and would last for a couple of weeks' travelling; and our water tank carried 120 gallons, which meant that even with four of us washing and showering we would always have enough for at least a couple of days without having to take on extra water.

It all seemed too good to be true. In the centre cockpit there was a gas refrigerator and in the main back cabin there was a gas fire as well as a gas cooking stove. The boat was extremely well designed and the hot-water tank so well lagged that after a good day's travelling we would still have hot water the following morning.

There were two single berths and a wash basin in the forecabin, then came the shower room and toilet, opposite were some shelves, cupboards and wardrobes. Steps led up to the central cockpit, which was canvas covered and could be opened up. Finally, there was a large rear cabin with two wide bunks, a pull-out table, a sink with hot and cold water, our gas oven and the gas fire.

There was plenty of deck space encompassing the whole boat, providing more than sufficient standing room for the crew manoeuvring the boat through locks.

Having loaded up everything under the sun (including a wine rack in the stern of the boat in the rudder housing) we set off on a beautiful sunny day in June, up through Wallingford to our first stop, Benson Lock, a deep lock with a beautifully maintained garden. Leaving the lock we passed through a lovely stretch of river lined by poplars just after Benson marina and boat house. We moved on, past the Shillingford Bridge Hotel, having first navigated Shillingford Bridge, to enter a stretch of river that wound through trees and meadows, passing what had once been a very stately home on the starboard side, now divided into three houses.

Further up the river we passed the entrance to the river Thame, and our next lock was Days Lock, where the lock keeper, Taffy, and his attractive ginger-haired wife always gave us a great welcome.

Taffy was a great RNLI stalwart. Apart from several fund-raising functions he had organised from his own lock, we had come across him raising money at Henley and various other spots in the year. Each year he would collect something in the order of £25,000 for the lifeboat fund.

He was also nationally famous for his 'Pooh' stick races from the footbridge just below the lock.

We moored for our first night about half way between

Days Lock and Clifton Hampden Lock. There was a lovely stretch of water meadow opposite a Cheshire Home.

It was a delightful place for dogs. Joe and Lyn had brought their border terrier and we'd brought Bertie, our white haired terrier and they were having the time of their lives. There were some lovely little beaches, rat- and rabbit-holes, as well as the river: it was a dog's paradise.

We were so far away from habitation that we were rarely bothered by fishermen or walkers. It was at least two miles to Clifton Hampden bridge and the Barley Mow made famous by Jerome K. Jerome's *Three Men in a Boat*.

We had an early morning breakfast, then travelled up river through Clifton Hampden Lock to the deep lock at Culham, with a glimpse of some beautiful barns and the multi-pastel-shaded Culham House. A slow cruise through the lock cut ended on a broad sweep of river leading into Abingdon.

Approaching Abingdon by river is quite beautiful. You first come to some of the oldest parts of Abingdon, with almshouses, churches and various other old buildings lining the river bank. There's one of the best chandleries on the river below the bridge, then on past the bridge on the left bank there's a park and a swimming pool and mooring for a good mile on the right.

We paid for a night's mooring in Abingdon, and this included a free ticket to Abingdon jail. (This didn't mean we were incarcerated for the night – the jail's been converted to a sports centre!)

Many a time previously we'd lunched at the Nag's Head pub on Abingdon Bridge, shopped in town, then gone above Abingdon Lock to moor for the night where there are open fields, streams and waterfalls.

Sadly for us, but due to promotion for him, our old friend the keeper at Abingdon Lock, Jack, had gone down river to run the old Windsor Lock. As a general principle the further you went down the river the larger it became, and the locks were much busier. We tended to go upstream where it was less crowded and the scenery more rural.

One problem I had to contend with on this maiden voyage was that once again I had a kidney stone, and, hoping to pass it, I was drinking gallons of water.

All this water meant that I had to get up in the night from time to time, and rather than disturb Joe and Lyn, who were in the forecabin, next to the toilet, I used to loosen the side covers in the cockpit and (albeit against the rules) would try and increase the volume of the river Thames. My symptoms told me I was near to passing the stone, so I stepped up my drinking rate.

One night I crept out at about two in the morning, undid the hatch covers, took up the appropriate posture and started to discharge my cargo into the Thames. Suddenly there was a tremendous splash as a rock plunged into the river, accompanied by a hoot of laughter.

'Your stone's gone all right now, Skipper,' said Joe from the bunk cabin.

Apparently he'd been sitting up half the night waiting for me to lean over the side. Once I was literally in full stream he had thrown in a boulder to encourage me.

In fact, I did not pass this particular stone until several weeks later.

Fortunately, apart from the first two stones that I had (one of which I passed in the middle of the Sahara and was absolute agony), further stones never seemed to bother me much. They caused only discomfort rather than pain.

Above Abingdon Lock we passed Nuneham Courteney, a beautiful old building with a folly and acres of landscaped fields. Radley College boathouse soon appeared, then we tackled the biggest lock on the river, Sandford Lock. A short cruise took us on to Iffley Lock, one of the prettiest locks which still had rollers to push the skips and punts over by hand, then we chugged down through Oxford, under Folly Bridge and into the town itself. The river here was almost like a street, with houses and allotments on each bank. We motored up to Osney Lock, which is followed by Osney Bridge, the lowest bridge on the river and which must have nearly decapitated many boaters. One year, on a hire boat, when Jane was about four years old, we had forgotten she was on the top deck, only remembering when we were halfway under the bridge. Fortunately she had the good sense to lie flat. We could have had a catastrophe.

We continued along the river cut up to Bossoms Boat Yard, where the river widened with the vast area of Port Meadows on the right bank which looked like the Camargue with horses and cows – it was a different world. We passed the Perch Inn on our left, which could be reached by an old landing stage, and journeyed on up to Godstow Lock, the last of the automatic locks. The lock keeper here is a fellow author and has written a first-class book on the middle Thames.

Through Godstow Lock, we passed the ruined priory, a difficult bridge, then the famous Trout Inn where you could get smoked-salmon sandwiches and where everybody who was anybody went to see and be seen. Starlets, dons, actors, politicians, all the fashionable, would sit round in the grounds with its tumbling waterfalls, peacocks and giant trout.

Leaving Godstow Lock we joined a completely different kind of Thames. It wound and twisted and from then on all the locks were manually operated and everything seemed to be at a slower pace. When the lock keepers were at lunch or were out working on the sluices we worked the locks ourselves.

The river steadily narrowed and on this first voyage we were blessed all the time by sunshine. We passed on, winding our way through countryside with marvellous views. From Kings Lock, the first of the manual locks, we journeyed to Eynsham. Our next lock was Pink Hill Lock having first passed a great reservoir on the left bank. Further on up river was a huge caravan/mobile home park on the right bank stretching upstream and ending at the Ferry Boat Inn. This view was unsightly, and not in keeping with this gentler part of the Thames. It was like a sudden lump of suburbia smack in the middle of the countryside. However, this was balanced by the amount of pleasure it must have given to the hundreds of people who came to stay there. It was ideal for family holidays.

A boat such as *Sea Grey* called for a certain amount of daily maintenance. I know nothing about engines and am no good at anything mechanical and had to be instructed on all the various things I had to do.

Each day I had to tighten two screws to make sure there was plenty of grease on the propeller shaft. I had to check the water level in the exchange radiator tank, and the oil level. I had to check the filter where the water-cooling system brought water in from the river, and clean it of any leaves or debris that might be choking it.

I had to start up the bilge pump to see if any bilge water came out from the bilge. The engine compartment was shut off from the rest of the boat and was not connected to the bilge area. If you pumped out your engine compartment in the same way you would have polluted the river with oil, so it had to be done on to the bank into some receptacle where it could be disposed of.

Normally there was nothing of any quantity in the engine compartment, just a little oily water in the channel at the bottom.

On our third day out, however, I noticed that we had collected a pool of blue fluid, not in the bottom of the engine compartment, but in an isolated area on one side. I thought it strange it didn't drain away and eventually I tackled the offending liquid with a mug and bucket. I managed to clear out several buckets and chucked the contents on to the bank, only to have the space fill up again. It also seemed to have a peculiar smell.

Joe, who knows much more about things mechanical than I do, was holding himself with laughter. 'Do you realise what's happened, Skip?' he said.

'No,' I replied.

'I'm afraid our flush toilet mustn't be flushed any more,' he chuckled. 'The holding tank is leaking into the engine compartment.'

And so it was. So, for the rest of our voyage, having liberally filled the engine compartment with Dettol, we had to go back to using public toilets, banks and bushes and when we got back home the Maid Boat Yard fitted a new bottom to our effluent tank.

Otherwise this first trip on our new boat was absolute heaven. The river was almost empty. We cruised up to Newbridge, having a meal at the Rose Revived on my birthday, past Radcott, where there'd been a terrible battle during the Civil War (you could almost feel and see

16

Cavaliers and Roundheads fighting on the bridge). Then as far as we could go with our boat, the last lock, St John's Lock, and on to Lechlade town, whose church stood out for miles.

Joe, who wasn't satisfied that we'd gone far enough, hired a rowing boat for the day and rowed it up to Cricklade.

We had a couple of days at Lechlade then ambled slowly down river, mooring each night out in the wild, enjoying pub lunches en route, eating on the boat at night to classical music on our tape recorder with lovely sunsets and unbroken beautiful weather.

Finally, we drifted back to our home territory, Abingdon, Culham, Clifton Hampden, Days, Benson Lock and Wallingford Bridge, easing up as we passed the Maid Boat Yard. Slowly we nudged our way (with perfect manoeuvring by the skipper) to our own landing stage at the bottom of the garden.

How very, very lucky we were. The sun doesn't always shine but it had for us those ten days and it had been quite perfect.

CHAPTER 3

Taking it Easy

Among the greatest joys of retirement are not having to get up early in the morning, not having to work weekends and, above all, not being called out of bed at night.

It took me some weeks to adjust to the fact that my sleep was not going to be disturbed. I felt guilty about enjoying this luxury after so many years of broken nights.

I love the mornings. Our radio alarm is set for 8 o'clock but the central heating gently coming on at 7 a.m. usually wakes me. About the same time I hear the thud of the morning papers falling from the letter box, accompanied by a growl from Bertie, our West Highland terrier. Confined to the kitchen at night, Bertie cannot make his usual terrifying leap at the letterbox, but his growl shows that the guardian of the house is up and alert and ready to take on all comers.

About 7.30 a.m. I hear the postman lean his bike against the wall then a patter as he pushes the day's post through the door. I try and guess how many letters have been delivered, hoping for a win on the football pools or at least a £50 premium bond prize.

Usually it is bills and a fistful of circulars which begin:

'You have been specially selected to take part in a draw for an enormous amount of money providing you take on approval a priceless book (or some other exclusive and valuable item) for half its worth.' A tremendous number of people want to insure me, give me unsecured loans or invest my money for me. With the wood pulp involved in the production of the circulars, it is a wonder there are any trees left standing.

I am spared the mass of giveaway medical magazines that used to fill my dustbin when I was in practice. Now I have some time on my hands I would quite enjoy them. But on asking why these journals were no longer arriving, I was informed that now I was retired I would have to pay for them.

I still receive the *British Medical Journal*, but this is the retired version and does not include the jobs section, which was the only thing I used to read.

I am no longer interested in such papers as 'Cytopatho-genic Protein in Filtrates for Cultures of Propionibacterium' or 'Acnes Isolated from Patients with Kawasaki Disease', though, to be honest, even when I was at my medical and intellectual peak I wouldn't have understood them.

The radio alarm goes off at 8 o'clock to be followed by the news headlines, and this is the signal for my wife, Pam, to get up and make me a cup of tea. This sounds like male chauvinism at its worst, but it is by mutual agreement.

A patient once gave me a teasmade and I loved the early-morning drama of it. You were first awakened as it started to bubble. The bubbling increased in tempo until the final climax of water coming to the boil, steam gushing out and the kettle tipping into the pot. At the same time a light came on and the alarm rang. It was just like a small volcano going off in your ear. It must have been invented by someone who lived near the San Andreas Fault who, knowing that one day they were going to be in a real earthquake, could practice by having a small one every morning.

I loved the teasmade, but Pam hated it. Not only did she lie awake all night listening for it, almost jump out of her skin when the alarm, light and teamaking all suddenly burst into action, but also had to suffer a rotten cup of tea because the pot hadn't been warmed first. She much prefers to get up and make a good cup of tea herself.

On the rare occasions that I actually get up with a fit of conscience and make the tea, it seems to unsettle her for the day, so I lie back and enjoy being spoilt.

While Pam is brewing up, Bertie is let out into the garden for morning ablutions. Then, as Pam enters the bedroom with the morning post, papers and tea, he comes hurtling on to the bed, has a quick lick of my nose then dashes off to look out of the window, front paws on the sill, back legs up straight, like a pair of white jodhpurs.

From the window, Bertie has a panoramic view of all the ground down to the river. We have a lawn in front of the house, then the service road for our row of houses. Beyond this is a long lawn leading to some concrete hardstanding, a further stretch of lawn, a public right of way and finally a grassy bank and the concrete steps of our mooring with a small slipway where our boat, *Sea Grey*, rocks gently at her moorings.

The right of way is a favourite walking place for dogs, and Bertie, from the security of the bedroom, can threaten any canine. From behind the window, he doesn't care how big they are.

People do not always appreciate that the right of way is through someone's garden so dogs tend to be slipped off leads as soon as they leave the main boat yard, one garden away, rather than kept restrained for another hundred yards until they reach the fields and towpath proper.

It does mean that we have some of the best manured grass in the district and it's important to inspect your shoes carefully if you walk down to the river.

Picnickers and fishermen do not always quite appreciate that I haven't actually cut and trimmed my lawn just for them, and that there are several miles of other river bank at their disposal. One of my neighbours tried the tactful approach and asked a very persistent group of picnickers if it would be all right if he took his tea round to their house!

The vast majority of people are careful, but the small minority seem hell bent on destruction and will uproot anything uprootable and pinch anything movable.

Now and again I protest if I find a dozen bikes on my bank with their owners scrabbling all over my boat. My remonstrations are usually followed by a posse of small boy cyclists, riding up and down the road shouting 'Fatty!' or 'Baldy!' every time they pass the house. It's very annoying when you're both fat and bald.

Any of them who ask permission to fish are given it and we rarely move anyone on if they are harmlessly enjoying themselves. We feel very privileged to enjoy the facilities we have and it seems a pity not to share them.

Our concrete hardstanding is a legacy from the last war. It runs right from the boatyard and on through the front lawns-cum-water-meadows of the last six houses of the

cul-de-sac. American troops had used it to practise river crossings and bridge building.

Our neighbour, a retired physician, asked a builder for an estimate to remove his bit. The builder quoted £50 and said he would have it done the next afternoon. Three days later they were still hard at it with power drills and bulldozers – the concrete was 12 feet thick.

Back to bed. I read the post and newspaper headlines then Pam appears again with my breakfast; cereal and a piece of toast with honey. She really spoils me, but it does mean that breakfast is now out of the way.

A friend, Trevor Robinson, once staying with us, watched this ritual and then said 'My God, Bob, you're lucky to have her.' I replied 'She's lucky to have me.' 'Yes,' said Trevor, 'but you're luckier than she is.'

By the time I've bathed, wshed, shaved and dressed, it's almost coffee time. After that, there's the rest of the day to play with.

Pam takes Bertie for his daily walk along the towpath. I square my conscience by saying it's good for her hip – she had a hip replacement some years ago.

On his walk, Bertie meets some of the dogs he's uttered abuse at earlier in the morning. He has an infallible technique if he meets a really big dog – he jumps straight in the river and hides under the bank.

One day we lost him completely and he was found by a lady who kept a horse by the towpath, shivering in the water almost hidden from view.

But all people and most dogs are Bertie's friends and he races up and down with Lally, Bock and Lilly, his three special friends, full of the joys of doghood.

Meanwhile I check the boat's moorings, pump out the bilge if necessary and generally mess about.

About once a week we have lunch at the delightful Trapp's Wine Bar in Wallingford, a place to meet friends as well as to eat and drink. It is underneath the Lamb Arcade, an old hotel rescued by the community and developed into a collection of about twenty antique and craft shops, with a first-class secondhand bookshop and a restaurant on the top floor.

Near the Lamb is the lovely old coaching inn, The George, which way back in about 1200 was owned by a Mr Baynton. Pam's maiden name was Baynton and we always hoped that one day, through some ancestral link, we would find we owned it.

There are many first-class eating places in Wallingford. Stoney's down by the bridge compares with any London restaurant. Across the road behind Wallingford Bridge, Boats is the curry house. There are also first-class Indian, Chinese and Greek restaurants. Many of the pubs serve full meals and bar food. There is Upstairs Downstairs in the precinct and the Egon Ronay guide *Have a Bite* recommended Annie's Restaurant, in the Wantage Road.

The old Row Barge pub changed its name to the Little House and produced a full-blown dining room. In addition there are several cafés, sandwich and pie shops. Eating must appear high on the list of any industries in Wallingford.

Market day is Friday with stalls piled with fruit, veg and flowers; there's also a fish stall and the usual accompanying array of clothes, cooking utensils and other nicknacks for sale.

We have our own excellent fresh fish and game shop coupled with a delicatessen shop, and half a dozen butchers some of whom still wear traditional boaters.

I started both a Philosophy class and an English class but, through various other commitments, reluctantly had to give them up. I particularly missed the English class which consisted of twenty-eight ladies and me – just the right proportion.

Wallingford is famous for its authors. Rex Warner, who wrote *Aerodrome*, was still alive when I arrived in the town, but unfortunately I never met him. Agatha Christie's boathouse is a hundred yards from our garden, and Jerome K. Jerome lived across the river in Ewelme. I hoped that some of this writing aura might rub off on me.

Wallingford Castle, or what is left of it, has been opened up as a park and you can stroll round the grounds climbing to the highest point after crossing the drawbridge, leading to a platform where there is a panoramic view for miles around.

Fundamentally, I am lazy and I find that Wallingford has all the facilities for busily doing nothing, at which I claim to be an expert.

Our Norman first came into our lives in Tadchester, when I was laid off work with chest pains, just before I had a coronary bypass. I was unable to do any heavy physical work and we needed some help in the garden. Norman volunteered and gradually became part of the family. His duties eventually included staying in the house and looking after Bertie (who loved him) when we were away.

After many years of working as a printer, he could have retired comfortably on his pensions but he preferred to do two or three days' work a week, as well as maintaining a big allotment, so that he could travel to the four corners of the earth which he literally did. This year he is off to Barcelona in the spring, Moscow and Leningrad in the autumn, squeezing in his annual month's touring in France in between.

To our great delight he had moved to Wallingford before us, since two of his children lived nearby. When we arrived he immediately resumed all his former tasks. He'd sometimes come round for a meal or we'd dine out together. We had a lovely couple of days on the river, just the three of us in *Sea Grey*, pottering up to Sandford Lock, just below Oxford.

He was the first of the clan of old friends and relatives who started to settle around us in Wallingford.

By sheer chance an old friend, Joan Gore, who we'd known since before the War, arrived in Wallingford. She didn't come because she knew us, in fact I don't think she knew we were there. She was later followed by her brother and sister. Then one of those strange coincidences, if they are coincidences, happened. I had some cousins up north – three boys. I hadn't seen them since my Bevin Boy days back in 1945–46, when they were tiny short-trousered tearaways. One of them, the oldest, Anthony, took a degree at Manchester University, then went into the air force as a pilot where, amongst other things, he won the Nato bombing award.

After doing a spell in the RAF he was seconded to the Saudi Air Force and he and his wife, Eunice, stayed out in Saudi for another ten years.

They had two sons just leaving school in the Isle of Man and felt if a job turned up on their next leave, they'd have to stay. If they left it much later the settling down in England again would be even more difficult and although they loved the Saudi life, they appreciated they couldn't stay there for ever. One day I had a 'phone call from Anthony's father to say Anthony had moved to Wallingford, 300 yards away from us – it was quite incredible.

They turned out to be a delightful couple, and it was a great comfort to know we had blood relatives in the town. Anthony was employed by a merchant bank and Eunice was working for the British Trust for Conservation Volunteers, which continues to grow in importance and makes a tremendous contribution to present-day society.

I wonder, are these things coincidences? A lot of philosophers have believed in the existence of overall patterns to our lives and that some people will keep turning up in them. Certainly I have noticed that there are some people I am always bumping into. And what, for example, are the chances of two cousins who hadn't met for nearly forty years, arriving unplanned in the same town to live 300 yards from each other?

Tony Murphy, a friend with whom I was at medical school, is one such example. When I was in practice in Tadchester, we twice bumped into him when we were on holiday in St Ives and he was on leave from his work in Mombassa. He, like Anthony and Eunice, felt that you had to return home at some stage and, by chance, he came to a practice in Reading and Pam bumped into him one day in a supermarket.

So we really were blessed and felt we did belong, in addition we had excellent neighbours and the whole small cul-de-sac we lived in, looked out for each other. We were indeed very lucky.

It all added to the fullness of life. It meant at the least that when one or all of us had flu, we could make sympathetic noises down the phone to each other. We weren't isolated strangers in a foreign land.

But Wallingford was that sort of place. It had an aura of something special about it, quite what I don't know, but I know of no other place where there are so many community projects going on and with so many people giving up their time voluntarily to see that they are carried out.

I remember so well the words of three wise old men

many years before when asked for the answer to life's problems or society's problems. They said: 'It's not better systems, it's just better people we need,' and Wallingford certainly seemed to have more than its share of these.

I have always maintained that cheaper travel and easier access to different countries could be a main factor in achieving world peace. We would find that people who lived in other countries weren't strange or alien creatures, but ordinary people like you and me.

The twinning of towns was a great step in that direction. Luxeil les Bains was twinned with Wallingford and when their orchestra came over to play in the town, we put up a couple of the visiting musicians. Our guests were a delightful girl from Reims, who was studying the cello, and a professor from Montpelier, who had the most superb baritone voice.

We made two new friends and there were two new places on the Continent where we would always be welcome; and they, of course, knew that they would always be welcome to return here.

They gave us a splendid concert in the Corn Exchange, a theatre-cum-cinema, despite a horrendous forty-hour coach journey.

Perhaps we'd return the visit when Wallingford visited Luxeil les Bains.

I did learn one thing from their stay: I'd always pronounced Reims like 'reams', but the French pronunciation is 'rance' – why, I don't know. This reminded me of the day I tried to find the Devon village of Woolfardisworthy – nobody knew it when I asked for it by name, apparently locally it was always pronounced as Woolsery.

By comparison Rance for Reims is just small beer. French beer, of course.

CHAPTER 4

Family Affairs

It was our turn to be hosts at Christmas. I really am turning into an old stick-in-the-mud.

The children with their new homes had bagged the last two Christmases. We had the first with daughter Jane and son Trevor at Brighton, where they completely spoiled us. The only disadvantage about their accommodation is that it's up four flights of stairs, which would have been fine if we hadn't had Bertie with us – it's an awful long way to go to take him to find a lamp-post and a much longer way to find a precious piece of greensward to complete his daily rituals.

They were very proud of their flat and really gave us a smashing time.

The next year it had to be the turn of our other son, Paul, and his wife, Gill. Their home is at Cirencester, where we had a repeat of the same formula. We were extremely lucky that we were able to gather as a family on these occasions. Daisy May, our new granddaughter was, of course, the centre of attention this Christmas, but being only about five months old, she wasn't too aware of what was going on.

So now it was our turn. They were all coming, Jane, Trevor, Gill, Paul, Daisy May, and Gill's parents, Eddie and Liz. We put mattresses from the boat in my study for Paul and Gill, Trevor slept on a camp bed in the lounge and Jane shared a room with Daisy May and it was her Christmas. Her main present was a Noddy Car – I think we were all more excited about it than she was.

Gill was ready with her ciné camera to film Daisy May getting up on Christmas morning and finding the car. Through the lens, Gill was able to capture for ever the look of astonishment on Daisy May's face at seeing this new gift, of her exploring it and climbing into it.

We had a great Christmas and we were so lucky that our children – of course, they were no longer children – were getting on so well.

Trevor had turned into a fine actor. I thought his series *Star Cops* on BBC 2 was excellent. It was hoped that it would go on to BBC 1 and they would do a second series – perhaps it will, but nothing to date.

He made a film called *Drowning by Numbers,* which he said his mother wouldn't want to see as his wife drowns him at sea. In fact, when they were filming it off Southwold on the Suffolk coast in October they hadn't rehearsed the drowning scene explicitly before they did the take and it was very realistic – he accidentally took a mouthful of water the first time she pushed him under and he really thought he was going to drown. Then, in the cold of October, he had to lie naked on the beach while they filmed him being resuscitated, or filmed people trying to resuscitate him because in the story he perishes.

(Not in the script, his wife, who had done this dastardly deed, nearly died of hypothermia.)

He was enjoying a variety of engagements: an advertisement for Schweppes in New Zealand; an educational film for the Inland Revenue; a commercial for a washing machine where he was in drag as one of two ugly sisters; a commercial in Dublin; and something he could really get his teeth into – three months at the Manchester Royal Exchange Theatre in *Twelfth Night*, where he was to play Sir Toby Belch.

Paul had taken a new job, when an opportunity came up. This was a step forward for him and just his cup of tea. He joined a newish firm selling an American product – and it meant Paul going off to Chicago two or three weeks a year for training, and a business conference in Florida. The firm was going to go into Europe and he was already destined to accompany one of the senior officials from the firm to visit Austria, Switzerland, Italy and Spain.

It seemed an extremely good company and when Paul was making his first trip to Chicago, they arranged for Paul and Gill to say the night at a Manchester hotel so Gill could see him off.

Paul loved Chicago, and what I thought was most refreshing was that the American head of the firm talked to him and explained that they were a firm that held on to the old values; they weren't 'fly by night' sales people; they had a product they believed in. He said 'For example, we've just asked our suppliers to increase their prices, which sounds crazy, but it isn't. They give us a good product and we don't want them to go out of business. We want the best, and so when one of my workmen comes in and complains that the materials he's working with aren't good enough, I'm not upset by this, I'm pleased. It means he believes in what he's doing, and I see he gets the better stuff, and that's the way we work.' This is similar to my own philosophy and I know it tallies with Paul's; I wouldn't wish him any other job. It's quite amazing that in a three-year period he's moved from a dull, routine job, from which he seemed to have no escape, to a post with an electronic component firm, slowly building up his confidence and travelling all over England, to now, a couple of years later, an international company salesman, travelling all over the world.

At the same time Gill, a trained jeweller and artist, had

31

begun to sell card designs to Gordon Fraser. They, too, seemed extremly nice people to work for and she made enough from her first batch of cards to buy herself a little car. This meant she would be able to come and see us more often and, now her husband was a world traveller, she would have a bit more freedom of movement.

. Jane was still the night stage doorkeeper at the Brighton Theatre Royal and although Jane always did find kind things to say about people, she met many famous theatrical people on pre-London runs down there and she always spoke of how nice they were to her.

During the day she plugged away at her dressmaking business, cutting out and designing clothes, then taking to market.

It was extremely heavy going and working on her own wasn't too much fun. Although she had some very good days, by the time she'd earned a bit of money, she had usually run out of material, so most of her takings went into purchasing material for her next batch. Her profit margins were too small and she wasn't a businesswoman.

She'd become a very able seamstress but was beginning to show signs of wanting to travel and this costs money. She was nursing a great ambition to go to New Zealand and although I had tentatively brought the subject up in the past, this time she accepted my advice and went on a shorthand-typing and word-processing course. This would mean that wherever she went she could always do some temping. It wouldn't stop her carrying on with her dressmaking once she'd learnt her new found skills, but at least she'd have another string to her bow.

In the Easter holidays, she had a marvellous week skiing in Austria with her friend, also called Jane. Prior to her holiday she was almost a vegetarian, and was not very good at getting up in the mornings, but a week in Austria made all the difference. They were up at 7 a.m. to tackle steeper and steeper slopes, and they came home in the evenings literally exhausted. Most of the food on offer was meat, potatoes and dumplings, and for that week all thoughts of being a vegetarian vanished. Both girls ate every bit.

They had only one accident, when they came down one of the steepest slopes at about 100 miles an hour and ran into each other, but apart from a few bruises they were both all right.

Of the fourteen group members that started the course only six survived. On the last day the instructor took them up a very high mountain (from Jane's description you'd have thought it was Everest). He just said, 'Right ho, off you go,' and off they went. But they came back sunburnt, full of beans and raring to go.

Pam integrated well into Wallingford. We both joined the Sinodian Players as non-active players – this was the nearby theatre-cum-cinema run by local people. Pam also helps out at the local Oxfam shop and the Wallingford Museum, which puts on two or three excellent exhibitions a.year. They were held in one of the oldest houses in the town, the Old Flint House.

I have become, I'm afraid, very lazy. I'm not a great gardener, but will cut the grass when necessary. I was very happy fiddling about with the boat and have helped out with the annual regatta. The first two regattas in which we were involved, although held on the first weekend in May, were bitterly cold.

We were the 'long start', which meant I had to take *Sea Grey* to pick up various items of equipment – tents, chairs, etc. – and people who were running the start, and take them down river to the point where the long river races used to be started, opposite Carmell College, a boys' boarding school.

I never realised what a complicated business it was.

There were about six or seven radio links with various points down the river, and teams of Sea Scouts had to man the stake boats, from which they held on to the back of race boats and steadied them before they set off.

I had some help from Bernard and Joyce Walter, some

33

old friends from Woolhampton. Bernard helped row the boys to and from the stake boats, and our boat, being the only warm place to shelter, became a mobile canteen. Joyce made over a hundred cups of tea for these little lads, who came on board with chattering teeth and gradually warmed up before they had to return to do their next stint on the boats.

The third year we were due to be at the long start with the biggest entry Wallingford had ever had for its regatta – 250 boats. I think it was about the third largest in the country and there were going to be races from eight in the morning till seven o'clock at night.

We had good cooking facilities on *Sea Grey* and anticipating warming up little boys and starting officials in bitterly cold weather, Pam got in a whole pile of beefburgers, with Coke for the younger members and whisky for the starters and senior officials. We set off, leaving our mooring at seven o'clock in the morning, and went down river as far as the Spastic Training College, which was the finishing post where all the officials and equipment were waiting. We picked up all the necessary gear and officials and headed back up river, ready for the first race at eight o'clock.

We had jumpers, anoraks, mackintoshes – everything for cold, wet weather – and it turned out to be one of the sunniest, hottest days of the year. It was absolutely glorious.

Fortunately the fridge was working and by chance we had a dozen cans of beer on board. I don't know how many races actually took place but with 250 crews and quarter finals, semi-finals and finals, the regatta seemed endless. What impressed me most were all the people who gave their time to this exhausting day. By the time all the races were over and we had collected up the equipment, plus one odd rowing boat we found abandoned on the way, it was about 8.30 p.m. when we got back to the race finish at the Spastic headquarters, a lovely building with a

34

beautiful lawn, loaned by the Society for many of the bigger social occasions held in Wallingford.

We got back to our mooring at about nine.

People were still working, pulling up buoys, taking down flags and markers – for many it had been approximately a fourteen-hour day, a real community effort.

Luckily this year, all had gone well. The previous year I'd commented on how refreshing it was to see all these young men tugging their hearts out against each other, literally hundreds of them, and what a good omen it was for the future etc., not knowing that at that very moment officials were shutting the bar at race headquarters because some louts had started to throw things about and abuse the people who were serving. There was a fight with the police, arrests and all sorts of goings on.

On the day of this regatta such problems had been forestalled. Some 'heavies' had been brought in to protect the establishment so there were no troubles at base and a most successful day was had by everyone.

I contributed very little, just appearing for a day with my boat, enjoying an outing in the sunshine.

Wallingford is certainly not short of community spirited people who give a tremendous amount of time to organise and set up this occasion. Because of people like this we are able to enjoy the theatres, the carnival, music in Wallingford Castle and St Peter's Church and many other functions.

So long as communities like this flourish I think society has nothing to fear. If there were more places with the spirit and enterprise of Wallingford, how much less the troubles in society would be.

CHAPTER 5

Encore Portugal

We felt that we would like some sun on our backs before the year closed. Having enjoyed one winter holiday in Portugal, we thought we'd go for another at the tag end of the season, so we set off for Lagos on the Algarve.

We'd loved the previous holiday in Faro, the capital of the Algarve, in the winter. We realised we were rather spoilt then as there weren't too many planes about and the planes weren't too big. On this particular trip we were on a wide-bodied jet and it seemed to arrive at Faro airport with about six other wide-bodied jets, all unloading at the same time and there was a tremendous scramble for luggage. You have to be fit to travel by plane nowadays.

There were scores of buses waiting to take passengers to their hotels.

Our departure from Faro airport at the end of our holiday was worse than our arrival as all the communication systems, the computer boards detailing flight times, had broken down, a couple of planes had engine trouble and the passengers had been waiting twelve hours to board.

There was a seething mass of people all wondering if they were going to fly out that night, and whoever was speaking over the public address system would never win a prize for English pronunciation: it was unintelligible.

We had a two-hour journey to our hotel, dropping people off at various places en route, passing near Albufeira which now, alas, could be mistaken for a popular Spanish resort with thousands of hotels and thousands more going up. We caught a beautiful view of the fishing town of Portimao with a huge sardine restaurant at the side of the bridge. There were rows and rows of tables and a hazy sardine smoke floating above the whole area – it looked most appetising. We had to drop some people off at Praia da Rocha which, although having lovely hotels and beautiful beaches, seemed like Albufeira trying to catch up with Spain.

And then on to our hotel, the Hotel de Lagos, which was quite beautiful and seemed to have twice as many lounges, all beautifully clean and appointed, as it did residents.

Our room was pleasant, but the dining room was rather disappointing. It was a bit like being back at school: you had to queue for a place, you sat where the waiter put you, and the food was very limited.

There was one financial puzzle that I could never work out. A notice outside the dining room stated that the cost of a meal was 2,000 escudos, however, if you decided not to eat in the dining room and opted for a meal in the grill bar, the hotel would give you 500 escudos towards your meal in the grill bar, which would cost considerably more than 2,000. I had the feeling that they were gaining on me somewhere.

On asking our courier about the food she said that all these things were cut down to such fine profit margins that their tour company wasn't even going to send tourists to this particular hotel that winter, which was a terrible shame. It was superbly equipped, the Portuguese were their usual charming selves, but of course they had to make a profit.

But the setting, a beautiful ascending staircase as you

38

came in the main gateway, lovely pillared landings, great deep armchairs in scattered lounges, pleasant bars – really first-class food was meant to go with these surroundings.

We did eat out a couple of times, which proved inexpensive and certainly better than the hotel fare. However, the food in the grill bar was superb.

There was a regular bus service to a beach ten minutes away where there were miles and miles of sand and for a very small sum you could hire a sun shade. The hotel also had its own swimming pool and restaurant there.

What amazed us was that the beach was empty, at most there were half a dozen people sitting on it, so it worked out to about two miles each. The water was warm, the swimming was good, but when you went past the wooden palings to get into the enclosure where the swimming pool and restaurant were, perhaps because it was Portugal, the people there looked as if they were in a sardine tin. There were probably a couple of hundred oiled bodies lying side by side, taking up every inch of space around the pool, and a dozen people actually in the pool itself. There was a very good restaurant at the side where inexpensively you could buy anything from a sandwich to a five-course meal, with wine, beers, the lot. It really was lovely.

I tried to reason out why everyone stuck round the pool and didn't go into the sea. I thought: well, I was young once, and I wanted to be where the crumpet was; but when I looked at the pool, quite a number of the people there were rather large ladies of the older age group wearing bikinis that were gestures rather than pieces of wearing apparel – not a pretty sight.

Lagos was a lovely little town. With its monument of Henry the Navigator on the sea front it was one of the places where it was thought he might have had his school of navigation, certainly the Governor's Palace was his headquarters.

It was a nice place to wander around. We went to the small unmarked arcade, a white two-storeyed building,

where the first slave auctions used to be held. There is the delightful St Anthony's Chapel with its carvings, beautiful altar, and on the floor, the tomb of an Irishman, Hugh Beatty, who was something to do with the Portuguese army in the eighteenth century. We visited the museum, the brewery, but enjoyed more strolling around the streets and shops which were often cool, shaded by tall buildings either side, with restaurants setting tables all the way down the middle of the street.

As far as I could see, the whole of the population of Lagos lived on a diet of grilled sardines. There were plenty of good bistros and bars to eat and drink in. It was not as big a town or quite as interesting a town as Faro, but a pleasant town and there's something about towns that makes them so much nicer than resorts. You felt that you were in Portugal and there were local people earning a living all around you; you weren't as yet in a faceless, concrete jungle as so many places in the sun are becoming.

Happily, the Portuguese, unlike the Spanish, are determined not to be taken over by the British and are now pulling down all English signs offering fish and chips, cream teas, etc., and replacing them with Portuguese equivalents.

We went for a coach trip into the mountains to see a most spectacular view, staying for a time and going round the old city of Silves. When the Moors occupied the Algarve in the eighth century, Silves was the capital, and their headquarters. Over the years the rivers leading to the sea have become silted up, but in those days Silves was a very important port and an almost impregnable castle was built on top of a hill. It wasn't until the middle of the thirteenth century that the Portuguese actually captured and threw out the Moors for good, and later transferred the capital of the Algarve from there to Faro, where it remains today.

There is an extremely well preserved castle and lovely cathedral adjoining it in the midst of this beautiful countryside.

Our day trip to the mountains was marred by the fact that we were two hours picking people up from other hotels on the way up and two hours dropping them off on the way back and, of course, we had several obligatory stops at various gift shops.

In spite of all that, we had a lovely day. The view for miles from the top of the mountains and certainly Silves were well worth a visit – you can't have everything.

This applied to our hotel and its food. The hotel was superb, the food was moderate with a very limited selection. You queued and were shown to a different place each evening which you shared with another couple.

We were lucky that all the people we met were nice; a few were quite fascinating.

The first couple were the Maguires. He was a salesman for an electronics company and she a nurse at a private nursing home. We saw quite a lot of Pat and Joy whilst we were there, going to the beach with them several times. They had some great stories to tell.

Pat was an Irish Roman Catholic from Belfast and obviously had been a bit of a wild lad in his younger days, and Joy was English and Protestant. The couple had met in England and had been going out together for some time when, though almost penniless, they decided to get engaged. They felt that Pat's parents in Ireland should be informed and that Pat should go home and tell them personally.

They clubbed together all the money they had, which would just pay the fare to Belfast, and Joy was set to have a few days on her own.

On the first day she bumped into her father, a poet who wandered in and out of their lives. On finding that Pat had gone to Ireland on his own because they hadn't enough money for them both to go, he produced money for an air ticket for Joy. She would be able to catch up with Pat and meet his thirteen brothers and sisters and his parents when he broke the news to them about his engagement to an English Protestant.

42

She had her hair done in a beehive, put her best silver fox fur round her neck (she'd bought it at an Oxfam shop), and set off for Belfast, tracking down Pat's address, eventually finding the right street and at last the right house.

She knocked on the door. A dark-haired young girl answered.

'I'm Pat's girlfriend,' said Joy.

'Which one?' said the girl.

This put Joy back a bit. 'Well,' she said, 'could I come in and see him?'

'I'm afraid you can't,' said the girl. 'He's in England.'

Pat had never made it to Ireland. With the money for his air fare in his pocket he'd bumped into somebody with whom he'd done his national service. They'd gone off to have one drink and by the time they'd finished reminiscing, he had no money left for his fare. He daren't go and face Joy.

Joy was eventually invited in and had to inform the family that she was Pat's fiancée. Eventually it all got sorted and and they later got married and had children: but Pat's mother, Joy said, always used to say, 'You've never looked as smart as that day you first arrived with your beehive hair-do and your fox fur round your neck, on a warm summer's day.'

The other couple with whom we became friendly were an older couple from Canada, Ken and Louise Edmondson, who were wandering around Europe. He was a strapping great man in his late sixties; a hunting, shooting, fishing man who had a farm out in the wilds in Canada somewhere. I could sit and listen to him for hours.

The stories I liked best were his Alaskan ones. He used to be taken fishing and shooting in deepest Alaska by Jack, a Canadian with the strangest accent, who was married to an Eskimo woman. Ken would tell tales of catching salmon and shooting caribou, but his stories of Jack and his Eskimo wife were the most interesting of all.

Jack used to say that his Eskimo wife literally kept him alive.

They needed to shoot twelve caribou to see them through the winter, and they'd go off to hunt them on their snow scooter. Sometimes a white-out (blizzard) would spring up and they would have to take shelter, or die. They would put the snow scooter on its side, the Eskimo wife would lay several caribou skins fur upwards on the snow by the scooter, then she and Jack would lie under another pile of caribou skins with the fur facing down. The snow would cover them and when it stopped snowing they would dig themselves out and in this way she kept them both alive.

Whilst Ken and his friends were out fishing with Jack, ever resourceful she would be busily bottling the fish they caught to store away for the winter.

Another of Ken's tales about Jack, this great brawny man of the wild, went thus.

One summer Jack had been fooling around with one or two other women in the encampment that they came to in the summer. They had a house built there, properly equipped with windows, doors, plumbing and other conveniences. This took a great deal of capital outlay as everything had to be brought from so far away.

One day after Jack had been at his shenanigans, his wife said, 'When the pilot comes from Winnipeg, will you ask him to bring me a bottle of gin?'

After the next trip to Winnipeg, the pilot duly delivered a bottle of gin.

Up to this stage Jack's wife had not mentioned anything about his extra-marital activities. She took the bottle of gin in her hand, sat down in the room with him, took a few slurps from the bottle and for the first time tackled the subject. 'I'm displeased with you,' she said, and took a few more slurps from her bottle. She added, 'In fact, I'm very displeased with you. You've been fooling around with women. You've disgraced our family name. You've made me look foolish. I'm very, very displeased with you.' She took two more slurps of gin then picked up a chair and systematically went round the house smashing every single window, knowing that the glass replacements would have to come 1,800 miles from Winnipeg. Mission accomplished she sat down, had one more gin and that was the end of the matter.

Whether he ever misbehaved again, Ken said he never knew, but they remained together. He said, 'But I did ask him about his accent. There was something odd about it; it wasn't true Canadian.' It's always difficult asking people about their accents, so Ken put it as tactfully as he could. 'Where do you hail from originally, Jack?' he said to this big Canadian trapper.

'Wolverhampton,' said Jack, and proffered no further information.

I wondered by what routes he had travelled from Wolverhampton to an isolated Eskimo settlement in north Alaska.

Another couple we sat next to one night had a daughter that once nearly became engaged to Ron Dickinson, our junior partner in Tadchester, and one night (I knew it as soon as we sat down) the couple sharing our table were a doctor and his wife from Bristol and, of course, we knew people who knew people who knew people.

All in all it was a very good holiday. The Portuguese are lovely, Portugal is lovely, there's sunshine, golden beaches and I think they're already taking steps to see it's not going to be spoilt. I expect it's because I'm getting old that I like towns rather than resorts. If I was twenty or twenty-one I expect all I would want would be sea, sun, girls and drinks. Historic places and views could always be saved for later years.

But the turmoil at the airport and an unpleasant train ride very late at night, rather put us off package holidays. The train was certainly the dirtiest, shabbiest train I've ever been on.

I noticed in each compartment an arrow indicating the

way to the luggage compartment for air travellers. Each arrow ended up at a toilet. I could see some very confused foreigners getting on this train.

It was so bad I wrote to British Rail about it, who apologised and said it was a train they were hoping to replace in the future.

Although we had had a good holiday in a very pleasant place, we thought afterwards how much easier it is to pop all your things in the back of the car and nip across the Channel to explore France which, along with outings on the Thames, was one of our great loves. And there was more of France left for me to explore than I could cover in a lifetime.

CHAPTER 6

Lucky for Some

I first met Robin Treaton on a disastrous Moroccan holiday when about fifty of us had a fortnight's tour through Morocco in a coach, staying in some frightful places, everybody being ill and nearly being lynched by the locals.

Friends you meet on holiday always swear to keep in touch, and it seldom happens. Robin Treaton was an exception. He has remained a friend ever since, and it must be at least ten years since we set out on this ill-fated expedition.

We became buddies during this trip, standing out from the rest – we were different from them. Not that we had any special talents but when we met the other members of the expedition we found, and this wasn't clear in the brochure, that this was a holiday for the under thirty-fives, and at the time Robin was forty-seven and I was fifty-three. We were practically geriatric compared with the rest, but we certainly held our own with the other males in the party, and even excelled ourselves on occasions such as when the eccentric Robin suddenly decided at 3 a.m. that the offensive toilet at this particular camp site at which we were staying needed cleaning out, and armed with palm branches he dragged me down to unblock these holes in the ground. That, plus a few buckets of water, made morning ablutions less offensive to the rest of the party.

I can quite believe Robin's story of when he was in Bangkok. Being at a loose end one evening he hired a rickshaw, and decided, under the direction of the rickshaw puller, to undertake a tour of the town's drinking establishments. Although drinking was not one of Robin's main interests, certainly not the main one, when he did sit down to drink he was one of these hollow-legged people who could drink vast quantities of alcohol without it having any great effect on him.

On this occasion they visited about ten establishments, and, defying local custom, Robin insisted that the rickshaw puller join him glass for glass on this glorified pub crawl. After twelve stops Robin was just getting into his stride, but the rickshaw puller, who probably hadn't had a square meal for a month, and was watching just about a year's wages going on drink, was out for the count. There was nothing for it other than for Robin to bodily carry his driver, dump him in his own rickshaw, get between the pulling shafts himself, and tow the chap back as far as his hotel. They had travelled further than Robin had estimated. It took him a good two hours to pull the chap along, by which time Robin was just about physically out on his feet, and the rickshaw puller sufficiently recovered to demand a fee from Robin for the evening's work.

A typical card arrived one day from Robin, who was in Turkey, to say, 'A little boy asked me if I would like a virgin. I asked him if it was his sister. "No," he said, "it's my mother."'

Robin was no Errol Flynn but was not far behind him in his success with the opposite sex. He wasn't the dashing swash-buckling type – in fact, he was almost a deadringer for Eddie 'the Eagle' Edwards of Olympic ski-jumping fame.

He resembled him facially, and seemed to have many of his mannerisms, and, as with Eddie the Eagle, they endeared him to everyone.

For many years Robin was unmarried though he always talked about his ex, which was a prolonged unmarried time with one particular lady who in the end married someone else. Although, even so he spent a lot of time with her and her new mate.

He was not really the marrying sort.

He was an engineer in a large aeronautical works in Birmingham. Part of his work necessitated travelling down to the west of England and often he would call in and stay with us.

He came on several boating trips, usually the short ones, and was very handy if the propeller got stuck. I remember our first trip with him: half the time he was diving under the boat unwinding something that had got stuck round the propeller shaft.

49

He drove a long green sporty-looking car of indeterminate age; it was always immaculate. He always meant to change it but could never afford to, mainly because all his money went on travel.

Robin went everywhere, South America, North America, India, Thailand, Nepal, Australia, and whereas most people who came back from these exotic places had stories of magnificent temples or ancient ruins, Robin would talk about the various conquests he'd made on each trip, and I would listen in envy and half belief.

He led a fairly hairy sort of life and many of the ladies he conquered on holiday had big hairy boyfriends at home, one or two of whom rang up and threatened him. Some of the ladies who went on these trips forgot to put on their wedding rings and when he came back he sometimes found there were unexpected husbands in the background who weren't always too pleased to see him.

Whatever he did he was always successful. There was something very appealing about him, just in the way you see Eddie Edwards stuffing newspaper into boots three sizes too big for him, competing against East Germans who'd been picked out as children and trained in army camps 24 hours a day to compete against the true amateurs of the world. Robin gave you this same warmhearted amateur, British feeling. But Robin, unlike Eddie the Eagle, rarely came last.

He came back disconsolate from a trip up the Nile. For once he'd been unsuccessful and for once he'd really liked somebody very much. He'd fallen for an American girl who, at the end of the trip, went back to her homeland, and America is much more difficult to commute to from Birmingham than is, say, Solihull or even London, so he had to pursue her from a distance.

Robin called this his 'lucky' year.

It began when somebody crashed into his car in a car park and went off without leaving a name and address, resulting in several hundred pounds' worth of repairs.

The next 'lucky' event happened when Robin was driving along the motorway one day. Suddenly he noticed a bouncing metal ingot coming over the barrier. By ducking just in time and pulling towards the hard shoulder the ingot smashed into the windscreen cutting into his right hand rather than his head. He could very easily have been killed.

A following motorist summoned an ambulance and all the emergency services; Robin was able to climb out of his car but he'd badly damaged his hand and, in fact, it never ever got completely better. What annoyed him most were the comments he received from everyone who attended him: 'My God, you were lucky.'

In a way he was; the ingot could have killed him but he felt that he was rather unlucky that it was *his* car that an unidentified object had collided with.

When he arrived at the hospital, they stitched him up, heard his story, and again they said how lucky he was.

Where he was definitely unlucky was that the police could not trace the owner of the ingot, so he got no compensation or insurance for the damage done to his car or the injury done to his person.

Robin did wonder from time to time what you had to do to be unlucky.

Eventually his luck did seem to change. He had continued to correspond with the American lady he'd failed to conquer and she, perhaps through some dull American winter, decided Robin wasn't so bad after all and agreed to come to Europe and go on a holiday with him to Portugal.

These were definite signs of surrender.

She had left all the bookings to him. He hired a car for a week and rented a villa.

The American lady arrived. They had a couple of free days before they went to their villa.

They picked up the car from the airport and set off to a beautiful luxurious hotel that Robin had picked out in the hills above Lisbon.

This was the night they were at last going to consummate their friendship, and they were going to do it in style.

The hotel was absolutely magnificent and surprisingly, not very expensive. The room had a huge four-poster bed, from which he could hardly keep his eyes. It had an en-suite lounge, a splendid bathroom with a toilet like a throne and a great high-walled bath, which was difficult to step out of. It all looked too good to be true. They were both tired and hot, sweaty and dirty after their travelling, so the first call was for a long, cool drink. Champagne was duly brought to the room. A plunge in the glorious bath was the next order of the day.

The American girl went first. He could hear her splashing around and singing, which was a good prelude as she knew a fate worse than death awaited her.

Eventually she came out in a tartan dressing gown and said, 'Well, I'll get into something comfortable whilst you go and have your bath.'

Robin, who had been busy exploring the room, had already uncovered a black negligée – this was going to be the night of nights. It was already early evening, but food and drink could wait till later.

He filled the bath and then wallowed in it with scented oils, in no hurry – everything was going to be just perfect. He stood up in the bath, half dried himself and took a step over the high bath wall. He put his foot straight down on a piece of soap, slipped, and skidded across the bathroom floor. There was a searing pain in the area of his nether regions and blood started to pour all over the floor. He shouted with pain as he slid, tearing something, he wasn't quite sure what. Hearing the shouts his girlfriend, now in a black, see-through neligée, came in to find the man of the moment lying naked on the floor in a pool of blood. She screamed.

A jagged tile edge had caused a seven-inch cut in his scrotum. It was bleeding profusely. They rang the desk for help; the assistant manager came up. In this particular

Portuguese hotel nobody understood very much English, particularly the word for scrotum, but by various hand sign language the assistant manager suggested he went to the hospital, which fortunately was only about three hundred yards away.

To stop the bleeding Robin and his girlfriend put a couple of towels on him like nappies and managed to pull his trousers over the top. Dressed thus he waddled off to the hospital where, thank goodness, the doctor spoke good English.

He looked down at Robin's injury. 'My God, you've been lucky,' he said. He didn't realise how near he'd come to Robin inflicting him with some grievous bodily harm.

He was stitched up under local anaesthetic, had various plasters and things stuck on the wound and was advised to go to a clinic near the villa they'd booked, to have his stitches out in about seven days' time. Once more as they were leaving the hospital the doctor patted him on the shoulder. 'You're a lucky man,' he said. 'It could have been much worse.'

The injury prevented any consummation of friendship but the pair made the best of their holiday, and had a smashing time in good weather, touring round northern Portugal, reporting to the clinic to have his stitches out. Very often a blow to the area where Robin had received his injury causes bleeding and swelling of the scrotum. Many men who have had vasectomies have staggered into the surgery with dangling lumps the size and shape of footballs.

Robin was fortunate that this hadn't occurred to him.

This fact was also observed by the clinic doctors, who were Swedish, for some reason doing a spell in Portugal. Their first comments were, 'You've been very lucky', little realising that they were putting their lives in peril.

This chaste holiday seemed to have done Robin and his American friend, Pearl, good. In his mid-fifties, for the first time Robin had been conquered. Pam and I went up to Birmingham six months later to a registry office wedding and Robin, the oldest swinger in town, had eventually met his match.

They had a flat for a short time and acquired a dog, and then bought half a house in the country that dated back to the time of William and Conqueror, the other half being occupied by a delightful couple with two small children.

There was a communal garden and was one slight problem: the children had a rabbit and Robin and Pearl had a dog. If they were careful and the children let them know when the rabbit was going to have a run (and anyway the dog didn't seem particularly interested in rabbits), they shouldn't have any problems.

Months went by and, even though they were in two separate halves of the same house, they saw very little of their neighbours.

To their horror, one dark night, in came the dog dragging a very dead rabbit.

They didn't know what to do. The rabbit looked a bit wet but didn't seem to have been too mangled. They got out the hair dryer, washed it, dried it and once all its fur was fluffy and clean there was no obvious injury.

Robin and Pearl were in a quandary.

'I know,' said Robin. 'Let's put it back in the hutch.'

They crept out quietly in the dark and from behind bushes, opened the hutch, which to their surprise was shut, and popped in the rabbit.

All was well until the next morning when they heard a sudden hysterical screaming and a knocking from the lady next door.

'The rabbit's back in his hutch,' screamed the neighbour.

'Well, shouldn't it be in its hutch?' asked Robin.

'No,' said the near-frantic woman. 'The rabbit died two weeks ago. We buried it.'

They calmed her down, pleading ignorance of the whole event, and agreeing with their neighbour that some supernatural force had been at work. Then they helped re-bury the rabbit.

Alone at last Robin turned to Pearl and said, 'I guess this is just the beginning of another lucky day for me.'

CHAPTER 7

Neither a Lender nor a Borrower Be

Part of the fun of having a boat was lending it to family
and friends who were either having a holiday for the first
time, or who were so broke they couldn't afford to go
anywhere else.

I knew when I lent it to Jonathan next door that it would
be in good hands. Jonathan, his father and brother are
engineer mechanics of the highest order, and if I glanced
from my balcony to the drive next door any weekend, I
could almost guarantee that if Jonathan wasn't taking the
engine out of his car, he was at least putting it back.

After a week on the boat with friends, Jonathan returned
it, gleaming clean as it had never been before, with the
enging purring like a kitten.

I do not have the same confidence in my own family:
none of us know one end of a spanner from another.

It was with some trepidation that I saw Trevor, Jane and
two friends, Fred and another Jane, sailing off into the
gloaming. Before they set off I had pinned a set of
instructions to the back of the cabin door, and put a lock
and chain in Trevor's hand saying, 'If you moor in Oxford
or Henley for the night, chain the boat to one of the fixed

rings on the towpath.' Unfortunately vandalism has reached our river banks, and some yobbos delight in cutting the moorings of boats at night and pushing the craft out into the stream. There is no doubt that if they haven't already done so, one day they would kill someone. I would rank the cutting of moorings of occupied boats as attempted manslaughter, and would impose the requisite penalty.

Trevor reached Oxford safely but rang from there to say the battery was flat and they couldn't start the engine. This surprised me: you have to use an awful lot of juice to flatten one of those batteries. They had also had an adventure. They had been playing cards when they heard a knocking on the side of the boat. They lifted the cabin flap to find a man in a punt asking them politely if they realised they were drifting downstream. Someone had cut their moorings.

The punt man kindly manoeuvred them back to their mooring, and Trevor belatedly chained the boat to the bank. Without the kindly intervention of the man in the punt, they could have had a tragic end to their holiday.

'What time was this?' I enquired.

'About 2 a.m.,' said Trevor.

I then realised that if they had had electricity burning till 2 a.m., there was every reason to have a flat battery.

Trevor went to the nearest garage and bought a new car battery. This was enough to get them going, but I doubted if it would be man enough for all the electrical equipment on the boat, so I decided to intercept them at the Rose Revived at Newbridge, and take off the main boat battery and bring it home to be charged.

As I thought, there was a call from the Rose Revived the next morning. Flat battery again. I took out the newly charged main battery and saw them get started up. Thankfully I also saw the sun come out; it had rained steadily for the whole of the holiday up to now, and the morale of the crew was low.

This was the turning point, from then on they had a splendid time – the sun blazed down, no more mechanical or battery troubles, and they chained themselves to quays both in Oxford and Henley. Paul, Gill and Daisy May came over on their last day. We had a rough idea where they would be, so met up with them below Goring Lock.

Paul, Gill and Daisy May joined them for the last few miles, whilst Pam and I went back to prepare hot baths and arrange a barbecue in the garden.

They brought a spotless boat into our mooring like seasoned sailors. Who knows, given time we might all become mechanics.

The next borrowing was by my godson, Tim, who was taking a mixed crew of old school friends. Their start was delayed by one lady crew member, who, when she arrived, looked as if she would be more at home at Ascot rather than on a river boat, and had caught a train to Wallington only to discover she couldn't find a river there and thought she should try Wallingford.

The main disaster on their holiday was to get a mooring rope entangled around the propeller shaft. It took three boys a whole afternoon's diving to clear it, but that's messing about in boats for you.

Tim is a delightful young man, he stayed the night with us after his week, and I had to listen patiently to him regarding all his affairs of the heart. He was in desperate need of advice. I gave him the following article which I had written many years ago as a medical student.

How to Choose Your Mate

Anatomically the best wives are stocky, wide hipped, thick waisted, full chested members of the female sex, with short strong fingers, powerful backs, tremendous stamina and of the intellect that wouldn't waste £1 on the housekeeping that could just as easily be spent on beer and fags. With this in mind the average male will look for the slimmest, fragile, most expensive looking bird he can find. The main factors influencing his decision being the size, mobility and shape of the soft tissue swellings on the front of the female thorax (chest), and the length, curvature, muscle balance of the trunk body supports (the legs). The main vote going in a ratio of three to two to the legs, or under-carriage.

From then on the rules are simple:

Pursue the bird object of your desire for forty-eight hours. Then stop. If you go beyond this time period she will lose all interest as she will think she has got you. She'll put it down in her book as another conquest and then devote her time to trying to pick up her best friend's boy who is an inch shorter than her but has never looked at her.

After the initial forty-eight hours you start paying attention to the object bird's best friend, who has a pleasant face but whose under-carriage doesn't fill your desired specification.

This changes your bird from being on the point of giving you up to deciding that you are all she ever wanted and she will fling herself at your feet; thus changing her from the austere, wonderful, unapproachable beauty that you were first attracted to, to something available and humiliatingly easy that you immediately lose interest in.

As her friend, who you have been chatting up (in spite of her bad legs), shows no reciprocal interest, as she has just become engaged, you find her the most irresistible female you have ever seen, and if she marries this chap who has swinishly tricked her into wearing his ring, life will hold nothing for you and you will apply for a job as a porter in Albert Schweitzer's leper colony.

If she is fool enough to break off her engagement for you, forty-eight hours after the initial victory, she will fall into the same category as the first bird and you will realise how mad you were to have considered having anything to do with a bird with legs like hers.

Your first bird will then have got over her disappointment with you and have paired off with some other swine, and immediately will recapture all her old allure.

You will then fling yourself at her, but you being now so available, become less attractive, as well as her remembering the last time. She won't have anything to do with you, unless of course you start chatting up her second best friend, then the whole cycle will repeat itself.

These permutations are great fun for a few years, but if by the age of seventy-five you have not broken the cycle, even though the citations of individual cases will prove me wrong, it is unlikely that this article will be of much use to you.

If you were able to remember back to the alluring stage, when a bird is humiliating herself at your feet, then it would be possible to actually pick for your own which ever bird you really wanted, but of course it never works out like this.

The best thing is to marry the girl next door if she will have you, as there is no doubt it's the birds who decide on who is going to be their mate; the average man has no say in the matter at all.

Tim read the article, then looked up thoughtfully.

'But, Uncle Bob,' he said, 'there aren't any girls next door.'

'Well, Tim,' I said, 'it will have to be girl next-door-but-one.'

CHAPTER 8

An Act of Doc

I had spent most of my working life in Tadchester.

Tadchester is a market town with a rising population of about 8,000. It stands on the estuary of the River Tad in one of the most beautiful parts of the Somerset coast, with the resorts of Sandford-on-Sea and Stowin nearby. Although primarily a market town, it still has some fishing, an increasing amount of light industry and a small mine that produces pigments, a residue from the time when the main industry in the town was coal-mining.

We were the only general practice in the town, and when I first arrived, the senior partner was the beloved Steve Maxwell, who had a special interest in medicine, the bluff Henry Johnson, the surgeon of the practice, was the second partner, and Jack Hart, who gave most of the anaesthetics, batted at number three. I joined as number four, and most of the midwifery came my way. In later years we engaged a fifth partner, Ron Dickinson, who took a keen interest in E.N.T.s and an even greater interest in running, jumping, squash, sailing and water-skiing. He was always bouncing about doing something physical, a sort of cross between Peter Pan and Tigger from *Winnie The Pooh*.

Later on, when I was off work for some months, we had a locum, Catherine Carlton, a dentist's wife. When I returned to work, we kept her on as a half-time partner.

How quickly the years pass by. I remember when I went to be interviewed for the practice vacancy in 1955. I thought then that Steve Maxwell and Henry Johnson were old men, and that Jack Hart was late middle-aged. In fact, Steve and Henry must have been in their mid-forties and Jack Hart about thirty-five. Now, sadly, Steve Maxwell and Henry Johnson are dead, Jack Hart has retired and I have retired to Wallingford. It is unbelievable to think that Ron Dickinson, now the senior partner, is fast approaching retirement age himself.

Since we've moved to Wallingford we've seen a lot of Ron and his wife Annette. They frequently come to stay and Ron hasn't changed or aged a bit. As soon as they arrive Ron changes into a pink tracksuit and goes bouncing off down the towpath for a couple of miles, then runs back, has a quick hot bath and dashes off to the nearest pub. After downing a couple of pints of draught bitter he is at last fit to face us and the evening. By the time we approach the small hours, he has usually divested himself of most of his clothes and sits grinning like a pixie in his underpants with a large glass of port in his hand. There is certainly never a dull moment when Ron is around.

We have become a popular stopping-off place for all and sundry coming up from the West Country, being near to both London and Heathrow; often friends leave their cars with us while they visit the big city or fly abroad.

Several have come on the boat with us – Pam and Bill Law, Eric, Zara and Nicholas – but, one trip I was really looking forward to was with my old friend Chris Parfitt (C.P.), the editor of the *Tadchester Gazette*. It was to be a combined fishing-cum-boating holiday with C.P. as crew and me as captain and chief cook.

We had had an unforgettable holiday together before, *en famille*, eight of us in France and I hoped this boat trip would be as successful.

Sadly, although it wasn't a bad holiday, it wasn't as good as I had hoped. C.P. was not as river-wise as I had expected – he wasn't desperately good in locks, or at jumping out to moor the boat – and in the end C.P. developed some mysterious stomach upset and we had to return to base early. I had quite forgotten that most of C.P.'s river experience was derived from sitting on the bank, under a green umbrella, pipe clenched firmly in his mouth, dreaming of the pint of beer he was going to drink at the end of the day's activities.

It was lovely seeing him, even for a short time, and happily he perked up when we got home and Pam took over the catering.

I used to take the fishing magazine in which C.P. wrote a weekly humorous philosophical column, supposedly on fishing. In fact it could be on anything from the Pope to tiddlywinks. I thought he was the wittiest writer in print.

On reading his column some months after our holiday, I realised its contents were C.P.'s side of our trip together. The article went as follows.

An Act of Doc

'There's an insurance man in the paper,' I said to Dearly Beloved across the breakfast table, 'who reckons that the average husband is worth £500,000.'

'Really?' she said, looking at me in my morning glory. 'I'll take 50p for cash.'

Some people. . .

On the way to work, I read of a fifteen-year-old Italian lad, the world champion table-soccer player, whose right index finger – the one he flicks with – is insured for £25,000.

Gad, I thought. If a little lad's index finger is worth that much just for flicking some plastic footballers about, what must mine be worth? Where would I be without its aid on the bank for such essential operations as taking the ring off a can, guiding the hook into a pinkie and out of a perchie?

Shock horror at the office. Phone call from Dave Bogart, the hunky American person and former demon angler of Upper Black Eddy on the Delaware. Dave couldn't come to work on account of he was on his way home the night before and he fell over a bloke who was cleaning his car in the dark. Broke both arms.

With both arms in plaster Dave would be in no condition for several weeks even to bait up, let alone cast out.

I'd better get myself insured, I thought, before something terrible happens. No use any longer relying on my lucky socks, rabbit's foot or Fozzie Bear mascot to keep me out of the old emergency ward.

The trouble with angling, though, is that accidents

are seldom straightforward. And it's rarely the likely one which gets you. Take my last trip out with Doc Thumper [my pen name], physician extraordinary and skipper of the luxury 27 foot *Sea Grey*.

Up the Thames we went, along the narrower upper reaches, as is our wont. We came to a lock, the keeper of which was away for din-dins.

'I'll operate the gates,' said Doc. 'And you can stay in charge of the boat.'

'Aye aye, Cap'n,' I said. 'Have no fear. Old Long John Parfitt'll see ee roight. Oh arr . . .'

'On second thoughts,' said Doc, 'I'll stay on board the boat. You work the gates. Sure you know how to do it?'

'Easy peasy Cap'n,' said I. I leapt on the towpath, tied a rope around one of those bollard things and opened the first gate.

Fired with enthusiasm, I ran up to the next set of gates and started winching away.

'Help!' cried Doc, as about twenty miles of Thames water started moving down towards him. 'You're supposed to close the other one first! And I'm supposed to be inside the lock!'

'What's keeping you?' I hollered, winching madly in reverse.

'Those twelve granny knots you tied around the bollard. Are you sure you've done this before?'

A bit further upstream it was Doc's turn to make a boo-boo. We passed an island in midstream. On the other side of the island, and running to the far bank, was a weir.

Once past the island, Doc said, 'There's a lovely little creek behind the weir, and I know an old lady who lives along there. She'll let us fish from the bottom of her garden.'

So saying, he swung the boat hard-a-starboard (who says I know nowt about it?) round the back of the island, and headed for the creek. The current was flowing strongly and we found ourselves moving swiftly towards the weir.

'Soon be there,' said Doc.

'Oh, what's it say on that board sticking out of the water?' he said.

'D-A-N-G-E-R . . . danger,' I said (as in 'banger'). My mind must have been on something else. 'No! Oh-my-gawd! It's DANGER! As in 'ranger'!'

'As in what?' shouted Doc over the noise of the engine.

'Ranger! As in Lone Ranger! Tonto! Hi-yo Silver . . . away!'

'This is no time to be playing cowboys,' shouted Doc. 'I think we might be in some small difficulty here . . .'

By a combination of skilful seamanship and pure fluke, Doc turned the boat around then guided it painfully upstream out of the fast water. The old lady up the creek could wait for another day.

Some time later we approached a couple of small bays on the left bank.

'This looks fine,' said Doc. 'We'll moor here.'

I crouched on the bows like a tar to the manner born, mooring rope in hand, and leapt on to the bank as we entered the first bay. The boat kept on going and dragged me halfway down the bank before I could let go and cling on to a handy tree.

'Why the hell didn't you stop?' I shouted.

'I meant the second bay,' said Doc. 'Now stop messing about in that tree and make yourself useful.'

The useful bit was to moor the boat. Doc threw up a couple of iron spikes which just missed my vitals, and a two-pound hammer which landed neatly on my foot.

'I'm getting a bit fed up with this,' I said.

'Not to worry,' said Doc. 'We're here now. Tell you what, while you're tacking up I'll cook us a lovely mixed grill on the stove.'

Now do you see all the possibilities for accident on

that one innocent trip out? The boat could have been turned over or washed away by the rush of lock water; it could have been swept over the weir; I would have had a ducking if it had not been for the handy tree; I just missed being speared by the mooring spikes and was actually struck a deadly blow on the big toe by the two-pound hammer. Bang would have gone the no-claims bonus. But it wasn't any of those that did the damage.

That night, both Doc and I were assailed by fearsome indigestion and drove each other potty by groaning until the small hours. Now that was the real hazard of the trip yet it probably wouldn't have been covered by insurance. It wasn't so much an act of God as an act of Doc.

Have you ever tried his cooking?

I rang C.P. after I had read it, swearing that I would never cook for him again.

'Put that in writing,' said C.P., 'and we are friends for life.'

C.P. was a true fisherman, and on the river it was always a bit fisherman versus boats, and crewing on a boat rather divided his loyalties.

Though C.P. and his wife often came to stay and C.P. was quite happy to fish from the end of the garden, I could never entice him back on board again, even though I promised not to cook.

CHAPTER 9

On the Air

In 1961 I sent my first unsolicited script off to the Talks Department of the BBC. My story was about two old ladies, one of whom had been bedridden for forty-seven years and how this lady had made a great success of her life, confined as she was.

My script was accepted and I went to Exeter and recorded it. Not only was it broadcast on *Woman's Hour*, but it was repeated. For this to happen in Tadchester was fame indeed and I grew at least six inches in stature overnight.

One mistake I made in my broadcast was to disguise the identities of the two ladies. I called them Miss Gill and Miss Booth, whereas their names were Miss Oake and Miss Lord, and many of their friends throughout England (and they had a wide number of people with whom they corresponded), recognised them. What I hadn't realised was that my broadcast would open up their world as it did. They became overnight celebrities and if I'd called them by their proper names, they would have been more famous still.

In the story the bedridden lady said, 'People come to me because I have time to listen.' And it became a catch phrase that people remembered.

Heady with success I sent my second script off to the BBC. This was about a man who knew he was going to die and who died on the exact day he was told he was going to, and it made quite a moving story.

Again the BBC accepted it and this time I went to Plymouth to record it. I wasn't very good at reading from scripts and it took two hours to record. I could talk well but I couldn't read scripts – you need to be an actor. It was interesting that the producer of this particular talk went down with stomach ulcers a couple of weeks after having to cope with me!

But again, like the first story, the BBC not only broadcast it once, but repeated it.

In Tadchester I was absolutely famous. People nodded to me in the street, happy to know me; even my partners looked at me with a sort of new-found respect.

Back in 1961 radio was very important. People listened to it just as much as they watched television.

After these successes I realised that anything I sent to the BBC would automatically be taken and broadcast – I was a natural. Unfortunately the next twenty-seven scripts I sent in were rejected.

In between the time of my second successful broadcast and before my rejections started to arrive, somebody from Tadchester told me that a friend of theirs was about to give a broadcast on Radio Bristol. Would I, with all my experience, i.e. six minutes on *Woman's Hour*, help?

I was, of course, very happy to help any struggling star who hadn't made it to the top as I had, and my friend Eric from the Tadchester Radio Services lent me a tape-recorder – even tape-recorders were rare in those days – and I suggested that this potential lady broadcaster should record her broadcast and listen to herself. I also volunteered to listen to the tape and said I would be happy to give an opinion.

I listened to it and thought it was terrible.

The lady had a broad Devon accent and her talk concerned her husband, the lodgers they had at their guest-house and the pigs on their farm.

Obviously not in my league.

I kept my thoughts to myself, told her it was very good and wished her luck, thinking it a pity she hadn't a golden voice like mine – poor lass. I knew she would never broadcast again.

This broadcast was the first of many hundreds she made for *Woman's Hour* at the BBC. She became a household name and the BBC made several records of her collective broadcasts for general release.

She was about five hundred times more successful than I was!

I soldiered on, sending out broadcasting scripts and having one or two more accepted. Then, because I was a doctor, I drifted into giving medical broadcasts, mainly involving the answering of medical questions.

It was very convenient. If I was going up to London for any reason, I would ring up *Woman's Hour* and ask whether there were any medical questions that needed answering, and very often they would fit me in for a recording, which paid my fare.

I also continued to have some success with submitted scripts.

One, which I felt was better than most, was quite a moving story of a man who had spent ten years of his life trying to get a play put on in the West End. He was actually our landlord when we'd lived in a flat in a big house; he'd lived in a room upstairs.

I sent it to the people at the BBC I'd been working with, and they sent it back, not with a normal letter but with a rejection slip. So I sent it to Radio Bristol, who accepted it, and it was put on the Rolfe Whiteman show.

What I didn't know was that the Rolfe Whiteman show that afternoon was going to be part of *Woman's Hour*, so it got on *Woman's Hour* after all.

Rolfe Whiteman was a very famous broadcaster. I once

said on a radio programme that he had a voice that sounded as if he'd been gargling with Devon cream. This gave rise to a lot of angry letters and 'phone calls saying that he was a Wiltshire man and I'd inferred he'd come from Devon. I don't know whether they make cream in Wiltshire.

My broadcast about the man upstairs, which I had to read from a script, was made from the Bristol studios.

It was very poignant. This delightful man whom we knew well, had isolated himself for ten years, writing away at his plays and also keeping himself available so that if a film or theatre company needed him he could be off, literally within 24 hours' notice, anywhere in the world.

I believe he kept a bag packed.

He had been an important man in the theatre and at one time a scriptwriter for British Columbia. He was one of the most remarkable men I have ever met and one of the bravest.

I made this broadcast live from Bristol.

Pam took the children to Bristol Zoo then they listened on the car radio just outside the studios. For some reason Rolfe Whiteman decided to join in my broadcast, interjecting ums and ahs. I don't think it helped.

There was one unfortunate aspect of this particular piece, which appeared in the *Radio Times*. The broadcast was advertised as 'The Available Gentleman', and underneath it was written, 'A West Country doctor talks about his relationship with the man upstairs' – it took me some time to live that down.

Gradually I got to do more and more on *Woman's Hour*, mainly on medical topics. The awful thing was that I got on to radio programmes, not because I was brilliant or because I had anything wonderful to say, but because I was simple and said things in a straightforward way that people could understand. Friends would say to me, 'What a marvellous broadcasting technique you have,' not realising that I hadn't any technique at all; it was just me being me. I was in demand because I was safe and simple – what an achievement.

I did, amongst other programmes, some *Tuesday Calls*. These were live 'phone-ins from nine to ten in the morning. My first was with a lovely lady who did the morning exercises, Eileen Fowler, an expert on health and physical fitness. I'd written a book on backache, she'd spotted it and asked for me, thinking that I might be an authority on her subject.

Eileen Fowler's programme was very popular; when I met her she was in her seventies and looked about forty-five.

I was fat and unfit at the time and during the course of the 'phone-in suggested to everybody that they went out and bought bicycles – this was probably as good a way of keeping fit as any.

My words of advice were heeded by many people, including some of my neighbours, who went out and bought bikes. Then someone put two and two together (I usually hid under some pseudonym for broadcasting) and realised that the fat slob of a man across the road had said 'Get on your bike'. This expression was subsequently picked up by some minor politician a good twenty years later, which showed how much ahead of my time I was!

I liked going up to the BBC to broadcast, and the *Woman's Hour* people were extremely nice to work with. During the time I was with them the general nature of the programmes changed and reading from scripts was abandoned in favour of not having scripts at all. This suited me much better as, unless you are an actor, it is very difficult to insert the right inflections in the right places, whereas if you just speak your own words in your own voice in your own way, it's much more convincing and, of course, it's you.

Of all the broadcasts that I did over many years – and in some of them I was trying to get deep messages across – the only complimentary remarks that I ever got from people who knew me who'd heard my broadcasts were on the following lines: 'Bob [or Doctor – depending on how well they knew me], we heard your broadcast the other day. It was marvellous. It sounded exactly like you. It could have been you standing in my kitchen [or dining room, or whatever].' They never made any comment on the content of the broadcast, just that it sounded exactly like me. How surprising. It was *me* – no wonder it sounded like me.

What they were saying wasn't quite as bad as it sounds.

Sound recording cannot reproduce the whole range of your voice, and it either flatters or distorts it. I was lucky. The radio flattered my voice and television made me look much more positive, whereas I knew a most accomplished speaker, a very distinguished lady with a very nice voice, who on the radio sounded like Mickey Mouse.

So perhaps all my friends and patients could be excused for complimenting me in the way they did.

The most stressful broadcasts of all were the *Tuesday Call* 'phone-ins. I think they were made unnecessarily alarming.

The usual set-up was to have a couple of charming, beautiful, calm ladies, like Judith Chalmers or Sue McGregor, sitting on one side of a table, plus one or two guests (to answer the questions), and a secretary at the end of the table. Outside, through a window, sat various producers, and behind them a bank of girls with telephones and then behind them a whole bank of other visitors, perhaps thirty Japanese guests touring the BBC. No wonder it could become quite stressful.

I remember once recognising one of the callers as someone who'd been at the Writers' Summer School with me in Derbyshire. It was on the tip of my tongue to say 'Hello, Jack. I hope you enjoyed last year at the Writers' Summer School. See you next year,' when it dawned on me that perhaps Jack wasn't supposed to be at the school – he might have told his wife a different story – and that would have been very much disapproved of by the BBC.

The most harrowing *Tuesday Call* I ever did was with Gill Parker, a lovely lady who was a general practitioner and the wife of the then head of British Rail. There was a rehearsal the night before, during which a lot of wine was splashed about. Afterwards I went out with some medical friends and a lot more wine was splashed about. I eventually went to bed with a headache, and couldn't settle. I was staying in a hotel in London's Half Moon Street and there seemed to be traffic going all night – it was very noisy. When I arrived at the studio in the morning, not only was I lacking in sleep, but I had an awful headache and I was also wearing, for the first time, a new pair of bi-focal glasses. Every time I looked up I felt giddy.

I sat in my chair and, glancing at the clock, realised that I had an hour's live spontaneous broadcast ahead of me. On this particular morning the subject matter was general medical questions and Gill Parker and I had to stretch ourselves to the limit to get through it.

The hour seemed like an eternity and I literally sweated it out, my head thumping. Inwardly I was swearing never to touch a drop of wine again when a question came through: 'My husband is an alcoholic. What does Doctor Clifford recommend?' I turned appealingly to Gill Parker. Bless her, she took the question in her stride and gave a very good answer – I wasn't up to it that morning.

As I started to write books I began to appear on other programmes.

I was interviewed by Esther Rantzen on *Start the Week*, chaired by the delightful Richard Baker, with Fritz Spiegel and Moira Lister (who was absolutely gorgeous) on my right to be interviewed by Kenneth Robinson; Lance Percival strummed a guitar in the background.

I was being interviewed by Esther on a funny book called *The Medical Handbook to End All Medical Handbooks*.

We were sitting quietly in a circle round a table when suddenly Kenneth Robinson got up and attacked Moira Lister rudely about a play she was in at Wimbledon. It was unbelievably embarrassing and quite uncalled for.

All the members at the table later wrote to Moira Lister saying how sorry they were, the whole attack being in the worst possible taste.

I don't know what it's called – provocative broadcasting or something – but I found it both extremely unpleasant and unjustified.

The same book got me on to *Stop the Week* with Robert Robinson, whose other guests were Richard Gordon, Edward Du Bono, Benny Green and the literary editor of the *Manchester Guardian*.

Having two funny doctors on the same programme, I thought medical humour would be a main feature, but it wasn't. We were questioned about doctors' pay, which we knew nothing about.

We also had to give in-depth reports on a new book on adolescence by Doctor Spock. I thought it was very good and had a lot to offer, but my fellow guests were pretty noncommittal, or even damning. I felt that these were harsh judgements for them to make.

Whenever a book of my own was published and I was being interviewed on radio or television it was always fun.

I didn't have to make any preparations.

Usually the interviewers have appeared interested and over the years I've been on various radio stations all over the country: the BBC's *Today*, *Late Night Extra*, as well as *Woman's Hour* programmes, *Home This Afternoon*, the London Broadcasting Company, Radio London, Radio 210, Radio Bristol, Radio Wiltshire, Radio Sussex, Radio Oxford – all tremendous fun.

On the whole I found that the radio programmes were often more professional than their television counterparts.

I remember doing one 'phone-in, I think it was on first aid, for Radio London. Instead of involving masses of people, like they did on the BBC's *Tuesday Call*, an interviewer, one man on the telephone and a television monitor were all that were needed and it seemed to work more smoothly.

I literally drifted into television. I'd done a couple of things for the *Today* programme, one in answer to a fiery letter I'd written about the treatment of doctors. I had to debate the issue with a trades unionist, Lord Cooper, under the chairmanship of Kenneth Allsop. Lord Cooper and I were supposed to be on opposite sides but, in the end, we ganged up on Kenneth Allsop and I think we won.

Then one afternoon in the surgery, a panic 'phone call. Could I go up to London? It was the tenth anniversary of the National Health Service. The BBC had been looking through their files and I was about the only person who'd ever said anything nice about the National Health Service. They were interviewing the Minister of Health and wanted some doctors to say some encouraging things about it. I said I couldn't go because there was a rail strike on and I wouldn't be able to get there. The BBC suggested I caught a plane.

I rang the airports. There were no planes going to London.

After exploring every conventional avenue, my receptionist, Pam Law, said, 'You know, my husband drives to London very quickly; he'll run you up in a couple of hours.'

It was in the middle of the holiday season so I had my doubts.

Bill Law and I set off at speed, haring in and out of the traffic, overtaking everything. Everybody was tooting at us, some actually trying to run us into the hedge.

We got as far as Shaftesbury, but were so behind time I rang the BBC and told them we couldn't make it.

'Keep going,' they said. 'We'll send a BBC car to meet you at Ruislip.'

We eventually made Ruislip and found the car. I wasn't going to miss the broadcast as I thought; the programme was an hour later than they told me.

We tore up to the BBC in the taxi, the producer met me in the foyer and said, 'I'll brief you in the lift going up. The Minister of Health is there with a few doctors. There'll be a film, then you will be questioned and you will be able to question the Minister.'

I felt like a real celebrity. I went into the studio. There were ten doctors sitting in a row. I did wonder how much

78

time we were going to have to speak to the Minister of Health.

The programme began with a ten-minute film on the start of the National Health Service and then Michael Barratt started asking the doctors some questions. He turned to me and said, 'In what way has the new ancillary help facility of nurses in general practice helped you?'

I said, 'Our nurses syringe ears and bandage varicose veins.'

I wasn't asked any other questions.

I didn't have to say another word.

Bill Law drove me back to Tadchester at a somewhat slower pace, finally arriving at six in the morning.

My real television career started when I was interviewed by Westward Television about my first book, *The Hairy Man's Guide to First Aid*, which I wrote under the pseudonym of Doctor Pheasant.

They had a great laugh in the studio; people dressed up

in rugby clothes threw water over each other, struggled to give mouth-to-mouth resuscitation – it was great fun.

After the programme I was asked if I would become the programme's resident doctor, i.e. appear about once a month and put into simple language various medical problems that might arise.

They were a very nice young team at Westward.

The chief presenter, Kenneth McCleod, was a most accomplished actor and broadcaster.

Amongst the rest of the team was Angela Rippon, as lovely a young girl as she is now a mature woman and a first-class interviewer. At one time she had her own woman's programme and I appeared on it to talk about a book I had written called *How to Put on Weight*.

This particular book had more media coverage than any other I've ever produced – it also sold less. It was good to talk about, but not to buy. Anglia Television also interviewed me about this book, but it was through a link-up from a London studio and I had to speak into a monitor. It was quite disconcerting – every time I answered a question from the interviewer my own face came up on the monitor and I had to speak to myself.

At Westward Television I made perhaps the worst six first-aid films of all time. I was asked if I could do it, foolishly agreed and suddenly realised I had to script and present the series.

I had no idea how to go about it. We used to film it in the lunchtimes, to the disgust of all the various studio workers, i.e. lighting men, scene shifters, etc. I remember we spent a long session showing how to cope with a cut finger, which involved holding the finger under a tap, putting some disinfectant on it, then putting on some Elastoplast tape.

When we came to look at it afterwards, it was thought to be so bad we had to do it again.

Harlech Television also interviewed me on the *How to Put on Weight* book, and afterwards I was asked to become the resident doctor on their *Women Only* programme, where a very young Jan Leeming was the presenter. This was a splendid show and years later when Jan Leeming became nationally famous as a newsreader, I always thought that so much of her talent was wasted. She was one of the best and most professional programme presenters that I've ever come across.

I did some interviewing on the *Women Only* programme for Harlech. I first interviewed a doctor's wife on her book about the National Health Service.

I made the mistake of giving away all my most penetrating questions when I was discussing the book with the author prior to the broadcast. Of course, when the broadcast time came round she had thought out new answers to my questions and I was the one to be non-plussed. I had to put it all down to experience.

I was next to interview the great Claire Rayner about her second novel, *A Time to Heal.*

It was arranged that I would go up to Paddington to meet her, then we were to travel down to Bristol together and discuss her novel over breakfast.

Claire is a marvellous person, has more energy than three people put together, and, I believe, employs six secretaries. She is a really lovely genuine lady, in the fullest sense of the word. This has been recently confirmed in a survey to find the best-liked woman in the country. She came second to Felicity Kendall.

Claire is also one of the great talkers of the world, on a par with Maeve Binchey. If ever I was asked to form a government, I would appoint Claire as prime minister and Maeve as foreign secretary, they would sweep everything before them, nobody would get a chance to get a word in edgeways; Margaret Thatcher is not in their league. I, of course, would be in charge of the Treasury.

Claire and I talked non-stop all the way to Bristol. She told me she wanted to write an operetta, and an on-going saga of novels following a family over a period of 150 years. It all sounded like pie in the sky, but she was true to her word, she produced a twelve-book bestselling series, as well as continuing with her agony aunt column, newspaper and magazine articles and radio and television. I last saw her at a publishing party in March, 1988. She looked just as fit and bouncing with energy as she had done when I had interviewed her back in 1972.

Because we were talking so much, we hardly touched our breakfast. As the train pulled into Bristol, we realised we hadn't actually got round to discussing her novel, which had been the object of the exercise.

It didn't matter. Claire is a very easy person to interview. I hailed her as the new H. G. Wells. *A Time to Heal* was about a cancer cure, and Claire had predicted all sorts of things like test-tube babies, long before they were implemented.

Some months later we were again on Harlech Television together. I don't know what Claire's contribution was, but mine was to talk about what a doctor carries in his bag, and for the only time on TV I had my medical case with me.

Claire and I travelled back by rail together and sat in the restaurant car at the back of the train.

Out in the wilds of the country the train made an unscheduled stop. A guard came along to explain that a man had been hit on the line.

I said, 'Well, I'm a doctor, and this lady is a nurse. Can we be of any assistance?'

'I don't know the exact position,' said the guard, 'but if you could make your way to the front of the train, I'm sure they would be extremely grateful.'

I grabbed my medical case, and Claire and I ran the whole length of the train, with me shouting 'I'm a doctor!' and Claire shouting, 'I'm a nurse!', whenever someone impeded our progress.

It seemed like miles before we reached the front of the train. We were helped down the steep drop to the ground, and led round to the front of the engine where two labourers were shovelling the remains of what had been a man on to a wheelbarrow. We trudged our way slowly back to the restaurant car, answering 'Everything is under control,' to anyone who asked. I never learnt who the poor fellow was or whether it was an accident or suicide; I don't think that Claire or I will ever forget it.

There is a public side to Claire, which is seen to engage in a prodigious amount of work. I also know that there is a private one that is just as busy, as there have been occasions when she has rung me about some medical aspect of a problem she is dealing with personally. She is a truly marvellous human being. I am unable to make the 'Wellsian' predictions that Claire makes, but I would very much like to predict that one day she will be honoured by being made a Dame. If she isn't, then she should be.

I enjoyed both radio and television, although I was very much on the periphery. I was never particularly well known as a broadcaster, but I did relish the atmosphere of the studio and loved meeting the people taking part in programmes, particularly in Harlech Television's *Women Only* programme, which always had a host of interesting celebrities.

It was a tremendous experience and so different from my world of medicine that it was a great help in maintaining my own equilibrium with all the problems and tragedies that I had to deal with in my daily round. It gave me a foothold in another camp and although ninety-five per cent of my time was spent in medicine, meeting all these people in a different world was my relaxation and a great stabiliser.

My last television appearance was in series called *Believe it or not*. It was chaired by Paul Heiney, Andy Price and a lovely girl from the TV series *Crossroads*. The item I was involved in was to feature in a pilot programme and, if all went well, in the first programme. There were to be six programmes and six components of each.

My particular spot related to Culpeper's *London Dispen-*

satory of the seventeenth century. This was a famous book detailing the pharmaceutical preparations that were used in those days, like dead bodies, stag's pizzel and elf hearts, and we were looking to see how many of them were still being used today.

Old-fashioned remedies had become topical, and leeches, for example, were once more proving useful in medicine, particularly in eye surgery.

We had a good pilot programme and it was decided to go ahead with the series.

In the first episode, where I did my piece about how medical preparations came and went over the years, Andy Price went into the audience and talked to some of the studio guests on camera.

Trevor and a friend were my guests and they were both interviewed. How nice, I thought, that we should both be on the same television programme together.

However, it was not to be. Somewhere along the line (and it was blamed on the Director General of the BBC) it was thought that the six programmes weren't up to scratch. They scrambled the six programmes they'd made, taking out the best items to make just three programmes.

I watched the programme when it was eventually broadcast. They didn't interfere with my piece but they chopped and changed the others around so much it became very confusing. One minute, for example, you'd see Paul Heiney in a green jersey, and the next minute he'd be in a yellow one, as they jumped from one episode to another.

I thought the programme I was in was excellent and the people I worked with were all terribly nice. They were all very upset about it being broken up. Knowing there was little chance of my appearing on television again, and having little to lose, I wrote a long letter to the supposed villain of the piece, Derek Hart, who was the then Director General of the BBC.

I received a charming reply, thanking me for my letter, saying he would find out who had cancelled the programme and ask them to write to me and explain why it had been edited as it had. He would also ask the said producer/director to send him a copy of the letter. So the Director General wasn't the culprit, it was somebody else; whoever it was, I would certainly never be his favourite person.

I received an explanatory letter in due course, and an exceedingly long one at that (remember, this man had to send a copy to the Director General).

He started by saying that if only the contents of the programme had been up to the standard of my contribution, of course, they would have had no trouble. I took this with the great pinch of salt with which it was intended. Unfortunately, he said, most of the other items fell far beneath the standard of my performance.

To me it seemed that he had dodged the responsibility for reducing the programme and passed the buck, and suddenly the buck had come back to him. I winced as I read his letter; I knew that somewhere I had made a deadly enemy. I felt pretty certain that nobody would ever invite me to appear on a BBC television programme again, and I was absolutely right. I was never asked and never appeared again.

CHAPTER 10

Singing for Supper

Although I now live in the south midlands and have written mainly about the west of England, the only real literary occasions I have been invited to speak at are in the north of England. The *Yorkshire Ridings' Magazine* were very kind to me, as were the *Lancashire Magazine*, and I did a number of speaking engagements for them at dinners and lunches. They usually coincided with the publication of a new book and involved signing sessions after the meal.

My first actual literary dinner was for the *Yorkshire Ridings' Magazine* in Bradford, and was shared with a delightful policeman author called Peter Walker. I had become pretty sure of myself as a speaker, in fact, a bit too sure. A few weeks before the Bradford dinner I'd gone back to the Writers' Summer School at Swanwick in Derbyshire, as one of the celebrity speakers, some twenty years after having first gone there as a 'new boy' without having anything published or broadcast.

We had a good dinner in Bradford, with perhaps a couple of hundred people in attendance. The publisher's representative had been brought back from holiday because of the dinner and I looked forward to a most enjoyable evening, not least because of hearing myself speak.

We had our meal then Peter spoke. He turned out to be a first-class speaker. At literary lunches and dinners, particularly, it's very difficult to follow someone who speaks well, especially if they've been amusing. If you've wined and dined well, and been amused and entertained, you often feel ready to go home after a good speaker.

My turn came. I got up full of confidence but made the great mistake of reading something that I thought was funny. Being a bad reader of scripts my talk didn't go down well at all. If only Peter Walker hadn't been quite so good I might have held the attention of the audience a bit better.

I rate my talks or speeches as wins, loses or draws, and this was definitely a loss.

At the end of the dinner we had to leave the dining room to go to a second room. I was escorted by this poor rep who had foreshortened his holiday, and there, on a table, were my books for sale, dozens of them in rows.

I got out my pen, ready to sign, but this wasn't to be my evening. A good crowd collected around Peter Walker, and, not only did nobody buy my book, but also nobody even spoke to me, except, just as the evening was drawing to a close, a man who walked up and said how much he loved books and that most of his friends were doctors.

I joined the queue at Peter's table and bought one of his books. Bless him, he repaid the compliment and bought one of mine. I hated to think what the publisher's rep must have thought about his ruined holiday.

We were being put up by the *Yorkshire Ridings' Magazine* at the Olde Silent Inn at Stanbury, on the moors near Howarth, a lovely old place. I went back in despair; I felt I'd let them down. 'Don't worry,' said Winston, managing director of the magazine, 'you've got to be professional about these things. You win some, you lose some – it may be quite different tomorrow.' His words of comfort were

endorsed by Joan Laprell, the features editor, both lovely
people who became great friends over the years.

But I had a restless night, picking over my speech.
Winston had tactfully said, and he was quite right, that
reading something was perhaps not the best thing.

I knew that I had to face an audience at Halifax at a
function the next day.

Winston was right – I had a completely different reception at Halifax. The speech went over well, I didn't bore
them to tears by reading something, and when it came to
the book-signing session, there was a whole queue of
people buying books, as well as a whole lot more coming
up to talk about books and writing. A most delightful
occasion, and my confidence was restored.

My next literary occasion for this magazine was a great
honour. It was during the Barnsley Book Week, and
apparently more people in Barnsley take out library books
than in anywhere else in the world. There was to be a
dinner in the evening and a lunch the following day at the

same venue. I was in most distinguished company here and we were billed as bestselling authors, which I wasn't – I considered myself as a sort of aperitif before the main course.

At the literary dinner in the evening the other two speakers were the marvellous James Herriot and the incredible Jeffrey Archer, and I certainly wasn't in their league but this was part of the fun I got out of writing.

At lunch the following day Jeffrey Archer was again one of the speakers and the other was a much underestimated writer, and a man who, over the years, became a great friend. Sadly he was taken terminally ill just a couple of days before he was due to spend a weekend with us at Wallingford and he was so looking forward to a trip on the boat. He was an author who had really reached a peak with one of his first novels, *Room at the Top* – of course, I'm referring to John Braine. He told me that just after *Room at the Top* was published he was approached by both the Conservative and Labour parties to stand as a candidate. He wisely refused both offers. John was a truly professional author, a disciplined writer whose manuscripts always arrived on time.

It was not always easy to get to know the real John under that rather bluff, almost aggressive, exterior, but he was a very kindly learned man and was full of commonsense.

Jeffrey Archer was a brilliant speaker. Fortunately I didn't have to follow him because he insisted on speaking last. At the luncheon at Barnsley this did not work to my advantage. I had been a Bevin Boy just at the end of the War, coal-mining in South Yorkshire. My colliery had not been too far away from Barnsley and I'd had an uncle in Maltby whom I often visited at weekends when I was there.

He died some years ago but I was very fond of my Uncle George and as I got up to speak, Uncle George and Maltby were very much in my mind because I was going to mention him fairly early on.

I started my speech by saying, 'This is my first visit to Maltby,' and had only completed a few sentences when I realised that, of course, this was my first visit to Barnsley not Maltby and I had to start again. I don't know what Jeffrey had prepared to say prior to my speech, but he devoted most of his allotted ten minutes to saying how confused he was because he thought he'd come to Barnsley and now he found he was in Maltby. He'd have to sack his agent, and where was Maltby anyway? I decided definitely not to vote for him at the next election.

Going to dinners and lunches up north allowed me to revisit areas that I'd known in the past, mainly from just at the end of the War and, of course, I am a Yorkshireman by birth. It was amazing how things had changed. In 1946 there seemed to be smoke and slag-heaps in evidence from Watford onwards, but now, as you go north, it is difficult to spot a mine or black smoke anywhere.

John Braine and I travelled to Preston to do a lunch and a dinner there for the *Lancashire Magazine* and I was amazed how clean and neat everything was. The girls from the magazine took me for a ride in the country in the morning before the luncheon, and I thought that the supposedly industrial north was more countrified and generally in better order than the south. The streets seemed to be cleaner, with no litter about, and overall a better sense of order prevailed. It was a real pleasure.

Another time, I did a literary lunch and dinner in Keighley with the marvellous Maeve Binchey who, as well as being one of our best contemporary novelists, is without any doubt the best after-dinner speaker I have heard. She is an absolute riot.

Before the dinner Maeve asked very sweetly, would I mind if she spoke first as she was a bit nervous?

I would have much preferred speaking first but, being the gentleman I am, I agreed. Maeve was brilliant and I had the most difficult time following her. I made my talk short and sweet; I could have listened to her all night.

The next day we were to attend a luncheon and book-signing session at Nostell Priory, a magnificent old country house. This time I made sure that my short and sweet contribution was delivered before Maeve brought the house down. I would love to be able to write her after-dinner stories, but I'm sure that one day we will see them all in print.

I managed to persuade Maeve and her husband Gordon, and John Braine and Janet Barber, to come down to Plymouth for the West of England Writers' Congress (of which I was vice-chairman), where I had the greatest pleasure of all, being able to sit back and listen to them without having to contribute myself.

It seemed that I was doomed to literary lunches only in the north of England. There was a one-off half way down, a literary lunch at Ross-on-Wye where the other authors were the lovely Dulcie Gray, a most prolific and excellent novelist, Michael Dennison and Peter York, who co-wrote the extremely successful *Sloane Rangers' Handbook*.

My old friend Robin Treaton came down from Birmingham as my guest at this luncheon. To my surprise, I sold a great number of books – apparently Robin had practically bludgeoned people into buying them. I thought I'd have to take him with me to every literary occasion.

I once was called upon to give a lecture, not a literary one, in my own home town.

Every year the good vicar of Wallingford, namely the Reverend Good, organises five Lent lectures and he invites people from different walks of life to speak in the lovely old town hall. The speakers are not necessarily religious people, more a cross-section of society. There's usually a central theme each year which relates to Christianity or the Church. The year before my lecture the theme had been ethics, and we went to hear Richard Ingrams speak on the ethics of journalism. He has a bookshop in Wallingford and although he's not the person who immediately springs to mind when this subject is under discussion, he gave a first-class talk. During his lecture I sat next to a lady who had brought her very young baby with her and, just as Richard Ingrams started to talk, it started to cry. Without a moment's hesitation, she pulled up her jumper exposing a bare bosom, stuck her baby on it and it suckled happily through the lecture, and why not? It would be interesting to know if in twenty years' time the baby becomes a gifted journalist.

In my year the theme of the lectures was the media. I had to talk on the media, medicine and the Church. I felt a bit out of my depth. Other speakers included Michael Grade's deputy talking about television and the Church; somebody else spoke on communications and the Church. I worked harder at this lecture than I have done for any other and by my reckoning would have rated it a draw.

Having resigned myself to always speaking in the north of England, out of the blue the London Street Bookshop at Reading asked me to speak at the civic centre to the UK Federation of Business and Professional Women. This was only sixteen miles from home and I thought a step in the right direction.

I do not know Reading very well, and do not enjoy driving into it. I set off on the Oxford–Reading road, which is a beautiful undulating run with wide expanses of fields and woods, coming into Reading over Caversham Bridge. This was the easy bit. Then I plunged into the subterranean maze that leads to the Hexagon, the civic centre and the Butts shopping centre. I thought that speaking at the civic centre might give me privileged parking, so warily picked my way through underground passages to a place where an official was putting some bollards down and where a notice proclaimed 'Civic centre car park'.

I explained to him that I was speaking at the civic centre but, instead of welcoming me, he directed me towards the Butts multi-storey car park, which caters for the big shopping centre. There was a long, winding ascending ramp that I felt had a sinister atmosphere about it. I went through the bottom of the ramp, expecting an automatic ticket machine, but there was no barrier or anything.

I drove up the long ramp, parked and looked round for signs about payment. There was none to be seen.

I came out of the first exit, went down to the civic centre and met the lady from the London Street Bookshop. I enquired as to whether the Butts car park was free at night and was assured that this was so. We went to the room in which the meeting was to be held but found it already occupied by a group of ten or so men having a meeting. On an indicator board outside, the business women's meeting was allocated to a much smaller room. As we went into our room, I wondered if someone had been switching the room markers. Not only was it quite inadequate for the numbers coming to the meeting, but also it had not been cleared up after the last occupants. There were tables arranged down the middle of the room, piled with dirty coffee cups and trays. To save time, these energetic business ladies rolled up their sleeves and cleared away the coffee cups etc., piled up the tables, and crammed in

93

chairs to hold the anticipated numbers. Slowly the room filled up with lady accountants, nurses, bankers, solicitors, health visitors, etc.

Later than expected, the chairperson, who had been held up in a traffic jam, came into the room in a soaking wet blouse. I wondered if she'd been posing for *Playboy* pictures but she assured me she had only been drenched in wine, which I thought was better still! (Apparently it was all quite innocent – she'd been carrying some boxes of wine for the do afterwards and one of them had burst, covering her.)

It was the fulfilment of one of my ambitions: there was I, the only man in a party of forty attractive women. I only wished there was some way I could have joined their Society.

We had a good meeting and they very kindly bought lots of books; in fact, it's the only time that I've ever sold out.

When it was all over, I went up into the gloom of the Butts centre, got into my car and drove home.

Three or four days later, when we were getting the car out, Pam noticed something wrapped round my windscreen wiper. It was a note saying I'd been fined £15 for parking in the Butts car park without a ticket. I hit the roof. I sent a long letter to the chief executive of Reading Council saying how difficult it was to pay for something if there was nowhere obvious to pay.

I went on to elaborate about the room that I spoke in, saying it was the first time I'd had to clear a room of tables, cups and chairs before I spoke and I said I looked forward to his comments. To the Council's great credit and, on enquiring, I found that if I had walked further into the car park, there were big 'pay and display' signs. However, they wrote back to me with a letter of apology, waiving the fine.

My next speaking engagement after Reading was, of course, back up north again. This was to a library lecture at a literary week in Stockport. The actual venue was Cheadle Hulme Library. This was quite exciting because

I'd been to Cheadle Hulme School when I was eight. I was able to go back and have a look at the house where I'd lived fifty years before, and the lady who lives there now very kindly showed me round.

I'd had to catch the only convenient non-stop train from Didcot to Stockport, which meant that Barry Richards, an old friend and the Pelham rep for the area, had to meet me at lunchtime and entertain me for the day. He offered me about six options, one of which was to go home to have a salad, which we decided to do. I thought it would put him to the least trouble. To my utter amazement he produced fifteen different types of salads, plus quiches, pâtés and all sorts. He kindly took me round to my old house and Cheadle Hulme School and when his wife Linda arrived home in the evening, I was offered a choice of haute cuisine dishes. Not wishing to cause them any extra work, I said I'd be very happy with an omelette, only to see the family tucking into the likes of chicken Kiev, coq au vin and poached salmon. And then when it came to a sweet, again there were about a dozen different desserts to choose from. 'So this is how publishers' reps live, is it, Barry?' I asked. But there was a secret behind it – they'd had a party the day before and some guests couldn't come so they'd had an abundance of food left over.

But I didn't let them get away with it. From then on whenever I wrote to Barry and Linda I addressed them as Mr and Mrs Richards, Caterers.

They were a most hospitable couple: Barry not only took me sight-seeing, fed me, ferried me to the meetings and back to my hotel, but also insisted on picking me up at 8 o'clock the following morning and running me to the station.

My talk to the UK Federation of Business and Professional Women in Reading had introduced me to southern society, and we had a marvellous literary dinner at the new Ramada Hotel, Reading, where the other two speakers were Nigel Rees, who's written a huge number of books, is an expert on graffiti, a well-known radio and television personality and who has now written his first (excellent) novel, *The News Makers*. The star of the evening and a great person to meet was Willie Rushton, one of England's really true wits. It was an extremely successful evening. It was a lovely hotel and we were able to get a lot of our friends to come along and I was quite amazed at the numbers of books that were sold in one evening.

One thing leads to another. Following the Ramada I was booked to speak to a Writing for Pleasure class in Newbury, invited to give a lecture at the Reading Literary Festival in June with a repeat performance in Stockport, this time to speak to the Conservative Ladies' Supper Club. Apparently they'd only ever had one other author and that was Jeffrey Archer when he was doing pre-election literary lunches. I was glad he wasn't going to be there as I'm sure I would have started off by saying, 'This is the first time I've been to Sale' or some other place than the one I was actually in.

I think all these literary-type occasions are of great benefit to the writer, though not in commercial terms. If you add up the profit made on the books sold at any luncheon or dinner, it's unlikely that it would pay the train fare to the venue, never mind the hotel bill. The main benefit, from the author's point of view, is publicity, which is always useful and, of course, it's good for your ego.

Writing is an isolated, lonely business and being flattered by having a captive public audience to listen to you speaking about your own work is a great boost to your morale.

In recent years writers have tended to get together more. The most important gathering of budding authors is the Writers' Summer School in Derby where about four hundred writers live under the same roof for one week. There is also the West Country Writers' Association. To join this latter set you must have some connection with the West Country, or have written about the West Country and had at least a couple of hardback books published.

I was their secretary for three years and remember the
first conference I organised for them. We had many
distinguished people, such as Henry Williamson, Kenneth
Allsop, the President, Christopher Fry, and our guest of
honour was Jenny Lee, then Minister for Arts. The West
Country Writers' meetings were rather special in that they
weren't workshops like most writing weekends. We would
meet in a different West Country town each year, and the
local authorities always gave us a civic reception. We had
an annual general meeting and a few celebrated speakers,
a large luncheon and then usually theatre on the Saturday
evening.

I remember the first one that I organised in Exeter. Pam and I had to escort Christopher Fry and Jenny Lee to the Northcott Theatre to see *The Tempest* performed in Edwardian dress, and afterwards the cast lined up to receive Christopher Fry and Jenny Lee as if they were royalty.

There are now writing weekends and organisations which have sprung up all over the country, mainly created by people who have been unable to get into the Derbyshire summer school, so there are alternatives if you're not one of the lucky four hundred.

One year I was a speaker and chairman of the Southern Writers' Conference at Chichester. I went up to speak at the Scarborough Writers' Weekend, travelling up on the train with the star of the weekend, Margaret Drabble, John Braine being one of the other speakers. I was a guest at the Leicester Writers' Circle, many of whom were established writers, and presented the prizes at their annual dinner. I also had a lovely weekend in the Lake District with the Northern Writers, in a beautiful lakeside hotel.

It's unlikely that I would have got into print or been invited to any of these occasions unless I'd been a doctor. Everybody has a consuming interest in medicine of some sort or another, and writing is something you can pursue from your home without it interfering with your job. You don't have to move house, or change your wife, and you can have a new career and explore the world with your pen without ever leaving your front door or giving up the way you earn your daily bread.

We all need our own formula for survival and mine was to practise medicine and dabble in writing and be involved with writers.

I used to say that I was completely schizophrenic: my doctor friends thought of me as a writer and my writer friends thought of me as a doctor. But this, in fact, was quite true. Somehow, confining myself to one rôle was more than I could cope with: I had to give an excuse for any inadequacies I might present in either rôle.

The main benefit of my writing was not financial – this was small – it was the fact that it helped me take a more balanced view of life. Wordsworth said, 'A poet's job is to describe people's experiences,' and of course, so is a writer's. Being a medical writer I was able, through my own experiences and those of the people I dealt with, to give comfort to others having to face similar situations. So, through my writing I was also practising medicine.

I will never, ever consider that I am a real writer. Real writers are creative people who explore new barriers. I'm just somebody who records day-to-day events, and as a doctor I have had privileged access to other people's lives. I consider myself fortunate to have had a few books published.

CHAPTER 11

It's Quicker by Tube

Although now officially retired from active medicine, I still do a lot of counselling on the telephone. Barely a day goes by without a former patient ringing me to chat about his or her particular ailments. I try to keep in touch by reading medical journals, noting all the incredible strides that medicine is making – unbelievable brain transplants, laser surgery, etc.

Amazing things were beginning to happen in the few years before I retired, particularly in the field of midwifery.

I experienced for the first time the techniques involved in test-tube babies and other new procedures which gave childless couples the opportunity of having a family that they otherwise wouldn't have had. This remarkable achievement usually solved all sorts of other problems for the couples involved, as was illustrated all too well in the case of Steven and Sonia Martin.

Steven and Sonia were favourite patients of mine. I had known them literally since birth, having attended both their arrivals as home confinements, back in the days when home was the usual place to be born. After Sonia's birth the family sent me a dozen bottles of champagne. As a result of all this I was an honoured guest at their wedding, sitting at the top table.

It was totally undeserved, as my only contribution to Sonia's arrival in the world was to sit drinking a cup of tea while our then midwife, the admirable Nurse Plank, did all the hard work.

Much of the credit one receives in general practice is not merited, as are the complaints but, as an elderly physician from Winchcombe once observed, we tend to get more than our fair share of praise.

Sonia and Steven were a very good-looking couple, and played a lively part in the young people's activities in the town.

Steven was captain of the Tadchester Rugby Club as well as being chairman of the Round Table. Sonia played hockey for Tadchester Ladies and was a busy member of the Inner Circle. Both played tennis, swam, surfed, sailed and took part in most physical activities that were going on.

They were quite delightful, had been a 'pair' since leaving school, and had been regular mates (probably in the full sense of the word) for seven years until their marriage.

There was little doubt that their marriage was going to be a success. Steven was an accountant; Sonia worked in a bank. They had a nice house, no financial worries and were quite the leaders of young Tadchester society.

They had been married about three years when I first began to notice something was amiss. They began to come into the surgery from time to time, separately, complaining of minor problems such as headaches, indigestion, insomnia. When we met socially, they seemed to have lost their sparkle; not that anyone could go on sparkling forever, but I couldn't help sensing that something was really wrong.

They began to visit me more frequently. Sonia began to exhibit the signs of an acute depression; Steven, also on the depressive side, began to drop hints that there were problems with the physical side of their marriage, in particular that the marital act was becoming more difficult for him. The collective signs and symptoms were suggestive of a third party mucking up their marriage. This I doubted; I would have known about it beforehand – in Tadchester you couldn't get away with anything; patients would even tell me if they saw Pam going into a bank.

Sonia's depression became progressively worse, and I couldn't get to the root of the problem. It was time for some positive action: I sent them a note saying I would like to see them together at the surgery.

After making and cancelling a couple of appointments they eventually came, puzzled about why I had sent for them, sitting sullenly in front of my desk with no sign of the togetherness that had been the hallmark of their relationship over a decade.

'Sonia and Steven,' I said, 'I've known you both now since the day you were born; you are more than just patients, and I'm worried about you both. Something is wrong and I don't know what it is. Won't you tell me and see if I can help?'

At this Sonia burst into tears. 'You tell him, Steven,' she sobbed – and then it all came out. All their friends had children, and although they had tried continually since they were first married they had not managed to conceive. This had become such an issue between them that Steven was now barely potent. Each thought it must be the other's fault.

'You silly pair,' I said. 'Why on earth didn't you come and see me before? This is a very common problem and there are all sorts of things we can do about it. From now on you tackle this problem with me.'

Facing the problem with me made a great difference to them. I gave both of them a general examination, could find nothing amiss, and arranged for them to be investigated at an infertility clinic.

Rarely was this unsuccessful – but what was surprising was the number of patients who became pregnant before ever reaching the clinic. It was as if just facing up to the issue gave them some sort of release that made conception possible.

Unfortunately with Steven and Sonia this was not the case. Over the next three years they underwent every infertility test known to the medical profession. There were sperm counts, inspection of fallopian tubes, infertility drugs, monitoring of vaginal temperatures, all to no avail. All the tests were encouraging but, in spite of the various drugs given to Sonia, they still didn't conceive. It was no comfort to them that I was able to tell them truthfully that, even in these circumstances, I had patients who had still gone on to conceive.

After three years of hoping, the couple were back in the depths of despair. Sonia was acutely depressed and Steven was barely potent again.

One evening they came to see me together, with very

determined looks in their faces. Steven, who had obviously been nominated spokesman, took some time to get to the point. 'We would like a test tube ... I mean a test-tube baby,' he said. 'Whatever it costs.' They sat holding hands, looking defiantly at me.

'In your circumstances,' I said, 'this is a perfectly sensible sort of action. I have no experience of the procedure, but I will try and find something out as soon as possible.'

Sonia came round the desk and hugged me, tears streaming down her face and sobbing, 'Oh, thank you, Doctor Bob, for being so understanding!'

At the time, this procedure was not available under the National Health Service and it took a while to find out who to send them to. Eventually everything was organised and they went up to a clinic near London.

It was found that there was no reason why they should not have a baby by this method, and although they were unsuccessful at their first attempt, Sonia's second admission produced results. She conceived twins, and nine months later gave birth to two healthy boys in a London hospital.

Once her pregnancy had been confirmed, Sonia asked if there was any chance of my keeping up the family tradition and delivering her offspring at home. I now delivered only about one baby a year, so it was a definite no. This was science-fiction medicine; hospital, and a special unit at that, was the only place for her.

The twins were the answer to Steven's and Sonia's problems. Depression and impotence disappeared, and the pair returned to being the happy young couple they used to be.

Medicine has made some great advances, test-tube babies being one of the more spectacular ones. There are still some problems to sort out in this field, like what to do with spare embryos and the ethics of research on embryos. There is also the frightening thought that you could freeze an embryo in liquid nitrogen in 1988 and, as far as one knows, keep it indefinitely...

But, these are problems for someone else – the Church, the state, the medical profession, who knows?

From my point of view it had been the means of restoring to good health a lovely young couple, with the added bonus of two strapping boys becoming part of a loving, caring household.

CHAPTER 12

How to Get a Book Published

When I was in general practice, I had found the pressures difficult to cope with. My main energies were taken up accepting the responsibilities that went with the job.

Sometimes you had to act on impulse and have faith in your own judgement. You couldn't always be right; you could only try your best and be as careful and conscientious as possible.

You also, however difficult, had to come to terms with the fact that you could not be all things to all men.

I had been lucky that the Tadchester hospital consultants were always ready to give advice and were willing to see patients in their own homes. We had a good relationship with the main hospital ten miles away, where there were full-time specialists and where we sent our more serious cases. As the local hospital began to reduce its services, more and more of our cases went to the main hospital. I hated to admit it but, in some ways, it was a relief.

Before, the vast majority of cases went into the local cottage hospital where we looked after them ourselves; now, once you knew a case was safely in an ambulance, it was somebody else's responsibility, the patient was going to

106

somebody who was better equipped, somewhere where there was a bigger team, somewhere where there were people with more specialised knowledge than we had.

In spite of all the stresses and strains that I had in general practice, including the awful trauma of a child dying while I was anaesthetising him, and deaths in the young and people whom I had known well, the area that I had not thought would be a main area of pressure, particularly never of strain, was my hobby of writing.

It had long been my ambition to write humorous books about medicine: one, because I enjoyed writing; two, because I think that writing is an important medium of communication.

It was interesting to hear from the editor of one woman's magazine to which I contributed, that the commonest single question she was asked for advice about by parents was masturbation in small children. I had never ever been consulted by a parent about this.

People liked the anonymity of confiding in someone they didn't know.

I realised that simple medical stories could possibly be of great comfort to people who were having frightening experiences. They would see that other people had these experiences, survived them, and that they weren't all that frightening after all.

I wrote a series of articles based on this theme, called *Our Village*, for one of the 'give-away' medical magazines, and when I had done a good number, enough to form a nucleus of a book with continuity of characters, I started to submit them to newspapers, thinking they might be serialised.

I tried every national daily and every national Sunday at least twice, without any result.

Then I sent them to streams of publishers, always with a negative reply.

I was also writing a number of lay medical articles and had been commissioned by a publisher to write a book on how to put on weight. One of my patients had said that he hadn't read it but kept a copy in the back of his car for a month and found that he had put on three pounds.

The publisher thought that in every office there was a thin girl who desperately wanted to wear a bikini, or a sleeveless sweater but was too bony to risk it.

It was good media material; however, hardly anybody bought the book but it did result in a leading British magazine asking me to write an article on the subject.

I managed to arrange a lunch with the deputy editor of the magazine. My article was misprinted but that didn't really matter very much as during the luncheon this very powerful deputy editor looked at me and said, 'Can you write anecdotal humorous medicine?'

'I think so,' I said, my ears pricking at the idea.

'Right,' he said. 'Go and write me three thousand words and I'll pay you a hundred pounds for the option of buying it.'

I, of course, already had thirty or forty thousand words written, so I sent him a sample three days later.

He was on the 'phone straightaway. 'This is marvellous stuff,' he said. 'Now write me thirty thousand words.'

I polished up the material I had already written, and sent it to him.

I was immediately summoned to lunch in the executive suite of this massive publishing house.

Coincidentally I had a friend in publishing who had edited all the other work I had done before. This was mainly on medical matters. He was moving to a general publishing house and said he would be happy to publish a book of my stories. It seemed as if all my dreams were coming true at once.

I managed to arrange for him to attend lunches with the deputy editor and features editor of this great magazine. It was quite frightening. The building was huge. You could have got virtually the whole of my West Country town inside it.

This magazine, which was world famous, had a floor of its own and before one of the eventual five lunches that we had with these two very senior people, I was taken round the whole of the office and introduced as their new, bestselling author.

They were delighted with the stuff that I had provided.

Not only were they going to publish it, but were also going to use it as the basis of their new-year television advertising as a balance to some articles they had done about a politician who had disgraced himself.

I thought I was going to become rich and famous.

I went to London for the final lunch, after which we were to sign the contracts. Also joining us for lunch was a delightful chap from a national daily, who was to do the actual serialisation.

I came bounding in, smiling, to meet frosty faces that remained so over lunch.

I was attacked by the deputy editor. Lord knows why.

Whether he had over-reached himself in some way or not I don't know, but I had changed in one week from being the best thing since sliced bread, to being an awful writer.

If only I could write like I talked, he said.

The only chance that the book might be serialised would be if the journalist could make something of it, and it was pretty doubtful that he could.

There would be no contracts signed today.

With this anticipated success I had managed to persuade a literary agent to take me on to guard my interests. I 'phoned her about the whole thing. She was quite bemused.

She said, 'There's nothing we can do about it. We'll just have to wait and see.'

The nice man from the national daily came down to see me at home and agreed to serialise my anecdotal stories. A fortnight later I had a 'phone call from the deputy editor saying that the stories were absolutely terrific and we would soon have a celebration lunch. I could have kicked myself for having so little faith.

After three or four weeks, having not heard about this celebration lunch, I rang the deputy editor to say that I felt this celebration lunch ought to be on me; I had already had five lunches on them.

He, rather cautiously, replied in a tone that gave rise to all sorts of uncertainties. He would prefer to get in touch with me, he said.

He did get in touch with me a week later. I had a letter saying they had decided not to do the serialisation of my work.

It was quite beyond my comprehension. I poured out my woes to my editor friend.

'Don't worry,' he said, 'we've still got the book to look forward to and that's coming on nicely.'

One month later the famous magazine sent a secretary in a taxi round to his publishing house saying that they wanted a copy of the manuscript of the book immediately.

They had decided to serialise it in their magazine after all, at the end of the next month.

A copy of what we had done so far was hastily assembled, bundled into the taxi, and we were smiling once more. Oh, we of little faith.

A month passed and nothing happened. I asked my agent to enquire as to the fate of my serialisation (I daren't ring them up myself).

She rang me back and said, 'I'm very sorry to say that they have decided, again, not to do it after all.'

I did wonder whether magazine editors ever slept at night; I understand they have a pretty high mortality rate.

I thought it might be worth trying to have the stories serialised somewhere else. When we had got near to finishing them in book form, I sent them to one of the national Sunday papers that I had contributed to in the past but they returned them saying they were sorry, it wasn't for them.

'Never mind,' said my book editor. 'The book's going to come out. Stop worrying. It'll hold its own.'

And it did come out. It had a smashing cover, now all that it needed was people to buy it.

The new book had been out one week when my book editor rang.

'Bob,' he said. 'I have some bad news for you.'

'Come on,' I said, 'tell me the worst.'

He said, 'I'm afraid the receivers are in.'

His new publishing firm had gone bankrupt. I thought this was the end, but in the dying moments of the publishing house the publicity officer had sent some review copies out. The national Sunday paper that turned my book down for serialisation, gave the book the most marvellous review any author could wish for. It must have struck a chord in the reviewer's heart for I felt he gave it a better review than it deserved. The newspaper, now reading the review in its own columns, decided they would serialise it after all.

My agent, God bless her, as soon as she heard that the publishing house was in receivership, got in a taxi and rescued the manuscript. Within a month we had a serialisation in a national Sunday paper pending, and had sold the book to a large established publishing house who turned out to be honest and fair. Over the years they have become almost like family and I've remained with them ever since.

But the ups and downs of this period had some effect on me. I had some swallowing difficulties, for which I had every test under the sun. My senior partner sent me to specialists; I had X-rays but nothing was found.

He called me into his surgery one evening after the latest batch of investigation results came in, all negative again.

'You know what the problem is, my lad?' he said.

'I wish I did,' I replied.

'I think it's this little bit of bother you've had with the

magazine. Once you've left all that behind I think your troubles will leave you.'

There was a period of fifteen years from when I started offering my series of anecdotal, humorous medical articles as a possible book, until they actually appeared in book form.

I had literally dozens of rejections, and the trauma of this inexplicable experience with the editors from this leading magazine. Yet, whenever I go to a writing week-end or to a writer's conference, my fellow writers will quite rightly say to me, 'God, you're lucky to get books published.'

There are a few requisites needed to become an established writer and to have books published, but you don't require great gifts, or even great skills.

What has never been told before is *your* story in *your* own words.

What you need is perseverance; of course, luck is an essential; and, if you are really lucky, a good agent.

It was interesting that the national Sunday that serialised my first book said they would be happy to serialise any subsequent book of the same type. However, when the second book appeared, they didn't like it, gave it a terrible review and didn't serialise it. The third book they gave a good review to, but no further serialisations.

Subsequent books have been serialised in other British magazines, and in New Zealand, Holland, Denmark, and there were German editions of the first four books of the series, plus paperback and large print editions.

I have been very lucky.

CHAPTER 13

Full Circle

There's little doubt when I look back over my life that some of the happiest times have been spent on holiday with the children, taking them to new, exciting places.

Children, of course, grow up and from sixteen onwards they tend to go on holiday on their own. Ours were very good and for many years continued the pattern, finding a spare week so that we could have a family get-together in some holiday situation.

Nowadays, holidays are no longer family affairs, and Pam and I tend to go off on our own or with a couple of friends.

The arrival of Daisy May, our first grandchild, provided the opportunity for family holidays again, and we, as doting grandparents, could offer the added service of mobile baby-sitting.

We had done some scouting in France and on a holiday with Jim and Tighe Reeves had found a delightful place in Dinard, Hotel Les Pins, which consisted of about a dozen very well-equipped apartments in a converted farmhouse.

There were all sorts of facilities – an indoor games room with Space Invaders, darts, table tennis and billiards; some lovely grounds and a big barbecue area at the back. There was, of course, a place for playing *boule*, and for a special Breton game in which you threw metal discs on to a board. In the evenings you could come down to a communal lounge which had its own bar.

The thing that made this particular place so attractive were the proprietors, Monsieur and Madame Perrier (as in Perrier water). They were absolutely delightful, nothing was too much trouble. They were always at hand for a chat, help and advice. They even produced a syringe for me to unblock one of Pam's ears. We had a maid service, we could have had petit déjeuner (breakfast) in the small restaurant there. If we wanted, bread would be delivered each day.

Monsieur Perrier's great love was fishing and a day's free fishing was thrown in with every fortnight's stay, or you could organise private trips with him. His boat was his pride and joy.

The farmhouse was on the top of a hill just outside Dinard. Being in the country it was completely quiet, and it was less than half a mile from the nearest beach.

We booked the biggest apartment they had, which was a six-berther, for the second half of May and the first half of June.

One of the many advantages of Dinard is the fact that it's only a few miles from the port of St Malo, and we hoped that family and friends would come to stay with us, travelling over on a night boat. Thus, they wouldn't have to bring a car as we could pick them up from the port.

We loved the Dinard, Dinan, St Malo area; it is a part of Brittany that never seems to get crowded. There are lots of glorious beaches, and in Dinard itself there is the most marvellous promenade walk for several miles, all on the flat, going right round the town. I remember one visit there with some friends, when we walked past the yacht club one spring evening, and the whole cliff face behind the club was covered in fairy lights and classical music was coming out of a series of loudspeakers along the promenade – it was quite delightful.

Pam and I travelled on our own from Portsmouth to Cherbourg. We wanted to be the welcoming party at the apartment as Paul and Gill and Daisy May and Gill's parents, Liz and Eddie, were arriving the next day.

A lovely morning dawned and we drove through the countryside, down to Portsmouth. We were blessed with a smooth ferry crossing, then motored about 150 miles to spend our first night in a quayside hotel at Cancale.

From our hotel bedroom window we could see oyster beds stretching out in the sea, and tractors were busy toing and froing, dragging literally tons of oysters off to local hotels, markets, etc.

The next morning we left early for Dinard as we wanted to call at the hypermarket in St Malo which Gill, my daughter-in-law, thinks is one of the seven wonders of the world. (If she had her own way she would spend her whole holiday there.)

It's absolutely vast – you can buy anything from a car to a packet of peppermints. A huge area is devoted to a fantastic array of foods of every kind, and there are restaurants, and shops for clothes, kitchen and garden equipment . . . everything.

The whole place is immaculate and the service is very pleasant. Moreover most things are inexpensive, particularly the wine. The wine that we bought for under a pound a bottle in the St Malo hypermarket would have cost £5 or £6 in a modest French restaurant.

We had a good hour's shopping in the hypermarket, packing the car with wine, cheese, eggs, etc., then set off for the Hotel Les Pins which was about fifteen minutes' drive away.

Our apartment consisted of a huge double bedroom with a six-foot bed and an en-suite toilet and bathroom, a general bathroom, two single beds to be made up in the main living/lounge/dining room, and another room with two bunks in it.

We waited anxiously for Paul, Gill, Liz, Eddie and Daisy May to arrive. It's lovely to show people something new. Like old times, we were back on holiday with the children again.

On the first night, the Perriers invited us to have a drink with them and, realising there were three pairs of adults, offered us, for very little extra money, a double bedroom next door to our apartment, so Liz and Eddie could have more room and privacy.

We all had a great time. Liz and Eddie had spent most of their time in India and this was their first visit to France for many years, although Eddie, in his younger days as a jockey, had ridden at Deauville. Paul, who is a bad traveller, had taken the shortest sea crossing, via Dover to Calais, and he and Gill had spent two days en route having a look round before joining us at Dinard. They had spent one night in Honfleur and one in Amboise, an island on which we had camped when Paul was a small boy.

Dinard was full of interesting things: a market twice a week, lovely walks, bays, beaches and shops. One day we took the ferry to the old walled town of St Malo where we lunched, Daisy May enjoying every minute of it. We went down to the golden sands of Sable d'Or, then, after a week, Paul and Gill drove Liz and Eddie back to Cherbourg for their return home, and the next day we picked up Jane from St Malo. She just had three days with us there, but somehow time has no real measurement – it could have been three hours or three weeks.

Although the apartment was well equipped for self-catering we sometimes ate out, most often at the Hotel de

117

Paix in the town. This was an old family hotel which had a very comprehensive menu that worked out at about £5 a head. It had a nice atmosphere and would have cost three times as much for its English equivalent.

Paul and Gill are superb cooks and really went to town with all the exotic food they could buy in the Dinard shops and markets.

We reluctantly said goodbye to Jane and then a few days later we had to wave farewell to Paul and Gill. Before they left we went for a splendid lunch at Erquy, further down the coast, where we sat on the top floor of a restaurant and had a superb meal as we watched the fishing boats come into the harbour. It's a large fishing port and as you look out over the main harbour wall you could see bay after bay along the coastline.

We weren't alone for long. A couple of days later I went down to the St Malo ferry to pick up Margaret and Terry and their son Nigel. Margaret types my books.

They also loved Dinard, especially the Hotel Les Pins, and we went with them to some of the places we discovered with Paul and Gill. Further along the coast we found a marvellous view from Cap Frehel. On one or two occasions we went walking with different visitors and scrambled over Fort le Latte.

Margaret and Terry thought they'd had their best French meal ever in the Hotel de Paix, and they made up their minds to come back to Hotel Les Pins again.

I think there's a lot to be said for a short holiday. By virtue of special travel concessions on the Portsmouth to St Malo ferry, Jane and Margaret's family were able to enjoy France and then return on the night of the third day, which worked out at less than staying in a two-star English hotel for a weekend.

The last couple to join us were our old neighbours, Stan and Pauline Williams, who came for ten days, bringing their Range Rover.

Outings were split between my little Ford and, for the

longer journeys, Stan's Range Rover. In the latter, being higher up, we got a much better view of the countryside.

We'd been to Dinard with Stan and Pauline before, so with Stan driving we ventured further afield. One day we travelled eastwards, following the coastline, past St Brieuc as far as Morlaix, exploring as we went. Perhaps the most picturesque stretch was the Baie d'Lannion which ran from St Michel en Grove to St Eclamp. It was a long day's drive, but worth it.

Having more time, we were also able to fulfil one of our ambitions, which was to catch the ferry that plied from St Malo to Dinard, and up the River Rance to Dinan and back. On reflection I think we should have taken the boat just one way and come back by bus, but we'd booked a return and there was a bar that served drinks and coffee, which was some consolation. The River Rance is cut off from the St Malo/Dinard bay by a great barrage and tidal power station which I believe is the only one of its kind in France.

We boarded the steamer with about a hundred school children and passed through one side of the barrier, then on past a whole number of riverside towns and marinas, right up into the town of Dinan itself. Or rather to the lower part of Dinan where we could get out and have a meal before the boat turned round and went back. The main town of Dinan is on top of a hill. What we hadn't appreciated was that on the way back, the boat went to St Malo before it went to Dinard, which made the journey longer. There was only one small problem; I found the steps from the ferry station at Dinard up to the top road pretty hard going; there were hundreds of them, but I made it all right with a bit of puffing and panting.

On Pentecost Sunday we went to Sable d'Or for a special meal at a hotel. We knew it would be difficult to get in somewhere, so we'd booked ahead – all the young confirmants were out having great family meals.

In the hotel there was one little boy who was king for the

day, with thirty or forty relatives all dining together after his confirmation. Their meal included a special cake which looked like a mountain of profiteroles. Everybody was dressed in his or her Sunday best, except one or two rather countrified gentlemen, probably farmers, firmly keeping their hats (trilbies or flat caps) on throughout the festivities.

After Stan and Pauline had gone, the next day Pam and I wandered round the town – we had just two or three days left to ourselves. We followed the promenade east out of Dinard, finding new bays and beaches that we'd never discovered before. We had parked our car in the town and had noticed a GB plate on a car parked a few yards from ours. When we returned to our car the other GB people were heading back to theirs, and lo and behold it was my midwife from Tadchester, Amanda Leak (our 'leaky midwife' as I called her), with her husband and very tiny baby.

So we had a day with them and they came back to Hotel Les Pins. They'd brought a caravan across and had all sorts of hair-raising adventures, and finished up based at Dole. They had heard on the grapevine that we were in Dinard.

We had a splendid holiday. I'd bathed in the sea with Jane, we'd got to know our granddaughter, who was a little angel, all our guests had been good fun, and most of them were good cooks, particularly Paul, Liz and Gill.

There was an abundance of *fruits de mer* in Dinard. The fishermen seemed very busy all the time, with boats coming and going, and fish and shellfish pouring in. We had the most gorgeous prawns and mussels, as well as fresh strawberries and always a plentiful supply of wine. Somehow the French seemed to have learnt how to live better and more fully then we do.

Dinard was neat and tidy, and its harbour absolutely chockablock with boats of every sort. It was nice to drive down to the end of one beach and see the boats come in; sometimes there'd be a passenger liner moored in the bay. We'd watch the Brittany ferry boats coming in and out in the morning and evening, and we'd see the Emerard ferry coming from the Channel Islands, as well as various cargo boats. The place was alive and there was something to see all the time. I would love a little apartment overlooking the bay where I could just sit and watch. Who knows? Some day . . .

Besides dining out at the Hotel de Paix, we also explored one or two other restaurants at various prices. At one, according to our translation, we ordered half a crab mayonnaise. We had a great shock when the dish arrived. There were two huge spider crabs and a whole set of instruments, and we had to get cracking and find the crabmeat ourselves. This involved a lot of hard work with only a little reward!

When we used to go seine-net fishing in Tadchester, we used to put the spider crabs back in the sea; they weren't eaten back there. But everything that moves in France gets eaten. We had a good laugh and I must have had at least a teaspoonful of crabmeat.

Dinard has many beaches and on the main one, where in summer the whole of the promenade is filled with tables and chairs, you can get any sort of meal. There's a huge flat expanse of beach and at low tide land yachts race to and fro. There's an ice-cream parlour tucked away in a sheltered corner, where everybody who is anybody goes with their dogs for morning tea or coffee or an ice-cream, and there are a couple of little cafés which seem to be open all the year round.

We had a splendid time. On our last night at Hotel Les Pins the Perriers asked us to join them in a bottle of champagne. Their daughter was just off to America and we'd already fixed for her friend, Patricia, to come and stay with Paul and Gill for a couple of weeks to learn a bit of English and see something of England. We hoped to see her too, and promised her a trip on the Thames.

One great surprise at the Hotel Les Pins was when Margaret brought with her a new German edition of one of my books. There were mainly German guests at the hotel and one of them recognised the book.

It had always been my ambition to find somebody who'd read one of my books, or to see someone actually reading one. It was strange that I'd at last found a fan club.

One family of Germans I met in Dinard possessed all the German editions of my books at home and knew all about our family. They would ask Pam questions like, 'Did your father really do this or that?' and 'How is Paul?' and 'What's Trevor doing?' and I know that from now on I shall have a regular sale of at least four German books every time I have one printed over there.

We set off home reluctantly. We had had a really good time and even having been there for a month, would have been happy to stay on. We were looking forward to seeing our dog, Bertie. We knew he was in good hands because 'Our Norman' looked after him and the house while we were away.

We had a good crossing but driving back through

England we couldn't help noticing how we English don't seem to bother about the verges or the cleanliness of the roadsides nearly as much as the French do.

I remember being particularly impressed by a group of tall, bronzed men in skimpy bathing trunks who walked up and down the promenade at Dinard with a shovel and brush. At first I thought they were life guards. Then I thought they were collecting litter, but I was wrong – they were there purely for picking up dog dirt and there was a notice that dogs were not allowed on the beach.

I couldn't see that happening in England and I knew that Bertie certainly wouldn't have approved of it.

Anyway, *vive la France . . . vive l'entente cordial*. We shall certainly go there again.

CHAPTER 14

Cheap at Half the Price

Every spring it has been our custom to go on a river trip with our friends Joe and Lyn Church. This year we were having to postpone it as their younger daughter, Catherine, was to be married in June and Lyn would need at least six months time for a nervous breakdown before the wedding occurred. (This is completely untrue – she is one of the calmest, nicest people anyone could meet anywhere.)

We were invited to the wedding; it only made me feel old. Both Catherine and Julie, the Church's two daughters, were my babies. I had looked after Lyn during her pregnancies and had delivered Julie at home in a small cottage on the side of a steep hill in Tadchester. Now here she was, a tall, striking blonde, a very capable business woman, in fact, an absolute stunner.

I'd have to see if I could get her paired off with Trevor.

Catherine wasn't my baby in the fact that I hadn't delivered her as I had Julie. She was born in Winchcombe Hospital, but I did look after Lyn before and after delivery and saw Catherine a few hours after she was born, never realising she would turn into the gorgeous bride I was seeing today.

Catherine was marrying an old college friend, Richard, and they had the great advantage that he and his parents have started from scratch and built up the most superb hotel near Tetbury in Gloucester. In just three years the hotel had earned itself a Michelin star.

In our younger days, Joe, Lyn, Pam and I used to go seine-net fishing in the surf at Sanford-on-Sea. Later, we'd gone boating together, never at any time really snappily dressed. Now, here we all were, gathered on a most beautiful sunny day, in grey toppers and tails. I can't remember going to a nicer wedding in a nicer setting. The church was about eight miles outside Tetbury, a little Norman church surrounded by lovely stone buildings. It was so tiny that they had to put nameplaces where people sat and the curate of the parish, who was to marry them, was in fact, an elderly bishop, complete with his bishop's regalia. He was a bit out of touch with conducting wedding services, he said, having not done one for a year or two, and it was a little confusing when we were asked to pray and sing a hymn at the same time, but in some way it added to the sweetness of the occasion.

The day was absolutely glorious, one of those golden sunny days when everything in England looks green and fresh and nothing in the world can really compare with it. Unfortunately sunshine like this in our country is only too rare.

The bridegroom, Richard, must have been very popular as he had great difficulty in deciding who were going to be his ushers, in the end he had thirteen and they worked like a well-trained set of guardsmen. They were all over the place, they showed us where our car had to be parked, directed us out of the car park after the service, then all the way along the route to the reception there were signs and ushers until we pulled in to a most beautiful Cotswolds stone hotel. Outside, on a huge expanse of lawn, a jazz band that Catherine had spotted in Bristol, were playing to the guests.

As we arrived white-coated waiters welcomed us with glasses of Bucks Fizz.

It was a really special day. If you'd tried to make a film set out of an English wedding in an English country house on a lovely summer's day, you couldn't have bettered this.

The rest of the wedding kept up this standard. The wedding breakfast was out of this world, and included a most beautiful coloured patterned pâté, and salmon specially brought up from the River Tad and cooked in pastry. One of the nicest things was that all the employees, waiters, cooks, chefs at the hotel were all part of the wedding itself.

Lyn looked quite gorgeous in a wide-brimmed hat and summer dress. I'd only seen her in jumpers and jeans before. Joe, a most accomplished lecturer and speaker, usually about birds of prey, proved that he was an even better and funnier speaker at a wedding breakfast giving away his daughter, without ever once mentioning his hobby-horse, river pollution.

We didn't know many people there but we knew both Joe and Lyn's mothers and we met a whole host of new people, friends who came from Holland, and of course, the thirteen ushers.

The food and wine were excellent and, as it happened, I was sitting next to a man who valued it as highly as I did, and he should have known, as for twelve years he had owned a very up-market West Country hotel.

He told me that he was judged to have the most comprehensive wine list in the West of England with prices ranging from £3 or £4 to £200 a bottle.

I've always been curious about expensive wine and asked him, 'Who would buy a bottle of wine for £150? Was it worth it or just snobbery?'

He doubted if it was even worth spending more than £10 or £15 for a bottle unless you were one of that exceedingly small, well-endowed group who had such cultivated palates that even minor changes in taste and bouquet could be of great meaning. What used to grieve him, he said, were businessmen entertaining other business-men on expense accounts where £100 bottles of wine would be bought to impress, and at the end of the evening the wines had not been properly appreciated and half-empty bottles littered the table.

He said it was usually the people who made the least fuss about the wine who knew the most about it, and he explained that a good wine for you was the one you liked best. He felt there was a great deal of snob value attached to many wines: many people did not know whether they were enjoying a wine until they'd read the label.

He told me, 'The shorter in supply any particular wine is, the greater the demand for it and the greater the virtues placed upon it.'

It reminded me of corned beef. The British tommy of World War I virtually fought the whole of the war on corned beef and, now, through various market variations, corned beef is really a delicacy. I've always loved it, irre-spective of the price; it used to be my favourite school dinner.

My wine-expert companion told me that once a year the managing director of one of England's biggest wine importers would come to stay for a single night in his hotel. This was an annual trip to check on some of his company's warehouses a few miles away. On the first occasion my neighbour watched with interest when this 'king of wine' went in to dinner. He wondered what he would order to drink.

To his great surprise the gentleman chose his cheapest wine, a claret costing £3.70.

This seemed utterly amazing. This particular guest cer-tainly wasn't short of funds; he was a wealthy man in his own right and, anyway, you could rest assured that his trip was being paid for by the firm.

My friend was completely puzzled and made a mental note to try the wine himself. However, other events intervened and he forgot all about it until the following year, when the wine company MD came down for his annual visit.

When the managing director went in to dinner, once again he ordered the cheapest claret.

The hotelier went down to his cellar and found that he had several cases of this wine. He opened a bottle, tasted it and found it was absolutely superb. He couldn't think why he'd never tried it before: in all probability it was because it was the cheapest wine on his list.

He approached the managing director after his meal and said, 'Sir, I do apologise for being so personal, but I've noticed that each time you stay you buy a bottle of our cheapest wine. I've just tried it and it's absolutely superb; as good a wine as I've ever tasted.'

The managing director, with a twinkle in his eye, said, 'You are absolutely right. It's really a trade secret, but my fellow directors and I decided that we would put ourselves in the position of being able to afford to buy the wine we like whenever we stayed out of London at some up-market hotel. So we priced one of our choicest wines at a very low price and made sure it was stocked at the very best hotels.' He added, 'I think that we're the only people who drink it. After all, if you're entertaining an important client and are given a wine list with a price range of £3.70 to £150, it's unlikely that you would go for the bottle priced at £3.70.'

There's a moral in this story somewhere, but the greatest tragedy is that although the hotelier divulged the name of this most precious wine, I failed to write it down and I have forgotten it.

We lingered on after the wedding breakfast, walking round the grounds of this lovely hotel. We saw Catherine and Richard off on their honeymoon, their car was covered with lipstick, balloons, confetti and all the usual paraphernalia that young people try to embarrass each other with at going away times. They were to have a motoring holiday in

France, staying at a lot of prime eating and drinking places.

It was a great occasion and we saw them off in a cloud of confetti.

We'd had lots and lots of photographs taken outside the church and in the grounds when we arrived. The poor photographer was still rushing around – he hadn't taken a photograph of the ushers.

Eventually after much hard work by Joe and Catherine's father-in-law, all thirteen ushers were rounded up.

The photographer, anxious to be off, said, 'Come now, gentlemen, adopt a relaxed pose.'

Immediately, all the ushers, for some reason, loosened their waistbands, and kept moving about until eventually he got them settled.

'Right, gentlemen,' he said, 'smile for the camera. Ready, steady, go,' and at the word 'go' he clicked his camera, to

be beaten by all the ushers dropping their trousers and showing thirteen pairs of Union Jack underpants.

The place was in an uproar, but somehow it was the perfect end to a perfect British wedding in the perfect British house on a perfect British day.

CHAPTER 15

Changing Direction

I'd been feeling off-colour for a while, not really ill, but was having all sorts of odd aches and pains in my chest. There must have been reasons for them but I tended to dismiss them.

We had a late boat holiday in October with our friends Lyn and Joe Church. Their daughter's wedding in the spring had prevented our usual trip and although Pam and I have had excellent boating holidays in October, this particular one with Joe and Lyn struck a patch of mid-winter. It was cold, wet and rainy with a very strong wind. We passed down river, missing the best of that most glorious stretch of river, the Goring Gap, where tree-lined slopes come down to the river's edge, because we were stuck inside as wind and rain buffeted the boat. The weather cleared a bit towards the evening and we found a mooring some way below Whitchurch Lock.

It was warm in the boat but it was so wet everywhere we were wandering around in oilskins. The weather forecast promised some improvement.

We cast off the next morning under gloomy skies and went through Mapledurham Lock. The last time we'd

been through here it had been flooded and the whole lock
was under water. We motored on through a grey-looking
Reading, one of the few industrial areas of the Thames. At
Caversham Lock we renewed our acquaintance with the
lock keeper, with whom we'd travelled in convoy up the
river the year before, when he was taking his boat up for
a month on the canals. Then down on to picturesque
Sonning Lock looking for the spot where we'd been stuck
for three days when the river had been flooded. We
remembered that we'd rung home to tell them we were all
right, only to be told that Trevor had fallen in Sark and
had broken his thigh.

We continued on in poor weather and moored early, not
out in the country as is our usual wont, but at the upper
end of the park in Henley. I was a bit cold so stayed in the
boat while the others went off to explore the town. There
was still plenty of room for the dogs, Bertie and Jenny, to
run around but it wasn't the sort of country they really
like.

It was raining when we set off the following morning,

passing under Henley Bridge and through the lovely broad sweep of river there. We moved on to Hambledon Lock, then to Temple Lock, where we called in on our friends, Bob Munro Ashman and his wife Sian. I'd borrowed two of Bob's books by Fred Archer, the old authority on the Thames, and I'd promised to take them down by boat. Bob had been a neighbour of ours in Wallingford when he was relief lock keeper on Cleeve, Goring and Benson Locks. Temple Lock was the first lock of his own and he seemed very happy there. Meanwhile it was still pouring with rain. Bob was optimistic; there was a good chance of it clearing up.

We continued on down river, through Marlow, passing, as we approached Marlow Lock, the huge weir stream that ran for several hundred yards on one side of the river. We somehow chugged through Cookham without even noticing, because before we knew where we were, we were in Cookham Lock. The stretch from Marlow to Cookham is unattractive compared with the Thames up river. The river's so wide you feel you're at sea and there's a lot of river development. Although there are some pretty parts, it's all rather drab.

Leaving Cookham Lock we entered what I consider is the most beautiful stretch of the river and this was our main objective, Cliveden Reach. We'd originally intended to spend a night there but it was blowing a gale so we moored up on one of the many islands, had lunch and cruised down as far as Boulters Lock and started on our return journey. It was quite lovely, with wooded slopes going up to Cliveden and clusters of islands. All through this stretch you could moor and have your own island. The dogs adored it.

Just after leaving Cookham Lock, the boat suddenly lost power; we hardly made any headway at all. There was a huge crosswind and it was pouring with rain – we were at a loss as to what to do. We debated whether to go into a boat yard, wondering if the clutch was slipping.

The stretch from Cookham Lock to Marlow took us over two hours. When I looked at the bank sometimes we didn't appear to be moving at all. We decided to negotiate Marlow Lock and then find a boat yard. I'd once had a similar experience when the throttle was slipping but it didn't feel quite like that. I was worried about passing the huge weir stream on our port side just beyond Marlow Lock. With so little headway on we could be in trouble. It seemed hours coming, I was quite dry-mouthed. There were hardly any other boats on the river, and there was a wind sweeping right across it. There was nothing to protect us. The engine could barely keep our nose into the wind.

Eventually, around a bend in the river, there was the shelter of Marlow Lock, and it was open. We pulled in to a perfect stop, with me putting the propeller astern to bring us to a complete halt.

I dreaded what it was going to be like coming out of the lock.

The lock filled up, the gates opened. I started up the engine and we cruised out, to our amazement, under full power.

'It must have been the clutch not properly engaged,' said Joe.

We pulled clear of the lock and moored up behind a boat with an experienced boatman aboard. He diagnosed our problem: 'You must have had a plastic bag round your propeller and by going astern in the lock you cleared it. You were very lucky.'

Sea Grey was built in such a way that it was extremely difficult to get at the propeller – it would have meant diving down beneath the boat and this wasn't the weather for it. The gale was blowing into the bank here but even so we lashed ourselves to the quayside with about three extra ropes. Joe went into the town to buy a Chinese takeaway and this, washed down with a bottle of wine, seemed to reduce our troubles miraculously.

134

It was a bit finer the next morning. We set off, with the engine under full power and we made good progress upstream, passing once more through Henley, which is such a lovely sight from the river, up through Shiplake and moored again, as we had on an earlier night, beside the field just below Whitchurch Lock. By now there was a tremendous gale blowing and we hardly dared get out of the boat. (Thank goodness for our inside toilet.)

Joe, mustering every item of waterproof clothing, volunteered to exercise the dogs from time to time. I was complaining to Pam that my chest was uncomfortable. This wasn't really surprising because all the wind and the rain had involved a lot more heaving and pulling than usual, and having had a coronary by-pass operation, the scar often gave discomfort when I did extra or, in particular, different physical movements.

We set off for home early next morning, passing Whitchurch, Goring, and Cleeve Locks, arriving at our homeward stretch to moor. We unpacked the boat in the pouring rain and I did find it very wearying plodding up and down to the boat with our stores and equipment. We all had a hot bath to revive us, Pam had nipped out for fish and chips, and we all had a good cup of tea, mission accomplished.

'Well,' said Joe, beaming, 'home at last. Do you know what the best part of that trip was?'

'No,' I said.

'The hot bath I've just had.'

I certainly did ache all over through carrying and pulling. It was very difficult holding the boat into the moorings waiting to go through locks. In all it was a very strenuous holiday and I made up my mind that my days of fighting the elements were over.

After the trip I allowed myself a few lazy days. The weather didn't improve much and the following week brought a hurricane.

The day after the hurricane we went down to Brighton

to see Trevor and Jane, who had damage to their skylight and Trevor's bedroom window had been knocked out.

Water was pouring in through the skylight. I had brought with me some sheets of rubber and various things I thought might help.

Driving down to Brighton reminded me of the Blitz. There were trees down everywhere, some lying across houses or cars. The roads were being cleared, but there were literally thousands of trees down; it would be hundreds of years before they could be replaced.

Trevor and I clambered out on to his roof and managed to seal the skylight. It was not an easy task – we were four storeys up and, about four feet away, there was a sharp drop to the ground; it also had such a high sloping roof that we had to hang on to the skylight frame with one hand holding the nails in our teeth.

'Should you be doing that?' said Trevor.

'Yes,' I said, 'I'm as fit as a flea!'

Between us we managed to get things watertight and Trevor fixed the double glazing across his broken window.

We came back home the next day and I had a go at some of my own damaged trees. A few of the willows looked very dangerous and, in spite of Pam's protests, just to show how young and fit I was, I climbed up some of the willows and sawed off great big branches, hanging on upside down with one arm, legs wrapped around the trunk, and sawing in a most difficult position. It was really hard work and at the end of it I'd used more muscles than I had in years and had a corresponding few more aches and pains.

The final straw came when a few days later a man arrived with some books. When a hardback book has gone into paperback and has been published for some time, if all the hardbacks have not been sold, the author has the option of buying them at a very cheap rate. There were four hundred of one of my hardbacks left and I decided to buy the lot.

The delivery man brought seven boxes of books to the

door. They must have weighed three-quarters of a hundred-weight each; Pam couldn't even lift one off the floor. I not only carried each one upstairs but also climbed the step ladder into the loft, or, shall I say, fought my way up into the loft. Then, once inside the loft, on my hands and knees, I had to lift them over the cross-beams to store them.

I had seven journeys to make and it really took the stuffing out of me. Again I used muscles I hadn't used for years; my shoulders ached like anything. 'I must be fit if I can do something like this,' I remarked to Pam.

She said, 'I don't know if you're fit or stupid.'

The aches in my chest continued; they weren't specific, nothing like heart trouble. I did go and have a medical check-up and nothing obvious showed up.

One Sunday night I awoke with a pain in my chest that I couldn't ignore and I realised I was having a coronary. The doctor was called and I was whipped off to the Royal Berks Hospital, and it was almost an advantage to have a coronary to experience the monitoring unit they have there. On arrival, a cheerful nurse said, 'Do we address you as Doctor Robert Clifford, Robert or Bob?'

I said, 'Bob.'

She said, 'Right, my name's Gill, this is Ian,' and so on, and in the next few days there I experienced nursing of the highest standard.

The ward was immaculate; everybody was cheerful; nothing was too much trouble. My symptoms settled down after a couple of days and I was spoilt by being able to stay on in the ward for a bit longer, as for once they weren't pressed for beds.

I have never been so impressed by such a degree of efficiency and care. When you find units of such a high standard there's usually one or two people who are the main motivators behind them. In this case I think there was a doctor and a ward sister who, with their enthusiasm, kept up these exemplary levels of nursing, care, and most important of all, kindness and consideration.

It was a mixed ward. It was very funny being next to a lady – fine when you were chatting, but not quite so fine when you had to have a bedpan with only a curtain to separate you.

On my fourth day I saw a man in the bed opposite me come in and die.

The house surgeon was taking a history from him. The man had been admitted in a lot of pain having had a coronary. He'd been given treatment for his pain, which had settled, but suddenly I saw him go limp and sag over, gone. The houseman kept on talking, then realised his patient was no longer responding. He shouted an order. In a few seconds there was a sound of running feet, of machines, doctors and nurses appearing from all over. I couldn't see what was going on as they drew the curtains, but there was a lot of activity: 'Turn him this way. Give him this. Right, give him one more shot.' They managed to revive him and pull him through this attack, and he was hanging on.

I was moved from the ward the next day but kept an interest in him and saw him improve generally. He was sitting up in bed reading the paper before I left. I was put in the main ward for a couple of days where, again, the nursing was excellent. The sister, who I think was West Indian, said to me, 'There's your bed, Doctor Clifford.'

'Actually, my name's Bob,' I said.

'Not in this ward,' she said. 'I'm one of the old school.' She laughed but she had her ward staff on their toes. Everything was efficient and well run and the nursing auxiliaries and the ladies who brought the tea round added a tremendous amount of colour to the ward. This was not just because they came from India, Pakistan, the West Indies and other far-flung places, but they were lively, smiling people who cheered us up. One nursing auxiliary, a Jamaican, was practically a music-hall turn on her own. We looked forward to her coming in. As well as being entertaining she was a most devoted and caring nurse and couldn't have been kinder or more gentle.

The hospital were very organised about my departure: an outpatients appointment was made, I was given tablets, and it was arranged that the district nurse would call on me. They even let me home a bit early as my new young GP had offered to keep an eye on me at home. I was lucky, I'd had an uncomplicated incident and there was no reason why I shouldn't, after a period of rest, get over it completely and resume most of the things I was doing before.

It was lovely to get home again, lie in my bed and look out at the river flowing past. I got myself an exercise bicycle, and pedalled away each day. It was not long before I was walking into the town, and doing circular trips around the boat yard. I'd been very lucky. I had to take various sorts of medication and it was a little while before we found the one that suited me the best and I fortunately had no further troubles.

My old friend John Bowler came up from Tadchester with his daughter, to stay. *Sea Grey* was out of the water for

139

the winter, looking absolutely huge on the hard-standing in the front garden. I asked him whether my boating days were over.

'Well, I think the time has come to be sensible,' he said. 'Both the episodes you've had, the one before your coronary by-pass and this latest one, have followed periods when you've done some excessive, strenuous physical activity. The first time it was carrying a dinghy on your back and this last time, I think it was carrying those books upstairs. I think you'll be fine providing you don't put yourself under extreme physical pressure. Walking, riding, running, going around, say, in a day boat would be fine. You've got your writing, and there's so much of France you haven't explored yet, but I think you'll really have to give up battling against the elements. Your boat weighs several tons, and if it gets stuck in the mud you'll have to push it off – it's just not worth it. My advice to you is to get rid of it. I know it's a bit sad, but you have so enjoyed your days on the river, it would be a pity to let it damage your health.'

He was right. I knew when we were down on Cliveden Reach that I didn't really want much more of gales, storms and hanging on to moorings for dear life; but it was sad – we'd been so happy and had had such good holidays on the Thames. But there were other things we could do. I have always claimed I had two main loves, the Thames and France; now I would have to concentrate on the latter.

The Williams, our ex-neighours, had invited us to join them in the spring on a touring holiday in France with me navigating and Stan driving his Range Rover ('the tank' as he called it). I'd just have to accept that I was getting a teeny bit older and mustn't look for physical battles.

The weather picked up in February for a short spell, one of those false springs and it was sunny. There were

one or two people out on the river. Pam and I walked down the garden and there was our boat, *Sea Grey*, perched on oil-drums on our hard-standing, covered in the new blue tarpaulin I'd bought at the beginning of the winter to protect her from the worst of the weather.

I tacked a 'For Sale' notice on her; I'd already let the Maid Boat Yard and Andrew Corless at the Sheridan Boat Yard know she was up for sale.

I stood back with Pam, looking at her.

It was sad to think that we'd had our last voyage on her.

Pam squeezed my hand.

'D'you know what?' she said.

'Yes,' I replied, 'You don't have to tell me: life is going to be different from now on.'

Postscript

There is the fable of the old man sitting outside a town, being approached by a stranger.

'What are they like in this town?' asked the stranger.

'What were they like in your last town?' replied the old man.

'They were delightful people. I was very happy there. They were kind, generous and would always help you in trouble.'

'You will find them very much like that in this town.'

The old man was approached by another stranger.

'What are the people like in this town?' asked the second stranger.

'What were they like in your last town?' replied the old man.

'It was an awful place. They were mean, unkind and nobody would ever help anybody.'

'I am afraid you will find it very much the same here,' said the old man.

If it should be your lot to ever visit Wallingford, this is how you will find it.

☐	Just Here, Doctor!	Dr Robert Clifford	£3.50
☐	Not There, Doctor!	Dr Robert Clifford	£3.50
☐	What Next, Doctor!	Dr Robert Clifford	£3.99
☐	Three Times a Day, Doctor?	Dr Robert Clifford	£9.99
☐	There You Are, Doctor!	Dr Robert Clifford	£3.50
☐	On Holiday Again, Doctor?	Dr Robert Clifford	£3.50
☐	You're Still A Doctor, Doctor!	Dr Robert Clifford	£3.50
☐	Only When I Laugh, Doctor	Dr Robert Clifford	£5.99

Warner Books now offers an exciting range of quality titles by both established and new authors. All of the books in this series are available from:

Little, Brown and Company (UK) Limited,
P.O. Box 11,
Falmouth,
Cornwall TR10 9EN.

Alternatively you may fax your order to the above address. Fax No. 0326 376423.

Payments can be made as follows: cheque, postal order (payable to Little, Brown and Company) or by credit cards, Visa/Access. Do not send cash or currency. UK customers and B.F.P.O. please allow £1.00 for postage and packing for the first book, plus 50p for the second book, plus 30p for each additional book up to a maximum charge of £3.00 (7 books plus).

Overseas customers including Ireland, please allow £2.00 for the first book plus £1.00 for the second book, plus 50p for each additional book.

NAME (Block Letters) ....

....

ADDRESS ....

....

....

☐ I enclose my remittance for _____

☐ I wish to pay by Access/Visa Card

Number ☐☐☐☐☐☐☐☐☐☐☐☐☐☐☐☐

Card Expiry Date ☐☐☐☐